INV 13

KU-215-007

THE BEST
PUB
QUIZ
BOOK

THIS IS A CARLTON BOOK

Copyright © Carlton Books Limited 1998

This book is sold subject to the condition that it shall not,
by way of trade or otherwise, be lent, resold, hired out or
otherwise circulated without the publisher's prior written
consent in any form of cover or binding other than that in
which it is published and without a similar condition,
including this condition, being imposed on the
subsequent purchaser.

All rights reserved.

1 85868 631 8

Editor: Tim Dedopulos
Designer: Paul Messam
Production: Garry Lewis

Questions set by The Puzzle House

Printed and bound in Great Britain

THE BEST
PUB
QUIZ
BOOK

CARLTON

Contents

Introduction

Quizzes are a strange thing. If you were to stroll up to some poor bloke on the street – let's say it's a Saturday lunch time, and he's out with the wife doing the weekly shopping, trying to get it over and done with so he can make it back home for kick-off – and started firing questions at him, one after the other, he'd probably take it pretty badly. He'd be nervous, irritated, and looking for quick ways to escape the maniac that's latched on to him. If you take a moment to picture it ("Quick, mate, what would you ride in a velodrome? What colour is an aubergine?"), you'll see how ludicrous it sounds. If he doesn't lamp you one, he'll probably run off screaming in terror.

However, get the same bloke later on the same Saturday, down the pub with his mates after the match, and then you leap up and start firing the same questions at him, at the very least he's going to rise to the challenge and prove he's the equal of your questions. If you've taken the time to sort things out with the landlord in advance, and you're asking the whole pub, you'll have a crowd of people enthralled, hanging on your every word, and not just our bloke. Even if – and this is the best part – there's absolutely no prize at the end of it. We all love glory, after all, and what could be more glorious than proving you've got the keenest mind in the bar? It beats getting onto a horse and charging at a cannon hands down.

This is the third volume of *The Best Pub Quiz Book Ever!* and it keeps getting better and better. Inside these hallowed covers, you'll find more than 10,000 questions covering a stunning range of topics, divided into laughably easy, reasonably medium, and brain-shreddingly hard. At the back, you'll also find a comprehensive set of guidelines on how to prepare for and run a successful quiz of your own down the local, and some handy answer sheet templates to photocopy and give out to contestants. There is one important thing you have to remember though, and that is never, ever, under any circumstances, give out your own pens.

More importantly than that though – seriously for a minute – when you are going to be running a quiz, prepare properly beforehand. Don't just take this book along and read out of it (because apart from anything else, some other wise guy might have bought a copy too, and be checking the answers). Note down all the questions and all the answers, and make sure you've got everything. If an answer makes you think "hang on a moment, is that right?" then double-check it to make sure that it is not only correct, but it is the only correct answer. While every possible effort has been undertaken to make absolutely sure that every answer is accurate, there is a slight possibility that an error may have crept in and the answer is wrong. Nothing is more humiliating than telling people who are right that they are wrong, in front of a lot of other people who will remember it and tease you about it mercilessly for the next three years. If you've made sure of your answers, you'll be absolutely 100% safe, not just 99.99% safe.

So, there you go. Wade in, and have fun. After all, that's what it's all about.

Easy Questions

The whole point of these questions is that they are, well, easy. As in not hard. That means that they shouldn't give you, or anyone else who speaks the same language, any problems. If you get these questions right, that's really not much to be proud of. In fact, it's close to the truth that getting these questions wrong is something to be worried about. If you find yourself doing badly on these questions, there are many possible reasons. The first thing to check is that you're looking at the correct answer block. If you've made that mistake, it'll throw your results right out. Alternatively, you may be extremely drunk. If reading this short introduction is proving tricky, that could be the cause. Try again later. Another possible cause is that you might only be three or four years old – again, try again later, only make it much later. Finally, you may have been born in the wilds and have spent your life being raised by a friendly family of otters, in which case you can be forgiven for your ignorance. They're nice creatures, but they're really not much cop when it comes to hits of the 90s.

So, when you're devising a quiz for people, you might like to soften them up with a few of these questions, ease them into the groove, fatten them for the kill, and lots of other clichés that mean you're gently preparing people for something nasty. If nothing else, it'll make sure that even the bloke in the corner who's so hammered he can't stand will get one or two points, and save face. Tomorrow, he may even be grateful enough to buy you a drink for being so considerate. It's worth a shot, so to speak...

Quiz 1 The Movies: Actresses

Answers - see Quiz 2, page 10

LEVEL 1

1 In which film did Uma Thurman play Emma Peel?
2 What part of her did Demi Moore remove completely for G.I.Jane?
3 How many films had Barbara Streisand been in before being the star of Funny Girl?
4 Which crime writer did Vanessa Redgrave play in Agatha?
5 Is Nicole Kidman shorter or taller than husband Tom Cruise?
6 Which Sandra starred in Speed and The Net?
7 What is the name of Audrey Hepburn's cat in Breakfast at Tiffany's?
8 Which blonde was the star of Some Like It Hot?
9 Which English actress was the first to play M in the Bond movies?
10 During which war was Land Girls with Anna Friel set?
11 Which Audrey played Eliza Doolittle in My Fair Lady?
12 Which Tallulah was known for calling everyone "Dahling"?
13 Who played Rita in Educating Rita?
14 Which Ms Foster had a son Charles in 1998?
15 Which actress Vanessa is Natasha Richardson's mother?
16 Ingrid Bergman and Judy Garland had what type of flower named after them?
17 What was the nationality of Ingrid Bergman?
18 What was Julie Andrews' first film, about a nanny?
19 Is Shirley MacLaine left or right handed?
20 Which Ursula co starred with Elvis in Fun in Acapulco?
21 Which blonde French actress's real name is Camille Javal?
22 Which Jane was one of the first actresses to produce fitness videos?
23 Which item of Madonna's underwear made £4,600 at auction in '97?
24 Brigitte Bardot had a theatre named after her in which French city?
25 Which Marlene said, "I acted vulgar, Madonna IS vulgar"?
26 Which Irish TV personality was named after Gloria Swanson?
27 Which actress Debra served in the Israeli army?
28 Which Christina played the sinister Wednesday in the Addam Family films?
29 What is Goldie Hawn's real name?
30 Catherine Zeta Jones supports which South Wales soccer side?

Answers

Nature: Animal World (see Quiz 2, page 10)

1 (African) elephant. 2 Wolf. 3 Warm blooded. 4 Tooth. 5 Voice box.
6 Alone. 7 Primate. 8 Duck. 9 Dog. 10 Sheep. 11 Sight. 12 Offensive
smell. 13 Brown. 14 (South) America. 15 Eye. 16 Hare. 17 Its ears.
18 Alaska. 19 Warm. 20 Carnivorous. 21 Cows. 22 Chimpanzee.
23 Neck. 24 Invertebrates. 25 One. 26 Tail. 27 Polar bear. 28 Milk.
29 Fingerprints. 30 Southern.

Quiz 2 Nature: Animal World

Answers - see Quiz 1, page 9

LEVEL 1

1 Which land mammal has the largest ears?
2 Which wild animal is the domesticated dog descended from?
3 Are mammals warm blooded or cold blooded?
4 Which part of the body has a crown and a root?
5 What is another name for the larynx?
6 Do tigers hunt in packs or alone?
7 Which group of animals shares its name with an archbishop?
8 What type of creature is an Aylesbury?
9 What was the first animal to be domesticated?
10 Cheviot and Suffolk are both types of what?
11 Shrews have acute sense of smell and hearing to compensate for which weak sense?
12 The opossum and the skunk are famous for what?
13 What colour is a grizzly bear?
14 The llama is native to which continent?
15 Which part of a human's body has a cornea?
16 A leveret is a young what?
17 What part of a Basset Hound is particularly long?
18 Which northerly US state is famous for the brown bear?
19 Does the moose live in a warm or cold climate?
20 Are crocodiles carnivorous or herbivores?
21 Which farm animals chew the cud?
22 Which primate species is the closest genetic cousin to humanity?
23 Where is human's jugular vein?
24 Are most animals vertebrates or invertebrates?
25 How many young does a kangaroo usually produce at any one time?
26 What part of the body of a Manx cat is missing which is present on most other cats?
27 Which bear is the largest meat-eating land animal?
28 What do all mammals feed their babies on?
29 Which part of a human includes loops and whorls?
30 In which hemisphere do penguins live in the wild?

The Movies: Actresses (see Quiz 1, page 9)
1 The Avengers. 2 Her hair. 3 None. 4 Agatha Christie. 5 Taller. 6 Bullock. 7 Cat. 8 Marilyn Monroe. 9 Judi Dench. 10 Second World War. 11 Hepburn. 12 Bankhead. 13 Julie Walters. 14 Jodie Foster. 15 Redgrave. 16 Rose. 17 Swedish. 18 Mary Poppins. 19 Left. 20 Andress. 21 Brigitte Bardot. 22 Fonda. 23 Black bra. 24 Paris. 25 Dietrich. 26 Gloria Hunniford. 27 Winger. 28 Ricci. 29 Goldie Hawn. 30 Swansea City.

Quiz 3 TV: Cops & Robbers

Answers - see Quiz 4, page 12

LEVEL 1

1 What is the surname of cop Maisie played by Pauline Quirke?
2 Michael French left which soap to become a Crime Traveller?
3 Who replaced Sue Cook as co presenter of Crimewatch UK?
4 Which series featured Ediie "Fitz" Fitzgerald?
5 Which early police serial is found at the end of the alphabet?
6 Which Yorkshire police series did Nick Berry leave in 1997?
7 In which US city was Cagney and Lacey set?
8 Dangerfield deals with what type of police personnel?
9 David Suchet played which Belgian Agatha Christie detective?
10 In which English county does Wycliffe take place?
11 Which assistant to Morse was missing from the show in 1998?
12 Michael Gambon played which French detective in the 90s?
13 How was The Bill's DC Lines, played by Kevin Lloyd, better known?
14 Which Glasgow detective was played by Mark McManus?
15 Which Hetty has a sidekick called Geoffrey?
16 What is the surname of detective Jack played by David Jason?
17 Which police station's blues were led by Captain Frank Furillo?
18 What is the first name of Commander Dalgliesh, created by PD James?
19 Which Jimmy starred in Evita and played Geordie Spender?
20 Which Victorian sleuth from Baker Street was played by Jeremy Brett?
21 WIn "Pie in the Sky", which profession did Henry combine with policing?
22 In which northern city was City Central set?
23 How is Cordelia Gray's creator Baroness James better known?
24 Which bald TV cop was Friends' Jennifer Aniston's godfather?
25 Where was the police sitcom Duck Patrol set?
26 Where did Sonny Crockett aka Don Johnson sort out Vice?
27 Who has played Jack Regan and Morse?
28 In which city was Cagney and Lacey set?
29 Which crime buster show shared its name with insects?
30 In which city did Maigret operate?

Pot Luck 1 (see Quiz 4, page 12)
1 Drinks. 2 Bread & cheese. 3 American. 4 The Sun. 5 Romantic. 6 Paris.
7 The Mouse Trap. 8 Waterloo. 9 Pyramids. 10 Sheep. 11 Gates.
12 Christmas. 13 Nile. 14 Dog. 15 October. 16 Lancashire.
17 Association. 18 Thistle . 19 Cattle. 20 80s. 21 Travel. 22 Wight.
23 Game. 24 Royals. 25 Hong Kong. 26 London. 27 Mont Blanc.
28 Pancakes. 29 29th. 30 Beijing.

Quiz 4 Pot Luck 1

LEVEL 1

1   What is usually sold at reduced prices during a happy hour?
2   What are the two main ingredients of a ploughman's lunch?
3   What was Martina Navratilova's nationality when winning her last Wimbledon title?
4   Which UK daily newspaper has the shortest name?
5   Dame Barbara Cartland is famous for what type of fiction?
6   In which city is the Louvre Museum?
7   Which Agatha Christie play has run in the West End for over 45 years?
8   From which London railway station do Eurostar trains depart?
9   Which surviving tombs were built for the Pharaohs of Egypt?
10 What type of animal was the first successful adult cloning?
11 Which Bill is the world's richest businessman?
12 Twelfth Night marks the end of which festive season?
13 On which river does Cairo stand?
14 What type of animal is a Chihuahua?
15 In which month did the 1987 hurricane take place in the UK?
16 Which county does TV detective Hetty Wainthropp come from?
17 In motoring terms, what does the second A in AA stand for?
18 What is the national emblem of Scotland?
19 What type of animal does BSE affect?
20 In which decade of the 20th century was Prince William born?
21 What sort of tickets would a bucket shop sell?
22 On which Isle is Parkhurst prison?
23 What is hopscotch?
24 Which family receives a payment from the Civil List?
25 Which British colony returned to China in July 1997?
26 In which city did rhyming slang originate?
27 Which alpine peak's name means White Mountain?
28 Which food is traditionally eaten on Shrove Tuesday?
29 If August 31st was a Wednesday what date would August Bank Holiday Monday be in England?
30 In which city is Tiananmen Square?

Answers

TV: Cops & Robbers (see Quiz 3, page 11)
1 Raine. 2 Eastenders. 3 Jill Dando. 4 Cracker. 5 Z Cars. 6 Heartbeat.
7 New York. 8 Police surgeon. 9 Poirot. 10 Cornwall. 11 Lewis.
12 Maigret. 13 Tosh. 14 Taggart. 15 Wainthropp. 16 Frost. 17 Hill St.
Blues. 18 Adam. 19 Nail. 20 Sherlock Holmes. 21 Chef. 22 Manchester.
23 P.D. James. 24 Kojak (Telly Savalas). 25 River Thames. 26 Miami. 27
John Thaw. 28 New York. 29 Bugs. 30 Paris.

Quiz 5 Rich & Famous: Names

LEVEL 1

Answers - see Quiz 6, page 14

1 How is Jeremy John Durham Ashdown better known?
2 Raymond Blanc is famous for being what?
3 Which Betty became the House of Commons' first woman Speaker?
4 Which Melvyn stopped starting the week when he became a peer?
5 Which one time husband and wife actors were dubbed Ken and Em?
6 Which trendy homeware store did Terence Conran found in the 60s?
7 Which part of you would you ask Nicky Clarke to cut off?
8 How was Yorkshire based murderer Peter Sutcliffe better known?
9 Which celebrity daughter was named after the song Chelsea Morning?
10 Who released an album in 1975 called Uri Geller?
11 Which 90s PM was in a university pop group called Ugly Rumours?
12 Who is taller, Kylie Minogue or Naomi Campbell?
13 Who launched Virgin Cola and Virgin PEPs ?
14 Which singer Sarah was once Mrs Andrew Lloyd Webber?
15 Who is Michelle Lineker's famous husband?
16 Which Monica was intimately associated with Bill Clinton?
17 Was Joan Collins born in the 1920s, 1930s or the 1940s?
18 Which British Party leader has the same first names as Bill Clinton?
19 Which model Jerry had a cameo role in Batman?
20 What colour is Dame Edna Everage's hair?
21 Which London football club does David Mellor famously support?
22 Which Scot Andrew was the Sunday Times editor from 1983 to 1994?
23 John Prescott is Deputy Leader of which political party?
24 Which Prime Minister had twins called Mark and Carol?
25 The names Saatchi and Saatchi are associated with which industry?
26 Which Rolling Stone Bill was 34 years older than bride Mandy Smith?
27 What title does the brother of the late Princess Diana have?
28 What type of shops did Tim Waterstone found?
29 Which designer Vivienne is famous for her outrageous clothes?
30 What is the nickname of Royal 'nanny' Alexandra Legge-Bourke?

Pot Luck 2 (see Quiz 6, page 14)

1 Donkey. 2 Italy. 3 Tipperary. 4 White. 5 Poppy. 6 48. 7 Lah.
8 A calf. 9 China. 10 Frank Sinatra. 11 Chequered. 12 Japan. 13 C.
14 Bach. 15 HM Customs & Excise. 16 Orange. 17 11. 18 Blue.
19 Dublin. 20 Florence Nightingale. 21 Pumpkin. 22 Bill Haley &
the Comets. 23 London. 24 Hans Christian Andersen. 25 The twins.
26 Shropshire. 27 Grapes. 28 Tennis. 29 Sound and noise. 30 One.

Answers

Quiz 6 Pot Luck 2

LEVEL 1

1   What kind of animal is Eeyore in the children's classic?
2   Which country produces Parmesan cheese?
3   Where, according to the song, is it a long way to in Ireland?
4   What colour were all guests asked to wear at Mel B's wedding?
5   Which flower is linked with Remembrance Sunday?
6   How many sides are there in a dozen quadrilaterals?
7   Which note follows the musical note 'soh'?
8   What name is given to a young elephant?
9   In which country was acupuncture developed?
10   Which singer was known affectionately as 'Old Blue Eyes'?
11   Which flag in motor racing signals the end of the race?
12   In which country is the yen the unit of currency?
13   Which vitamin is found in oranges and lemons?
14   Which composer had the forenames Johann Sebastian?
15   Which Government department collects V.A.T?
16   What kind of fruit is a satsuma?
17   How many players are in a hockey team?
18   What colour is the shade of cobalt?
19   The Abbey Theatre is in which Irish city?
20   Which nurse was called 'The Lady with the Lamp'?
21   What was Cinderella's coach made from?
22   Who rocked around the clock in 1955?
23   Which zoo is found in Regent's Park?
24   Who wrote The Ugly Duckling?
25   What is the Zodiac sign Gemini also called?
26   Shrewsbury is the county town of which county?
27   Which fruit when dried produces raisins?
28   In which sport did Ivan Lendl achieve fame?
29   What is measured in decibels?
30   How many horns was a unicorn supposed to have?

Answers

Rich & Famous: Names (see Quiz 5, page 13)
1 Paddy Ashdown. 2 Chef/Restaurateur. 3 Boothroyd. 4 Bragg.
5 Kenneth Branagh and Emma Thompson. 6 Habitat. 7 Hair. 8 Yorkshire Ripper. 9 Chelsea Clinton. 10 Uri Geller. 11 Tony Blair. 12 Naomi Campbell. 13 Richard Branson. 14 Brightman. 15 Gary. 16 Lewinsky. 17 1930s. 18 William Jefferson Hague. 19 Hall. 20 Mauve. 21 Chelsea. 22 Neil. 23 Labour. 24 Margaret Thatcher. 25 Advertising. 26 Wyman. 27 Earl Spencer. 28 Bookshops. 29 Westwood. 30 Tiggy.

Quiz 7 Sport: Football UK

Answers - see Quiz 8, page 16

1 Messrs Docherty, Atkinson and Ferguson have all managed which team?
2 Who was the first football boss to marry one of her former players?
3 Which Arsenal player's autobiography was called Addicted?
4 Which Stanley was first winner of the European Footballer of the Year award?
5 Which was the first Rovers side to win the Premiership?
6 Graham Taylor was likened to a turnip after a defeat in which Scandinavian country?
7 Who did Ruud Gullit replace as manager of Newcastle Utd?
8 In which Asian country did Gary Lineker play club soccer?
9 What colour are the stripes on Newcastle Utd's first choice shirts?
10 Which side moved from Roker Park to the Stadium of Light?
11 Was Alan Shearer sold to Newcastle for £5 million, £15 million or £25 million?
12 In which country was George Best born?
13 What is the nationality of Dennis Bergkamp?
14 Which ex Anfield goalie Bruce was charged with match fixing in '95?
15 How many clubs were in the Premier league in 1997/8?
16 Which Yorkshire side was involved in a plane crash in March 1988?
17 Which Paul was the first black player to captain England?
18 Who was known as El Tel when he managed Barcelona?
19 Who in 1997 became Arsenal's all-time leading goal scorer?
20 How is the Football Association Challenge Cup better known?
21 Which Welshman Ian said living in Italy was like "living in a foreign country"?
22 Which club Charlton were promoted to the Premier League in 1998?
23 Which colour links shirts at Liverpool, Middlesbrough and Southampton?
24 Which Brian managed Notts Forest for 18 years?
25 At which international stadium were the 1993/4 FA Cup semis held?
26 Which Charlton brother was the first to be knighted?
27 Which Eric was the first overseas PFA Player of the Year winner?
28 Who was dubbed Duncan Disorderly?
29 Which London side does ex PM John Major support?
30 From which group of islands does Graeme Le Saux hail from?

Quiz 8 Pot Luck 3

Answers - see Quiz 7, page 15

1   Vienna is the capital of which European country?
2   What name is given to a young deer?
3   Which fruit when dried produces prunes?
4   Where was Achilles hit with a fatal arrow?
5   Which relation gave actor Clive Dunn a hit?
6   Which musical note follows ray?
7   What do you find in a bunker on a golf course?
8   Who wrote The Tale of Peter Rabbit?
9   Winchester is the county town of which county?
10 What is the name of the French National Anthem?
11 Which animal was Androcles very friendly with?
12 Which black wood is used for piano keys?
13 Which island is affectionately called the Emerald Isle?
14 In which sport is the Ryder Cup competed for?
15 What is the clock tower in the Houses of Parliament usually called?
16 Which animal is linked with the Zodiac sign Taurus?
17 Which town is home to the Bayeux Tapestry?
18 What kind of meat can be silverside and topside?
19 What is the unit of currency in Italy?
20 What is the name of the Queen's youngest son?
21 How many notes are there in an octave?
22 What do you measure with a protractor?
23 Ronan Keating heads which boy band?
24 What is it said an ostrich does, if it thinks it is in danger?
25 After a selling price, what do the initials O.N.O stand for?
26 Which type of soup is a consomme?
27 What colour is magenta?
28 What type of fruit is an Orange Pippin?
29 Which London based football club are known as 'The Hammers'?
30 In which county is Sherwood Forest?

Answers

Sport: Football UK (see Quiz 7, page 15)
1 Manchester Utd. 2 Karren Brady. 3 Tony Adams. 4 Matthews. 5 Blackburn.
6 Sweden. 7 Kenny Dalglish. 8 Japan. 9 Black & white. 10 Sunderland.
11 £15 million. 12 Northern Ireland. 13 Dutch. 14 Grobbelaar.
15 20. 16 Leeds Utd. 17 Ince. 18 Terry Venables. 19 Ian Wright. 20 FA
Cup. 21 Rush. 22 Charlton Athletic. 23 Red. 24 Clough. 25 Wembley.
26 Bobby. 27 Cantona. 28 Duncan Ferguson. 29 Chelsea. 30 Channel Islands.

Quiz 9 Hobbies and Leisure 1

Answers - see Quiz 10, page 18

1   The art of self defence aikido originated in which country?
2   Which Bank Holiday comes immediately before Easter Day?
3   Pools is a gambling game based on which sport?
4   Where might you be entertained by a redcoat?
5   Which reptiles feature in a popular board game?
6   Which is bigger Disneyland or Disneyworld?
7   What do you play baccarat with?
8   Which leisure park Towers are near Stoke on Trent?
9   In which game is the object to gain checkmate?
10 What is the minimum number of players in a cribbage game?
11 Which quiz board game involves the collection of coloured wedges?
12 Brass rubbing usually takes place in what type of building?
13 How much is it for one game in the weekly national Lottery draw?
14 In which English city could you watch Rovers and City play soccer?
15 Which part of a pub shares its name with an area of a law court?
16 Which End of London is famous for its theatres?
17 Microlighting takes place in what sort of craft?
18 What name is given to the hours that a pub can open to sell alcohol?
19 Which property board game had a World Cup version in 1998?
20 What colour is the L on a normal learner driver's L plate?
21 What sort of accommodation is provided in a B & B?
22 Knitting needs needles, what does crochet need?
23 Which pier is to the north of Blackpool's central pier?
24 What type of castle do young children enjoy jumping up and down on?
25 'The dogs' involves races of which breed?
26 What colour are the segments on a roulette wheel?
27 Which Planet is a celebrity-founded restaurant chain?
28 What colour are Scrabble tiles?
29 Which gambling game's best hand is Royal flush?
30 What colour is the M on the McDonalds logo?

Answers

Pot Luck 4 (see Quiz 10, page 18)
1 Green. 2 Fish. 3 Friar Tuck. 4 Coal. 5 Leo. 6 Motor racing. 7 Public Limited Company. 8 Switzerland. 9 Bear. 10 Alexandra. 11 April. 12 76. 13 Pancakes. 14 On board ship. 15 A snake. 16 Linda McCartney. 17 Yellow/orange. 18 Apple. 19 George Orwell. 20 Isle of Wight. 21 60s. 22 Before they're hatched. 23 Holland. 24 Saturday. 25 A pup. 26 Malta. 27 Bill Clinton. 28 Eucalyptus leaves. 29 White coffee. 30 The Tower of London.

Quiz 10 Pot Luck 4

Answers - see Quiz 9, page 17

1 If you mix blue and yellow paint what colour is made?
2 What is usually eaten with Tartare Sauce?
3 Who was Robin Hood's priest?
4 What is normally kept at home in a bunker?
5 Which sign of the Zodiac is normally shown as a lion?
6 Which sport is associated with Silverstone and Brands Hatch?
7 What do the initials plc stand for after a company name?
8 Berne is the capital of which European country?
9 What type of creature was Baloo in The Jungle Book?
10 Which London palace is also called 'Ally Pally'?
11 St George's Day is in which month?
12 How many trombones led the big parade according to the song?
13 What are Crepes Suzettes a type of?
14 Where does a purser usually work?
15 What is a black mamba?
16 Which member of Wings died in 1998?
17 What colour is ochre?
18 What kind of fruit is a russet?
19 Who wrote Animal Farm?
20 On which island is Osborne House, home of Queen Victoria?
21 In which decade did Yuri Gagarin become the first man in space?
22 When must you not count your chickens, according to the proverb?
23 Which country makes Gouda cheese?
24 What day of the week is the Jewish Sabbath?
25 What name is given to a young seal?
26 Which island was awarded the George Cross in 1942?
27 Kenneth Starr produced a report about which famous American?
28 What does a koala have for its main source of food?
29 What is cafe au lait?
30 Where are the Crown Jewels kept?

Hobbies and Leisure 1 (see Quiz 9, page 17)
1 Japan. 2 Good Friday. 3 Football. 4 Holiday camp (Butlin's). 5 Snakes (& ladders). 6 Disneyworld. 7 Cards. 8 Alton Towers. 9 Chess. 10 Two. 11 Trivial Pursuits. 12 Churches. 13 £1. 14 Bristol. 15 Bar. 16 West End. 17 Plane. 18 Licensing hours. 19 Monopoly. 20 Red. 21 Bed & breakfast. 22 Hook. 23 North pier. 24 Bouncy castle. 25 Greyhounds. 26 Red, black. 27 Hollywood. 28 Cream. 29 Poker. 30 Yellow.

Quiz 11 Pop: Musical Babes

Answers - see Quiz 12, page 20

LEVEL 1

1   Which Spice Girl advertised Milky Bars as a child?
2   Was Billie Piper 10, 15 or 20 when she first went to No 1?
3   Which Tina sang the title song from Whistle Down the Wind?
4   Who put her famous Union Jack dress up for auction?
5   What is singing babe PJ Harvey's first name?
6   How many girls make up N-Tyce?
7   Janet and La Toyah are from which famous family?
8   What is the first name of the welsh babe from Catatonia?
9   Whose album Always and Forever gives a clue to their name?
10 Which 60s babe's first hit was written by the Rolling Stones?
11 Heather Small found fame with which band?
12 What is the surname of sister Kylie and Dannii?
13 How many girls make up Alisha's Attic?
14 Which Michelle left EastEnders to pursue a pop career?
15 Where do Scary Spice and Princess Anne's daughter have a stud?
16 Who share their name with an Egyptian queen?
17 Which Aussie soap did Natalie Imbruglia appear in?
18 How many babes make up B*witched?
19 How did the Bangles Walk?
20 Shaznay is in which all girl band?
21 Which 60s singer now hosts Surprise Surprise?
22 Which Capstan sang with the B52s and guested with REM?
23 Which babe was the lead singer for Blondie?
24 Which musical instrument is Vanessa Mae famous for?
25 Wendy James was the lead singer with which Vamp band?
26 Alanis Morissette and Celine Dion are from which country?
27 Who sang about Baboushka and Wuthering Heights?
28 In which decade did Bananarama have their first hit?
29 Miss Nurding dropped her surname and became known as whom?
30 Tracy Shaw's pop career began when she was in which soap?

Pot Luck 5 (see Quiz 12, page 20)

Answers

1 July. 2 Bull/cow. 3 Cider. 4 Peru. 5 A savoury snack. 6 1969.
7 Venice. 8 Mount Ararat. 9 Forbidden fruit. 10 A will. 11 France.
12 Norwich City. 13 Vincent van Gogh. 14 Aries. 15 Calligraphy.
16 Harley Street. 17 Pinocchio. 18 Tanks. 19 Friday. 20 A bird.
21 Caernarvon. 22 Cherry. 23 17. 24 September. 25 Devon. 26 Baptism.
27 Bee Gee. 28 A.A. Milne. 29 Hippopotamus. 30 Sausage.

Quiz 12 Pot Luck 5

Answers - see Quiz 11, page 19

LEVEL 1

1 St Swithin's Day is in which summer month?
2 Who or what is an Aberdeen Angus?
3 What drink did writer Laurie Lee share with Rosie?
4 Where did Paddington Bear originally come from?
5 What are pretzels?
6 Did man first land on the moon in 1966, 1969 or 1972?
7 In which Italian city is St Mark's cathedral?
8 On which Mount is the resting place of Noah's Ark?
9 Which fruit tastes sweetest according to the proverb?
10 What does a testator make, in law?
11 Which country produces Camembert cheese?
12 Which football team is known as 'The Canaries'?
13 Which Dutch painter cut off his ear?
14 Which Zodiac sign is normally associated with the ram?
15 What is the study of handwriting called?
16 Which London street is associated with the medical profession?
17 Which wooden puppet was written about by Carlo Collodi?
18 Shermans, Grants and Cromwells are all types of what?
19 Which day of the week is the Muslim Holy Day?
20 What is a quail?
21 In which castle was the investiture of the Prince of Wales?
22 Which fruit is used to make kirsch?
23 How old should you be to apply for a car driving licence in the UK?
24 In what month is Michaelmas Day?
25 Which county has Exeter as its county town?
26 For which religious ceremony is a font normally used?
27 Was Lulu's first husband a Beatle or a Bee Gee?
28 Who wrote about Tigger, Eeyore and Piglet?
29 Which animal has a name which means 'river horse'?
30 What would you be eating if you ate a saveloy?

Answers

Pop: Musical Babes (see Quiz 11, page 19)
1 Emma (Baby Spice). 2 15. 3 Tina Arena. 4 Geri Halliwell. 5 Polly.
6 Four. 7 Jackson. 8 Nerys. 9 Eternal. 10 Marianne Faithful. 11 M
People. 12 Minogue. 13 Two. 14 Gayle. 15 Tongue. 16 Cleopatra. 17
Home & Away. 18 Four. 19 Like an Egyptian. 20 All Saints. 21 Cilla Black.
22 Kate. 23 Debbie Harry. 24 Violin. 25 Transvision Vamp. 26 Canada.
27 Kate Bush. 28 80s. 29 Louise. 30 Coronation Street.

Quiz 13 The Movies: Blockbusters

Answers - see Quiz 14, page 22

1   Which early Spielberg blockbuster was about a shark?
2   Who played the title role in the Orson Welles directed Citizen Kane?
3   In which 90s musical film did Madonna change costume 85 times?
4   What was the name of the movie based on TV's The X Files?
5   Scarlett O'Hara was heroine of which Atlanta based epic?
6   Who was the star of the Western The Alamo?
7   Which musical about Danny and Sandy was re-released in 1998?
8   Which creatures dominated Jurassic Park?
9   What was Crocodile Dundee's homeland?
10 Hook was based on which children's book?
11 Which lizard-like monster's name is a mix of the Japanese words for gorilla and whale?
12 Who left Kramer in the 70s movie with Hoffman and Streep?
13 From Here To Eternity is set before the Japanese attack on where?
14 Raging Bull was about which sport?
15 Which film was an abbreviation of Extra Terrestrial?
16 The Empire Strikes Back was a sequel to what?
17 Raiders of the Lost Ark was about which Mr Jones?
18 Robin Hood was Prince of what in the 1991 blockbuster?
19 Was Snow White and the Seven Dwarfs released before or after World War II?
20 Where was Gary Oldman Lost in the 1998 hit movie?
21 Which Caped Crusader was the subject of one of the top 80s films?
22 Which watery film succeeded Waterworld as the most costly to make?
23 Gene Kelly was An American ... where in the Vincente Minnelli movie?
24 Which star of Grease and Saturday Night Fever is a qualified pilot?
25 Was The Sting a hit in the 50s, 70s or 90s?
26 Which Disney animal movie was a 1994 blockbuster set in Africa?
27 Amadeus told the story of which composer?
28 Home Alone shot which child star to fame?
29 Was Schindler's List in colour or black and white?
30 Which Kevin played Mariner in Waterworld?

Answers

Pot Luck 6 (see Quiz 14, page 22)
1 Switzerland. 2 Charles. 3 Golden Hind. 4 The Gondoliers. 5 Thrillers.
6 Fleet Street. 7 Suffolk. 8 V-shaped. 9 St Patrick. 10 Pisces. 11 Beetroot soup. 12 16 years. 13 4. 14 A Question of Sport. 15 Reindeer. 16 Golf.
17 Astrology. 18 Rome. 19 Alpha. 20 A dog. 21 France. 22 Lawn.
23 Herbs. 24 Green. 25 Katrina and the Waves. 26 A newspaper. 27 Eel.
28 Seaweed. 29 The Sound of Music. 30 Dorchester.

Quiz 14 Pot Luck 6

LEVEL 1

1 Which country produces Gruyere cheese?
2 Who was invested as Prince of Wales in 1969?
3 Francis Drake's ship Pelican was renamed what?
4 Which opera by Gilbert and Sullivan is set in Venice?
5 Did John Le Carre write thrillers or romantic fiction?
6 Which London Street was home to several British newspapers?
7 Which county has Ipswich as its county town?
8 What shape are the teeth on pinking shears?
9 Which Saint is commemorated on the 17th of March?
10 Which Zodiac sign is normally associated with two fishes?
11 What kind of food is borscht?
12 What is the minimum age for leaving school in England?
13 In snooker, how many points is the brown ball worth?
14 Which TV programme has the logo QS?
15 What kind of animals were Cupid, Donner and Blitzen?
16 In which sport would you use a caddie?
17 Which science looks at the planets and the stars?
18 According to the proverb, which Italian city was not built in a day?
19 What is the first letter of the Greek alphabet?
20 What is a Shih-Tzu?
21 Which country does the wine claret come from?
22 In tennis, what does the initial L in LTA stand for?
23 What kind of plants are sage, lovage and basil?
24 Which London park is the name of a colour?
25 Who were the UK's first Eurovision winners after Bucks Fizz?
26 If you bought Le Figaro in France what would you be buying?
27 An elver is a young what?
28 What is kelp?
29 Which film featured the Von Trapp Family?
30 What is the county town of Dorset?

Answers

The Movies: Blockbusters (see Quiz 13, page 21)
1 Jaws. 2 Orson Welles. 3 Evita. 4 The X Files. 5 Gone With the Wind.
6 John Wayne. 7 Grease. 8 Dinosaurs. 9 Australia. 10 Peter Pan.
11 Godzilla. 12 Kramer. 13 Pearl Harbor. 14 Boxing. 15 E.T.
16 Star Wars. 17 Indiana Jones. 18 Thieves. 19 Before. 20 Space.
21 Batman. 22 Titanic. 23 Paris. 24 John Travolta. 25 70s. 26 The Lion
King. 27 Mozart. 28 Macaulay Culkin. 29 Black & white. 30 Costner.

Quiz 15 TV: Quiz & Game Shows

Answers - see Quiz 16, page 24

LEVEL 1

1   On which channel is Countdown broadcast?
2   What is the version of 100 Per Cent for the over 50s called?
3   Which show does Dale Winton present from a supermarket?
4   Eric Knowles is the resident expert on which antiques quiz?
5   Which game show with Jim Davidson is based on snooker shots?
6   Who was the first 'female' presenter of Blankety Blank?
7   Which Noel Edmonds show was originally called Telly Quiz?
8   What completes the culinary challenge show Can't Cook,_____?
9   Through the Keyhole looks at which celebrity possessions?
10 How many students make up one University Challenge team?
11 In Blind Date a choice is made from what number of the opposite sex?
12 Which Ms Jonsson was the first female presenter of Gladiators?
13 Which darts based show offered losers a 'bendy Bully'?
14 Who hosts Bruce's Price is Right?
15 In the first Blockbusters were the contestants students or OAP's?
16 In which show do celebrities try to find True and Bluff?
17 Who presented the celebrity version of Countdown?
18 Which half of Richard and Judy hosted Cluedo?
19 Who was the only presenter of Mastermind on TV?
20 Which Angus says Have I Got News For You??
21 Does Carol adjudicate over letters or numbers in Countdown?
22 What night of the week is the National Lottery midweek draw?
23 Which Des hosted Take Your Pick in the 90s?
24 How many people start out on William G Stewart's afternoon quiz?
25 Which Frank was a team captain on Call My Bluff?
26 Which Gaby offered contestants Whatever You Want?
27 Who would have fulfilled your request to "Give me a K please, Bob?"
28 Which magician first presented Wipeout?
29 Which show had a Big Ticket challenge with Anthea Turner and Patrick Kielty?
30 What were contestants Going For in Henry Kelly's TV quiz show?

Pot Luck 7 (see Quiz 16, page 24)
1 Tax. 2 Insects. 3 The Boy Scout Movement. 4 Shrove Tuesday. 5 Pink.
6 Sagittarius. 7 Aylesbury. 8 Badger. 9 Liam Gallagher. 10 Romeo and
Juliet. 11 England. 12 Egypt. 13 Little Acorns. 14 Nazareth. 15 A tutu.
16 Take Your Pick. 17 Clouds. 18 In water. 19 Wood. 20 John Cleese.
21 Ontario. 22 Adolf Hitler. 23 Chelsea. 24 Blood. 25 Venice.
26 Silence. 27 Warwickshire. 28 A toad. 29 Gladys Knight. 30 Aldershot.

1 What does T stand for in the initials V.A.T?
2 What does a Venus fly-trap trap?
3 Which movement was founded by Lord Baden-Powell?
4 What day precedes Ash Wednesday?
5 In snooker, is the pink ball or the brown ball of higher value?
6 Which sign of the Zodiac is pictured by an archer?
7 What is the principal county town of Buckinghamshire?
8 Which animal is often given the name Brock?
9 Who was Patsy Kensit's third husband?
10 Which Shakespeare play features the Capulets and Montagues?
11 Which country was called Albion by Greeks and Romans?
12 In which country is the battle site of El Alamein?
13 Great oak trees grow from what, according to the proverb?
14 Which town did Jesus grow up in?
15 What is the name of the dress worn by a ballerina?
16 Which TV show features the Yes/No Game?
17 Stratus, Cirrus and Cumulus are all types of what?
18 Where do mosquitoes lay their eggs?
19 What are clogs traditionally made from?
20 Which actor played Basil Fawlty in Fawlty Towers?
21 Toronto is the capital of which Canadian province?
22 Who wrote Mein Kampf?
23 Which football team plays at Stamford Bridge?
24 What do your arteries carry from your heart?
25 In which northern Italian city is the Doge's Palace?
26 If speech is silver, what is golden according to the proverb?
27 Which county cricket team plays at Edgbaston?
28 What is a natterjack?
29 Which Gladys sang the theme song to the 007 movie Licence to Kill?
30 Which Hampshire town has England's largest military camp?

Answers

TV: Quiz and Game Shows (see Quiz 15, page 23)
1 Channel 4. 2 100 Per Cent Gold. 3 Supermarket Sweep. 4 Going For A
Song. 5 Big Break. 6 Lily Savage. 7 Telly Addicts. 8 Won't Cook.
9 Houses. 10 Four. 11 Three. 12 Ulrika. 13 Bullseye. 14 Bruce Forsyth.
15 Students. 16 Call My Bluff. 17 Richard Whitely. 18 Richard.
19 Magnus Magnusson. 20 Deayton. 21 Numbers. 22 Wednesday.
23 O'Connor. 24 15. 25 Muir. 26 Roslin. 27 Bob Holness. 28 Paul
Daniels. 29 National Lottery. 30 Gold.

Quiz 17 Leisure: Books

Answers - see Quiz 18, page 26

LEVEL 1

1   Which detective did Dr Watson assist?
2   Which egg shaped nursery rhyme character appears in Alice Through the Looking Glass?
3   Mrs Beeton was most famous for writing on what subject?
4   Are Penguin books hardbacks or paperbacks?
5   Was St Trinian's a school for boys or girls?
6   What type of animal is Winnie the Pooh?
7   What relation was Charlotte to Emily and Anne Bronte?
8   Who is Agatha Christie's most famous female detective?
9   Which ex MP Edwina wrote A Parliamentary Affair?
10 How is crime writer Baroness James better known?
11 Who's Winter Collection of recipes sold 1.5 million copies in just eight weeks?
12 What sort of Factory is associated with Roald Dahl's Charlie?
13 In which book are there four accounts of Jesus's life called gospels?
14 Which African president's autobiography was called Long Walk to Freedom?
15 Which animal was Beatrix Potter's Mrs Tiggywinkle?
16 What was Schindler's Ark renamed when it was made into a film?
17 Where was Douglas Adams' Hitchhiker's Guide to?
18 What type of tales did the Grimm brothers write?
19 What is the nationality of novelist Maeve Binchy?
20 Which novelist Dame Catherine died in 1998?
21 Which Jilly penned The Man who Made Husbands Jealous?
22 Who was Ian Fleming's most famous secret agent creation?
23 Who did Laurie Lee write of Cider with...?
24 Which soccer coach's World Cup Story 1998 caused an outrage over breaches of confidentiality?
25 Which Stephen is famous for horror writing such as The Shining?
26 What was Dick Francis's profession before he turned to writing?
27 What was Bram Stoker's most famous monstrous creation?
28 In which century did Charles Dickens live?
29 Which comedian Ben wrote Gridlock and Popcorn?
30 Which Frederick's first success was The Day of the Jackal?

Pot Luck 8 (see Quiz 18, page 26)

1 November. 2 The tail. 3 Oprah Winfrey. 4 An alkali. 5 A small wood.
6 Hamlet. 7 Angels. 8 Conservatives. 9 Afrikaans. 10 Kenya. 11 Willow.
12 Seven. 13 An eyrie. 14 Threadneedle Street. 15 Doncaster.
16 Goodbye Yellow Brick Road. 17 £1. 18 Ballet. 19 Violet. 20 Adder.
21 Nepal. 22 Agoraphobia. 23 Mercury. 24 Pasta. 25 Spencer. 26 A
Minister/Clergyman. 27 Norwich. 28 A News agency. 29 Mars. 30 Four.

Answers

Quiz 18 Pot Luck 8

Answers - see Quiz 17, page 25

1   In which month is Thanksgiving celebrated in America?
2   Where is the rattle in a rattlesnake?
3   Which talk show hostess looks back on founding Harpo Productions?
4   What is the opposite of an acid?
5   What is a spinney?
6   Who said, "To be or not to be, that is the question"?
7   In The Bible, what were seraphim and cherubim?
8   Which political party had Benjamin Disraeli as a leader?
9   Which South African language derives from the Dutch settlers?
10 Which country has Nairobi as its capital?
11 Cricket bats are traditionally made from which wood?
12 How many colours are in the spectrum?
13 What name is given to the home of an eagle?
14 On which Street is the Bank of England?
15 The St Leger is run at which Yorkshire race course?
16 The original Candle in the Wind was on which album?
17 Which coin was first introduced in the UK in 1983?
18 For what type of dancing did Anna Pavlova achieve fame?
19 What colour is an amethyst?
20 What is the only poisonous snake in Britain?
21 Which country is native homeland to the Gurkha troops?
22 Which phobia is the fear of open spaces?
23 Which chemical is also known as quicksilver?
24 Penne, rigatoni and tagliatelle are all types of what?
25 What did the initial 'S' stand for in Winston S Churchill?
26 Who lives in a Manse?
27 Which Norfolk city stands on the River Wensum?
28 What is Reuters?
29 Who was god of war in Roman mythology?
30 How many times does the letter 'S' appear in Mississippi?

Leisure: Books (see Quiz 17, page 25)
1 Sherlock Holmes. 2 Humpty Dumpty. 3 Cooking. 4 Paperbacks. 5 Girls.
6 Bear. 7 Sisters. 8 Miss Marple. 9 Currie. 10 P.D. James. 11 Delia
Smith. 12 Chocolate. 13 Bible. 14 Nelson Mandela. 15 Hedgehog.
16 Schindler's List. 17 The Galaxy. 18 Fairy tales. 19 Irish. 20 Cookson.
21 Cooper. 22 James Bond. 23 Rosie. 24 Glenn Hoddle. 25 King.
26 Jockey. 27 Dracula. 28 19th. 29 Elton. 30 Forsyth.

Answers

Quiz 19 Sport: Record Breakers

Answers - see Quiz 20, page 28

1   Mark Spitz won seven Olympic golds at record speeds doing what?
2   Which South American soccer team has won most World Cups?
3   Was Tessa Sanderson competing in her second, fourth or sixth Olympics in 1996?
4   Lyn Davies broke the British record in which jump event?
5   David Campese was leading try scorer for which country?
6   Which Sally was a world record hurdler and '92 Olympic champion?
7   Who was made England's youngest ever football coach in 1996?
8   Did Roger Bannister run the first four minute mile in Oxford or Cambridge?
9   Was Martina Hingis 13, 15 or 17 when she first won Wimbledon doubles?
10   Which ice dancers won a record six successive British championships between 1978 and 1984?
11   Which Nigel was the first to win both F1 and Indy Car world championships?
12   Which record breaker Sebastian went on to become a Tory MP?
13   Which Tony made the first televised hole in one in Britain?
14   Who won the 100m in Seoul in record time before being disqualified?
15   Which Steve was six times World Snooker Champion in the 80s?
16   For which former Iron Curtain country did Marita Koch break records?
17   Which English Steve won four Olympic golds between '84 and '96?
18   How many events were in Daley Thompson's speciality event?
19   Which Pete equalled Borg's five Wimbledon singles wins in 1998?
20   Which Gareth became Wales youngest ever Rugby captain in 1968?
21   Alain Prost was the first to win the F1 world title for which country?
22   Bob Beaman held which Olympic jump record for over 20 years?
23   Who was Britain's only Men's 100m world record holder between 1983 and 1993?
24   Which David did Graham Gooch overtake to become England's highest scoring Test player?
25   World record breaker Kip Keino is from which continent?
26   Did Nadia Comaneci first score a perfect Olympic 10 at 14, 18 or 21?
27   Which two Steves were record breaking middle distance runners of the 70s and 80s?
28   Colin Jackson was a world record holder in which event?
29   Who was the first player to score 100 goals in the Premiership?
30   Duncan Goodhew held British records in which sport?

Pot Luck 9 (see Quiz 20, page 28)
1 Oliver Twist. 2 Gin. 3 Taj Mahal. 4 Dingoes. 5 Actor/Actress. 6 Violins.
7 Greece. 8 June. 9 Bridges. 10 May. 11 Rumpelstiltskin. 12 A stipend.
13 Red. 14 Kite-mark. 15 New York. 16 Albatross. 17 Barrels.
18 Sherry. 19 The worm. 20 Paul McCartney. 21 Bread. 22 45. 23 In the mouth. 24 Andrew Lloyd Webber. 25 St Paul's Cathedral. 26 Vertical.
27 Theatres. 28 Sugar, almonds. 29 Evangelism. 30 Magpie.

Answers

Quiz 20 Pot Luck 9

Answers - see Quiz 19, page 27

LEVEL 1

1 In which Dickens' novel is the character Bill Sikes?
2 Which alcoholic drink contains juniper as a flavour?
3 By what name is the mausoleum at Agra, India normally known?
4 Which dogs are a serious pest in Australia?
5 What would your profession be if you were a member of Equity?
6 Which instruments did Antonio Stradivari produce?
7 Which country is famous for moussaka?
8 In which month is Father's Day in the UK?
9 Pontoon and suspension are both types of which construction?
10 What did the 'M' stand for in Louisa M. Alcott's name?
11 Which name did a fairytale Queen have to guess or lose her child?
12 What is a salary paid to a clergyman called?
13 What colour is cochineal?
14 The British Standards Institute uses what mark as a sign of approval?
15 Which American city is served by Kennedy Airport?
16 Which bird has the largest wing span?
17 What does a cooper make?
18 What kind of drink is Amontillado?
19 What does an early bird catch, according to the proverb?
20 Which Beatle's daughter is a dress designer?
21 Bloomers and baps are both types of what?
22 How many years are there in four and a half decades?
23 Where are your incisors?
24 Who, together with Tim Rice, wrote Evita?
25 Where is Lord Nelson buried?
26 On a staircase are the risers flat or vertical?
27 The Cambridge, Adelphi and Lyric in London are all what?
28 What are the two ingredients of marzipan?
29 Billy Graham is famous for which branch of Christianity?
30 Which black and white bird is usually accused of stealing?

Answers

Sport: Record Breakers (see Quiz 19, page 27)
1 Swimming. 2 Brazil. 3 Sixth. 4 Long jump. 5 Australia. 6 Gunnell.
7 Glenn Hoddle. 8 Oxford. 9 15. 10 Torvill & Dean. 11 Mansell. 12 Coe.
13 Jacklin. 14 Ben Johnson. 15 Davis. 16 East Germany. 17 Redgrave.
18 Ten. 19 Sampras. 20 Edwards. 21 France. 22 Long jump.
23 Linford Christie. 24 Gower. 25 Africa. 26 14. 27 Ovett & Cram.
28 Hurdles. 29 Alan Shearer. 30 Swimming.

Quiz 21 Science: Communication

LEVEL 1

Answers - see Quiz 22, page 30

1   Is 0171 the dialling code for central Manchester or central London?
2   Which mobile phone company shares its name with a fruit?
3   If you dial 1471 whose number are you given?
4   Which four letters preface access to an Internet website?
5   What is the normal size of a floppy disk?
6   What sort of cards can you use in a cardphone?
7   What is held in the hands to communicate through semaphore?
8   The fingertips represent which five letters in sign language?
9   112 is an alternative to which number?
10 A modem connects a computer to what?
11 Qantas Airways originated in which country?
12 Which cross Channel link has its French terminus at Coquelles?
13 Tresco airport links which Isles to the UK?
14 What is the regulatory body of the telecommunications industry called?
15 What did Le Shuttle change its name to in 1998?
16 What does D stand for in IDD?
17 Which character divides the person from the place in an email address?
18 Which type of clock works from shadows?
19 Numbers beginning with 0800 usually cost how much to the caller?
20 What do Demon and AOL offer access to?
21 Combinations of which two signs are used in Morse code?
22 What country are PanAm based in?
23 Before '81, telecommunications were under the authority of which Office?
24 Which number do you ring to contact a BT operator?
25 Which country's airline has the code PK?
26 What is the American version of the British post code?
27 With BT calls when does daytime end Monday to Friday?
28 What does 'I' stand for in IT?
29 Which two digits are the first to dial for an international number?
30 Ryan Air is a budget airline from which country?

Answers

Pot Luck 10 (see Quiz 22, page 30)
1 Pastry. **2** Mr Hyde. **3** Jewellery. **4** Red. **5** Loudspeakers. **6** Marriage.
7 Flamingo. **8** Table Mountain. **9** The Rank Organisation. **10** China.
11 Senorita. **12** Russia. **13** Hudson (Butler). **14** Disraeli. **15** Dame Edna
Everage. **16** Hong Kong. **17** Church/Cathedral. **18** Agenda. **19** Andrew.
20 Three. **21** Pears. **22** Shrew. **23** The Mayflower. **24** Oil Rigs.
25 Green. **26** Wuthering Heights. **27** Bridgetown. **28** Sultana.
29 Penultimate. **30** Fern Britton.

Quiz 22 Pot Luck 10

LEVEL 1

Answers - see Quiz 21, page 29

1   Choux, puff and short are all types of what?
2   Who was the more unpleasant - Dr Jekyll or Mr Hyde?
3   Generally what is Hatton Gardon in London famous for?
4   What colour is carmine?
5   What are tweeters and woofers?
6   Which ceremony is associated with orange blossom?
7   Which pink bird sleeps on one leg?
8   Which mountain overlooks Cape Town, South Africa?
9   Which British film company used a symbol of a man striking a gong?
10 Which country is renowned for sweet and sour cooking?
11 What is the Spanish word for a young or single lady?
12 Where was the news agency Tass based?
13 Which part did Gordon Jackson play in Upstairs, Downstairs?
14 Who was the first Jewish Prime Minister in Britain?
15 Comedian Barry Humphries plays which female character?
16 Which colony ceased to be British in June 1997?
17 Where would you be if you were in a transept?
18 What is the list of the subjects to be discussed at a meeting called?
19 Which Prince served in the Falklands War?
20 In the old saying, how many makes a crowd if two are company?
21 Conference and Cornice are types of which fruit?
22 Which animal needs 'Taming' in the title of the Shakespeare play?
23 Aboard which ship in 1620 did the Pilgrim Fathers sail to America?
24 What type of rigs are Ekofisk, Forties and Frigg?
25 What colour is angelica?
26 What connects singer Kate Bush with novelist Emily Bronte?
27 What is the capital of Barbados?
28 What is a wife of a sultan called?
29 What word describes something being next to last?
30 Who first presented Ready Steady Cook?

Answers

Science & Nature: Communications (see Quiz 21, page 29)
1 London. **2** Orange. **3** Last person to have called you. **4** http (not all have www). **5** 3.5ins. **6** Phone cards and credit cards. **7** Flags. **8** Vowels. **9** 999. **10** Telephone. **11** Australia. **12** Channel Tunnel. **13** Scilly Isles. **14** Oftel. **15** Eurotunnel. **16** Dialling. **17** @. **18** Sundial. **19** Nothing. **20** The Internet. **21** Dots & dashes. **22** USA. **23** Post Office. **24** 100. **25** Pakistan. **26** Zip. **27** 6 pm. **28** Information. **29** 00. **30** Ireland.

Quiz 23 Pop: 70s

Answers - see Quiz 24, page 32

LEVEL 1

1   Which country did Abba come from?
2   Which 70s pop movie with John Travolta was re-released in 1998?
3   Which band did Diana Ross leave at the start of the decade?
4   T Rex was led by which singer?
5   What colour was Debbie Harry's hair which named her band?
6   Maggie May provided who with his first No 1?
7   Kiki Dee's biggest 70s hit was with whom?
8   Where did Supertramp have Breakfast in 1979?
9   Who was lead singer with the Boomtown Rats?
10 Who cleaned Wimbledon Common and cleaned up in the charts in '74?
11 What went with Peaches in the 70s charts?
12 Who had a posthumous hit with Way Down?
13 Song for whom was Elton John's first instrumental hit?
14 Which World Cup football squad did Rod Stewart have a hit with?
15 Which Rollers had two No 1's in 1975?
16 Who had a single hit from their album Bat Out of Hell?
17 Izhar Cohen and Alphabeta won Eurovision for which country?
18 Which brothers included Wayne, Donny and Little Jimmy?
19 Whose first hit was Wuthering Heights?
20 Which 70s B side for Queen became a football anthem?
21 Which Abba hit became the name of an Alan Partridge spoof?
22 Which Gary's first hit was as Tubeway Army?
23 Which hostel did the Village People visit in the 70s?
24 How many performers made up The Carpenters?
25 Which soccer side had a hit with I'm Forever Blowing Bubbles?
26 Tubular Bells is credited with establishing which record label?
27 Which band were Part of the Union?
28 Which Bryan founded Roxy Music?
29 Who celebrated his Ding-A-Ling in song?
30 Who had the last 70s Xmas No 1 with Another Brick in the Wall?

Answers

Pot Luck 11 (see Quiz 24, page 32)
1 The Jungle Book. 2 Cumberland. 3 Michael Jackson. 4 Tailoring. 5 Yellow.
6 Two. 7 Swan. 8 Elvis Presley. 9 Otters. 10 Ballet. 11 Portugal.
12 Tenor. 13 White. 14 Open University. 15 Attila. 16 Louis Braille.
17 Stephen. 18 Carrot. 19 Count. 20 Julie Andrews. 21 The Sound of
Music. 22 South America. 23 Eight. 24 Johann Strauss. 25 Ginger Rogers.
26 Cheese. 27 Monopoly. 28 Gordonstoun. 29 Red. 30 Asia.

31

Quiz 24 Pot Luck 11

LEVEL 1

1   Which Disney film is I Wanna be Like You from?
2   Which British sausage is traditionally sold in a coil?
3   Which pop megastar celebrated his 40th birthday on 29th August 1998?
4   Which profession is associated with Savile Row?
5   What colour is the flower of an oil seed rape plant?
6   How many packs of playing cards are needed to play Canasta?
7   Bewick, Black and Whooper are all types of what?
8   Which pop star is linked with blue suede shoes?
9   Which animals live in a holt?
10 With which type of dance was Nijinsky famous?
11 In which country is the Algarve Coast?
12 Which voice is higher - a tenor or a baritone?
13 What colour is the St Andrew's cross on the Scottish flag?
14 Which University is based in Milton Keynes?
15 Who in AD 434 was King of the Huns?
16 Who invented the dot system with which the blind can read by touch?
17 On whose feast day did King Wenceslas look out?
18 Which vegetable are people told to eat to help them see at night?
19 An abacus helps you do what?
20 Which actress sang A Spoonful of Sugar in Mary Poppins?
21 Which musical does Climb Every Mountain come from?
22 The anaconda is native to which continent?
23 How many legs does a spider have?
24 Who wrote the waltz called The Blue Danube?
25 Who was the most famous dancing partner of Fred Astaire?
26 What are Gorgonzola, Dolcelatte and Pecorino?
27 On which board game are The Strand, Mayfair and Park Lane?
28 At which Scottish school was Prince Charles educated?
29 What colour is the spot on the Japanese flag?
30 Which continent is native home to the tiger?

Answers

Pop: 70s (see Quiz 23, page 31)
1 Sweden. 2 Grease. 3 The Supremes. 4 Marc Bolan. 5 Blonde. 6 Rod Stewart. 7 Elton John. 8 America. 9 Bob Geldof. 10 The Wombles. 11 Herb. 12 Elvis Presley. 13 Guy. 14 Scottish. 15 Bay City Rollers. 16 Meat Loaf. 17 Israel. 18 Osmond. 19 Kate Bush. 20 We Are the Champions. 21 Knowing Me Knowing You. 22 Numan. 23 YMCA. 24 Two. 25 West Ham. 26 Virgin. 27 Strawbs. 28 Ferry. 29 Chuck Berry. 30 Pink Floyd.

Quiz 25 TV: Sitcoms

Answers - see Quiz 26, page 34

LEVEL 1

1   What is the profession of Geraldine Grainger of Dibley?
2   How do Men Martin Clunes and Neil Morrissey behave in the sitcom?
3   Which Scottish pop star played Adrian Mole's mum?
4   Which Duchess made a cameo appearance in Friends as herself?
5   Whatever Happened to the Likely Lads? was the sequel to what?
6   Which sitcom classic was about self sufficiency in Surbiton?
7   How did Hyacinth pronounce 'Bucket' in Keeping Up Appearances?
8   Which show about Grace Brothers' store had a rerun in 1998?
9   What was the sequel to Yes Minister?
10 Which sitcom about the Trotters was originally to be called Readies?
11 Craig Charles was Dave Lister in which sci fi sitcom?
12 Which Penelope alias Audrey was To the Manor Born?
13 How many children feature in the sitcom about Bill and Ben Porter?
14 Which Ronnie played Arkwright in Open All Hours?
15 Ian McShane starred in which sitcom about a shady antiques dealer?
16 In which historical sitcom did Baldrick first appear?
17 Which show was originally to have been called Your Bottom?
18 Which Felicity was the star of Solo?
19 In which sitcom did Joanna Lumley play champagne swilling Patsy?
20 What are the names of the Birds in Birds of a Feather?
21 In Dad's Army, who called Sgt. Wilson Uncle Arthur?
22 Frasier was a spin off from which series based in a Boston bar?
23 What was the occupation of the stars of Common as Muck?
24 Which wartime sitcom featured Rene and Edith Artois?
25 Who played Jean, husband of Lionel, in As Time Goes By?
26 Goodnight Sweetheart is set in the 40s and which other decade?
27 Which series was based on Butlin's and Pontin's?
28 What was Anton Rodgers' legal job in May to December?
29 Which Family is a sitcom with ex Mrs Merton Caroline Aherne?
30 What is Mrs Victor Meldrew's first name?

Pot Luck 12 (see Quiz 26, page 34)

Answers
1 Butterflies. 2 Pork Pie. 3 The Sahara. 4 Horse racing. 5 Wright Brothers.
6 John Ridd. 7 Medicines/Drugs. 8 Pinocchio. 9 Fox. 10 Red/green.
11 Asp. 12 Three. 13 Evita. 14 Small pieces of wood. 15 Haricot.
16 Flower/Shrub. 17 Otter. 18 Flanders. 19 Baloo and Mowgli. 20 Pepsi
Cola. 21 Four. 22 1970s. 23 Italy. 24 Stamps. 25 Blue. 26 Peppermint.
27 Dove. 28 Aintree. 29 Soprano. 30 The English Channel.

Quiz 26 Pot Luck 12

Answers - see Quiz 25, page 33

1 Red Admirals, Fritillaries and Tortoiseshells are all what?
2 Which pie is Melton Mowbray renowned for?
3 Which has more rainfall the Sahara or Antarctica?
4 Which sport would you see at Chepstow?
5 Which brothers made the first manned powered aero flight in 1903?
6 Who is the main male character in the novel Lorna Doone?
7 What was sold in an apothecary?
8 From which Disney film is Give a Little Whistle from?
9 Which animals live in an earth or lair?
10 Along with white, what colours appear on the Italian flag?
11 Which snake is it said Cleopatra used to poison herself?
12 How many ships came sailing by according to the carol?
13 Which musical does Don't Cry for Me, Argentina come from?
14 What is chipboard made from?
15 What bean is made into a baked bean?
16 What is a poinsettia?
17 In the novel what kind of animal was Tarka?
18 Bruges is the capital of which part of Belgium?
19 Which characters sang The Bare Necessities in the Jungle Book?
20 Madonna's Like A Prayer advertised which soft drink?
21 How many wings does a bee have?
22 In which decade did Britain convert to decimal currency?
23 Sardinia is part of which country?
24 What are collected by a philatelist?
25 What colour is the background of the Scottish flag?
26 What flavour is creme de menthe?
27 What type of bird are Ring, Turtle and Collared?
28 On which horse race course are Becher's Brook and the Chair?
29 Which is the highest female singing voice?
30 Which sea is called La Manche by the French?

TV: Sitcoms (see Quiz 25, page 33)
1 Vicar. 2 Badly. 3 Lulu. 4 Duchess of York. 5 The Likely Lads. 6 The Good Life. 7 'Bouquet'. 8 Are You Being Served? 9 Yes Prime Minister.
10 Only Fools and Horses. 11 Red Dwarf. 12 Keith. 13 2 Point 4.
14 Barker. 15 Lovejoy. 16 Blackadder. 17 Bottom. 18 Kendall.
19 Absolutely Fabulous. 20 Sharon & Tracy. 21 Pike. 22 Cheers.
23 Dustmen. 24 Allo Allo. 25 Judy Dench. 26 90s. 27 Hi-De-Hi!
28 Solicitor. 29 Royle. 30 Margaret.

Quiz 27 The Movies: Comedies

LEVEL 1

Answers - see Quiz 28, page 36

1 Which Rowan played a vicar in Four Weddings and a Funeral?
2 Which Carry On film was set on board the SS Happy Wanderer?
3 Who played the bowler hatted Tramp in The Kid?
4 Addams Family Values was the follow up to what?
5 Which west London borough is associated with classic comedies?
6 What age group are the performers in the gangster film Bugsy Malone?
7 Which cartoon set in Bedrock starred John Goodman in the human version?
8 What type of Adventure did Bill and Ted have?
9 What sort of farm animal was Babe?
10 Which Tom starred in Jerry Maguire?
11 What type of animals were Lady and the Tramp?
12 Who's World did Mike Myers and Dana Garvey live in?
13 A Fish Called ... what was a John Cleese & Jamie Lee Curtis classic?
14 What was Whoopi Goldberg disguised as in Sister Act?
15 Which group sang the theme song for Four Weddings and a Funeral?
16 Which Jim was the shy bank clerk in The Mask?
17 Forrest Gump said life was like a box of what?
18 Which Julia was the Pretty Woman in the film's title?
19 Which British comedy duo were the stars of The Magnificent Two?
20 What did Robin Williams in Mrs Doubtfire and Dustin Hoffman in Tootsie have in common?
21 What unusual handicap did Bernie have as a host in A Weekend at Bernie's?
22 Which film of a Book featured The Bare Necessities?
23 Which Sid's first Carry On was Carry On Constable?
24 To whom did someone say 'I Shrunk The Kids' in the film title?
25 Which spinach-loving cartoon character was played by Robin Williams?
26 Which 1980 film title suggests normal working hours?
27 Was Patrick Swayze or Demi Moore the Ghost in the 1990 film?
28 Look Who's Talking Too was the sequel to what?
29 Who was the Queen of the Desert in the transvestsite comedy?
30 Which Inspector played by Peter Sellers was in The Pink Panther?

Answers

Pot Luck 13 (see Quiz 28, page 36)
1 Red/Yellow. 2 Stop bleeding. 3 The King and I. 4 Canada. 5 Sir Cliff Richard. 6 Tower of London. 7 Blue/violet. 8 Suffolk. 9 General Strike. 10 Cricket. 11 Russian. 12 Australia. 13 24. 14 Sturgeon. 15 Heart. 16 White. 17 Manchester City. 18 Spirit level. 19 Anna Sewell. 20 Maundy money. 21 Kayaks. 22 Oranges. 23 All for one and one for all. 24 Doncaster. 25 Windsor. 26 A Sharp. 27 Rolf Harris. 28 Cambridge. 29 Red/white. 30 Amy Johnson.

Quiz 28 Pot Luck 13

Answers - see Quiz 27, page 35

1   Along with black which colours appear on the German flag?
2   What is a tourniquet used for in First Aid?
3   Which musical is based on a book called Anna and the King of Siam?
4   The chipmunk is native to America and which other country?
5   Who was pop's first Knight?
6   Where in London is the ceremony of the keys held each night?
7   What colour is indigo?
8   Which East Anglian county is often called "Constable Country"?
9   In 1926 which General crisis happened in England?
10 Which sport links Ted Dexter, Peter May and Ray Illingworth?
11 What was the nationality of composer Rimsky-Korsakov?
12 Budgerigars are native to which country?
13 How many carats in pure gold?
14 Caviar comes traditionally from which fish?
15 What does a cardiologist study?
16 What colour are Aylesbury ducks?
17 Which football team plays at Maine Road for its home matches?
18 What is used to check something is level by a builder?
19 Who wrote Black Beauty?
20 What does the Queen give out on the day before Good Friday?
21 What are the sealskin boats used by Eskimos called?
22 What did Nell Gwyn sell when Charles II first saw her?
23 What was the motto of the Three Musketeers?
24 On which course is the horse race the St Leger run?
25 Which castle is in the royal county of Berkshire?
26 If a musical note is lowered by a flat, what raises it?
27 Who was the first presenter of Animal Hospital?
28 In which city is the River Cam?
29 Apart from blue, what two other colours appear on the Dutch flag?
30 In 1930 which female aviator flew from England to Australia?

Answers

The Movies: Comedies (see Quiz 27, page 35)
1 Atkinson. 2 Cruising. 3 Charlie Chaplin. 4 The Addams Family. 5 Ealing. 6 Children. 7 The Flintstones. 8 Excellent. 9 Pig. 10 Cruise. 11 Dogs. 12 Wayne's. 13 Wanda. 14 Nun. 15 Wet Wet Wet. 16 Carrey. 17 Chocolates. 18 Roberts. 19 Morecambe & Wise. 20 Dressed in drag. 21 Dead. 22 The Jungle Book. 23 James. 24 Honey. 25 Popeye. 26 Nine to Five. 27 Patrick Swayze. 28 Look Who's Talking. 29 Priscilla. 30 Clouseau.

Quiz 29 Geography: The UK

Answers - see Quiz 30, page 38

LEVEL 1

1   Is Holy Island off the east or west coast of England?
2   What is a native of Aberdeen called?
3   Is London's Docklands, north, south, east or west of the city?
4   Where do people go to spot Nessie?
5   Which English gorge takes its name from a nearby village famous for its cheese?
6   Which county has the abbreviation Beds?
7   St Anne's lies to the south of which British seaside resort?
8   Which Royal residence stands by the river Dee?
9   In which country is the UK's highest mountain?
10 What sort of an institution in London is Bart's?
11 On a London Tube map the Central Line is what colour?
12 In which Scottish city did you find the Gorbals?
13 Where is London's most famous Dog's Home?
14 Which Isle off the south coast of England is a county in its own right?
15 What is Britain's most southerly country?
16 Norwich is the administrative centre of which county?
17 In which city did the National Trust buy the childhood home of Paul McCartney?
18 Which motorway runs almost parallel to the A4?
19 With which profession is London's Harley Street associated?
20 What is Britain's largest international airport?
21 In which county is Land's End?
22 Would a Scotsman wear a sporran at the front or at the back of a kilt?
23 Which motorway goes from Lancashire to Yorkshire east to west?
24 In Ireland what is a lough?
25 In which part of the UK is Land of My Fathers a traditional song?
26 Winchester is the adminstrative seat of which county?
27 Aston University is near which Midlands city?
28 Most of the Lake District is in which county?
29 What red flower does Lancs have?
30 In which city is the Barbican Centre?

Pot Luck 14 (see Quiz 30, page 38)

Answers

1 101 Dalmatians. 2 Mozart. 3 A peach. 4 Sark. 5 Brown. 6 He who laughs last. 7 1953. 8 Carpets. 9 Diagonally. 10 Spain. 11 Charles Dickens. 12 Black/Yellow. 13 A vixen. 14 Cakes. 15 Pinocchio. 16 Fencing. 17 Colour. 18 Isle of Wight. 19 A fish. 20 39. 21 Blackberry. 22 Zambezi. 23 Herring. 24 Marie Antoinette. 25 Spam. 26 Victor Hugo. 27 Puffin. 28 Red, yellow & blue. 29 Four. 30 Italy.

Quiz 30 Pot Luck 14

LEVEL 1

1 Pongo and Perdita appear in which canine film?
2 Who composed the opera The Marriage of Figaro?
3 What type of fruit is a nectarine?
4 Which of the four Channel Islands is the smallest?
5 What colour is sepia?
6 Who, according to the proverb, laughs longest?
7 In which year was Everest conquered?
8 Which house furnishing is associated with the town of Kidderminster?
9 How does a bishop move in chess?
10 The drink sangria comes from which European country?
11 Who wrote The Old Curiosity Shop?
12 What two colours other than red appear on the Belgian flag?
13 What is a female fox called?
14 What is sold in a patisserie?
15 When You Wish Upon A Star comes from which Disney film?
16 In which sport would you need a foil or epee?
17 What can a chameleon lizard change?
18 The rocks called The Needles are close to which island?
19 What is a barracuda?
20 How many steps were there in the title of the novel by John Buchan?
21 A loganberry is a cross between a raspberry and what?
22 Which river are the Victoria Falls on?
23 Sardines and pilchards are part of which fish family?
24 Which French Queen was executed in the French Revolution?
25 What name was spiced ham given during wartime?
26 Who wrote The Hunchback of Notre Dame?
27 Which seabird is associated with Lundy Island?
28 What are the three primary colours in art?
29 How many wings does a moth have?
30 From which country does the football team Juventus come from?

Quiz 31 Sport: Who's Who?

Answers - see Quiz 32, page 40

LEVEL 1

1 Who was tennis star Martina Hingis named after?
2 Which lauded soccer-star was born Edson Arantes do Nascimento?
3 Which French footballer David advertised L'Oreal hair products?
4 Golfer Ernie Els is from which African country?
5 Which British tennis player was born on Greg Rusedski's first birthday?
6 Jonah Lomu plays for which international side?
7 Athlete Kelly Holmes was formerly a member of which armed service?
8 Which swimmer Sharron is married to athlete Derek Redmond?
9 Which snooker champ Ray was nicknamed Dracula?
10 What sort of eye accessory does Chris Eubank wear?
11 Who replaced David Coleman on A Question of Sport?
12 Which Monica was stabbed in the back by a fanatical Graf supporter?
13 Was tennis's Michael Chang from Hong Kong or the USA?
14 Which Irishman Alex won his last World Snooker Championship in 1982?
15 Which TV presenter ended her relationship with Stan Collymore during France 98?
16 Which four legged, three times Grand National winner died in 1995?
17 Which Greg rejected a maple leaf for a Union Jack in the 90s?
18 Who founded the book known as the cricketer's Bible?
19 Rachel Hayhoe Flint is a famous name in which sport?
20 Who was Ben Johnson running for when disqualified in Seoul?
21 Which Princess won the '71 European Three Day Event?
22 Who replaced Mike Atherton as England cricket captain?
23 Which temperamental tennis player was dubbed Superbrat?
24 Which Jenny was the first woman to train a Grand National winner?
25 Who was John Fashanu's late brother?
26 Which boxer's catchphrase was "Know what I mean 'Arry"?
27 Which disappearing horse last won the Derby in 1981?
28 Who founded the Stewart motor racing team?
29 What was cricket umpire Harold Bird's nickname?
30 Who became the first black manager of a Premiership club when he took over at Chelsea in 1996?

Pot Luck 15 (see Quiz 32. page 40)

1 Four. 2 Loire. 3 Kristin Scott Thomas. 4 Cornwall. 5 South-south-east.
6 Thomas Hardy. 7 Slavery. 8 King. 9 Red/White. 10 USA. 11 Seven.
12 Kew. 13 Hadrian's Wall. 14 Purple. 15 Mont Blanc. 16 Venice. 17 June.
18 Malta. 19 Blue Peter. 20 Apple. 21 Queen's Counsel. 22 The Black
Death/Bubonic Plague. 23 New Orleans. 24 A spring tide. 25 Argentina.
26 Daisy. 27 Shropshire. 28 Pigeon racing. 29 Melon. 30 Switzerland.

Answers

Quiz 32 Pot Luck 15

Answers - see Quiz 31, page 39

LEVEL 1

1   How many wings does a butterfly have?
2   Which river is the longest in France?
3   Who is older – Kristin Scott Thomas or Kate Winslet?
4   In which county is Bodmin Moor?
5   Which compass point is opposite North-north-west?
6   Which Thomas wrote The Mayor of Casterbridge?
7   Which trade was abolished in 1807 in the British Empire?
8   Which chess piece should be protected at all costs?
9   What two colours are on the Austrian flag?
10 In which country was there a North v South civil war from 1861-65?
11 How many players are in a netball team?
12 Where in Britain are the Royal Botanic Gardens?
13 Which ancient wall crosses England from Wallsend to Solway?
14 What colour is an aubergine?
15 Which mountain is the highest in the Alps?
16 The artist Canaletto was associated with which Italian city?
17 In which month is the Trooping of the Colour?
18 Which island is also called the George Cross Island?
19 Which children's show did Anthea Turner present?
20 Cox, Braeburn and Gala are all kinds of which fruit?
21 In legal terms, what do the initials QC stand for?
22 Which disaster struck England in the 1340s?
23 Where, in America, is jazz supposed to have been born?
24 What is the opposite of a neap tide?
25 Which country lies immediately east of Chile?
26 Who was asked to ride "a bicycle made for two" in the song?
27 In which English county is the town of Telford?
28 The National Homing Union is involved with which leisure pursuit?
29 What kind of fruit can be cantaloupe?
30 Which country as well as France is Lake Geneva in?

Answers

Sport: Who's Who? (see Quiz 31, page 39)
1 Martina Navratilova. 2 Pele. 3 Ginola. 4 South Africa. 5 Tim Henman.
6 New Zealand. 7 Army. 8 Davies. 9 Reardon. 10 Monocle. 11 Sue
Barker. 12 Seles. 13 USA. 14 Higgins. 15 Ulrika Jonsson. 16 Red Rum.
17 Rusedski. 18 Wisden. 19 Women's cricket. 20 Canada. 21 Anne.
22 Alec Stewart. 23 John McEnroe. 24 Pitman. 25 Justin Fashanu. 26 Frank
Bruno. 27 Shergar. 28 Jackie Stewart. 29 Dickie Bird. 30 Ruud Gullit.

Quiz 33 Pop: The 80s

Answers - see Quiz 34, page 42

LEVEL 1

1   Who went straight to No 1 in 81 with Stand and Deliver?
2   What colour Door gave Shakin' Stevens an 80s hit?
3   Which ex Beatle had a hit with Stevie Wonder in 1982?
4   Whose album Thriller provided several hit singles?
5   Who was KC's backing Band?
6   Which Scot had chart success after Esther Rantzen's The Big Time?
7   Which BBC Radio station banned Relax?
8   Ravel's Bolero charted because of which skaters' Olympic success?
9   Which actor Robert was named in a Bananarama song title ?
10 Which Superstar Rat sang Love Me Tender?
11 Which Alison's nickname was Alf?
12 Which Elaine and Barbara topped the charts in 1985?
13 Which Mrs Andrew Lloyd Webber had a hit with Pie Jesu?
14 David Bowie and Mick Jagger had a hit after which Concert?
15 Elton John charted with Nikita at the same time as Sting had which coincidental hit?
16 Who had hits as part of Visage and Ultravox?
17 Who told you that you were In The Army Now?
18 Who fronted Culture Club?
19 Graham McPherson of Madness was known as what?
20 Which Kim reached No 2 in 1981, 24 years after dad Marty?
21 Which Spanish singer had the UK's first chart topper in Spanish?
22 David Sylvian was part of which Asian sounding band?
23 Who was the first ventriloquist in the charts with Orville?
24 Who teamed up with Annie Lennox in The Eurythmics?
25 Who was the then oldest man in the charts with New York New York?
26 Who joined Cliff Richard for his 80s Living Doll?
27 Which TV puppets sang The Chicken Song?
28 Which red haired Royal liked Lady in Red?
29 Which future England coach joined Waddle on Diamond Lights?
30 Who had a Xmas No 1 in 88 after 30 year in the charts?

Answers

Pot Luck 16 (see Quiz 34, page 42)
1 Ian McCaskill. 2 Raymond Briggs. 3 13. 4 Soft fruit. 5 Surrey.
6 A monologue. 7 Isle of Man. 8 Queen Victoria. 9 Oranges. 10 French.
11 Horse Guards Parade. 12 Drugs. 13 Your Old Kit Bag. 14 Hats.
15 Honey. 16 Five. 17 Distillery. 18 His tools. 19 The Jordan. 20 Needles.
21 Blackbird. 22 Richard I. 23 Whales. 24 American Football. 25 Capricorn.
26 Pears. 27 November. 28 Agatha Christie. 29 Boxing. 30 Harp.

Quiz 34 Pot Luck 16

Answers - see Quiz 33, page 41

1   Which weatherman featured in a BT ad with the song Bring Me Sunshine?
2   Which cartoonist was the creator of The Snowman?
3   How many are there in a baker's dozen?
4   What would you find in a punnet?
5   In which county are Britain's Royal Botanic Gardens?
6   What is a speech or scene with only one actor called?
7   Douglas is the capital town of which Isle?
8   Who was wife to Prince Albert of Saxe-Coburg and Gotha?
9   The Spanish city of Seville is famous for which fruit?
10 What is the nationality of pianist Richard Clayderman?
11 Where does the Trooping of the Colour take place in London?
12 Pharmacology is the study of what?
13 Where, according to the song, should you pack up your troubles?
14 What is usually kept in a band-box?
15 What is the main ingredient in the drink mead?
16 In music, how many lines are there in a stave?
17 What name is given to the building where whisky is made?
18 According to the proverb, a bad workman always blames what?
19 Jesus Christ was baptised in which river?
20 What are inserted into the body during acupuncture?
21 According to rhyme which bird pecked off the maid's nose?
22 Which King was known as the 'Lionheart'?
23 Beluga, Sperm and Blue are all types of what?
24 Which sport is played on a grid iron?
25 Which Zodiac sign is known as the sign of the goat?
26 What is perry made from?
27 In which month is the State Opening of Parliament in England?
28 Who created sleuth Miss Marple?
29 With which sport do we associate Larry Holmes?
30 Which musical instrument is a national emblem of Ireland?

Answers

Pop: The 80s (see Quiz 33, page 41)
1 Adam and the Ants. 2 Green. 3 Paul McCartney. 4 Michael Jackson.
5 Sunshine Band. 6 Sheena Easton. 7 Radio One. 8 Torvill & Dean.
9 Robert de Niro. 10 Roland. 11 Moyet. 12 Paige, Dickson. 13 Sarah
Brightman. 14 Live Aid. 15 Russians. 16 Midge Ure. 17 Status Quo.
18 Boy George. 19 Suggs. 20 Kim Wilde. 21 Julio Iglesias. 22 Japan.
23 Keith Harris. 24 Dave Stewart. 25 Frank Sinatra. 26 The Young Ones.
27 Spitting Image. 28 Duchess of York. 29 Hoddle. 30 Cliff Richard.

Quiz 35 Leisure: Food & Drink 1

Answers - see Quiz 36, page 44

LEVEL 1

1　Which batter mix is an accompaniment to roast beef?
2　Which blackcurrant drink was advertised by Michael Portillo when he was a child?
3　What colour wine is Beaujolais Nouveau?
4　What colour is the flesh of an avocado?
5　What is the traditional colour for the outside of a stick of rock?
6　Would you eat or drink a Sally Lunn?
7　What type of egg is covered in sausage meat?
8　Scrumpy is a rough form of what?
9　Which mashed vegetable tops a shepherd's pie?
10　Which food has given its name to a road network near Birmingham?
11　Is a Spotted Dick a first course or a pudding?
12　Which fruit is associated with tennis at Wimbledon?
13　Champagne originated in which country?
14　Is a Melton Mowbray pie sweet or savoury?
15　What is a pistachio?
16　What sort of fruit is in a teacake?
17　What is a slice of bacon called?
18　Which is more substantial, afternoon tea or high tea?
19　If you ate al fresco would you be indoors or out of doors?
20　What is the usual shape of a Camembert cheese?
21　Which soft pulpy peas are eaten with fish and chips?
22　What type of food may be served clotted?
23　What would you make in a cafetiere?
24　What type of drink is Bristol Cream?
25　Is chowder a soup or a pudding?
26　A 'pinta' is usually a pint of what?
27　Should red wine normally be drunk chilled or a room temperature?
28　Is there milk in a cappuccino coffee?
29　Are you more likely to eat a croissant at breakfast or supper?
30　A gateau is a creamy type of what?

Answers

Pot Luck 17 (see Quiz 36, page 44)
1 Edward. 2 Staff/stave. 3 Everton. 4 Films. 5 Drowning Men. 6 Hillary Clinton. 7 Eyes. 8 A fool. 9 101 Dalmatians. 10 Baghdad. 11 B. 12 Four years. 13 Portugal. 14 Damon Hill. 15 Wood. 16 Fish. 17 Beta. 18 Ear, Nose & Throat. 19 Assisi. 20 Stitches. 21 Cancer. 22 Tammy Wynette. 23 Brown. 24 New Zealand. 25 St Bernard. 26 California. 27 21. 28 Michael and John. 29 Norway. 30 Roald Dahl.

43

Quiz 36 Pot Luck 17

LEVEL 1

Answers - see Quiz 35, page 43

1   Which English King was also called 'The Confessor'?
2   What are the lines called on which music is written?
3   Which football team play their home games at Goodison Park?
4   PG, 15 and 18 are all classifications for what?
5   According to the proverb, who clutches at straws?
6   How is US lawyer Hillary Roddam better known?
7   In Cockney rhyming slang, what are your mince pies?
8   According to the proverb, who is soon parted from his money?
9   From which Disney film does Cruella De Vil come from?
10   What is the capital of Iraq?
11   Which letter describes a soft lead pencil?
12   How long is an American president's term of office?
13   The Azores are a part of which European country?
14   Who, surprisingly, won the 1998 Belgian Formula 1 Grand Prix?
15   What are the bars on a xylophone made from?
16   What is a mud skipper?
17   What is the second letter of the Greek alphabet?
18   In medicine, what do the initials ENT stand for?
19   With which Italian town is Saint Francis linked?
20   Blanket, back and buttonhole are all types of what?
21   Which Zodiac sign is known as the sign of the crab?
22   Whose life story was called Stand By Your Man?
23   Which wire is live in modern three core electric cable?
24   From which country other than Australia did Anzac troops come from?
25   Who is the patron saint of mountaineers?
26   In which state of the US is the resort of Palm Springs?
27   How many consonants are in the English alphabet?
28   In Peter Pan what are names of Wendy's brothers?
29   The port of Bergen is in which European country?
30   Who wrote the original Tales of the Unexpected?

Answers

Leisure: Food & Drink 1 (see Quiz 35, page 43)
1 Yorkshire pudding. **2** Ribena. **3** Red. **4** Green. **5** Pink. **6** Eat. **7** Scotch egg. **8** Cider. **9** Potato. **10** Spaghetti (junction). **11** Pudding. **12** Strawberries. **13** France. **14** Savoury. **15** Nut. **16** Currants and/or other dried fruit. **17** Rasher. **18** High tea. **19** Out of doors. **20** Round. **21** Mushy peas. **22** Cream. **23** Coffee. **24** Sherry. **25** Soup. **26** Milk. **27** Room temperature. **28** Yes. **29** Breakfast. **30** Cake.

Quiz 37 TV: Soaps

LEVEL 1

1　Which Coronation Street character had the names Fairclough and Sullivan?
2　In which country is The Sullivans set?
3　Characters from which UK soap went to the '98 World Cup Final?
4　What was Channel 5's first major soap called?
5　Which soap sparked the campaign to 'Free the Weatherfield 1'?
6　Lisa Riley was in which soap before You've Been Framed?
7　Danielle Brown of Emmerdale has a sister in which pop band?
8　In which soap were the Battersbys introduced as the family from hell?
9　In Albert Square did Sharon marry Grant or Phil Mitchell?
10　In which northern city was the docu soap Hotel set?
11　In Coronation Street is Spider a pet or an eco warrior?
12　Which soap has an omnibus edition on Sunday afternoons?
13　Gillian Taylforth's sister Kim joined which northern soap in 1998?
14　In which soap did Bobby come back from the dead?
15　The docu soap Lakesiders took place in what type of venue?
16　Which soap has featured aristocrat Lady Tara?
17　Who started soap life as Alma Sedgewick?
18　Which soap has a car repair business at The Arches?
19　What sort of road is Brookside?
20　What time does Coronation Street usually start?
21　Which actress Anna found fame as Beth Jordache in Brookside?
22　Who is Nick Cotton's long suffering mum in Albert Square?
23　How had the Carringtons made their money in Dynasty?
24　What is the first name of Phil and Grant Mitchell's mum?
25　Which Baldwin in Coronation Street hasn't a northern accent?
26　Which Jack and Vera took over the Rovers from the Bet Gilroy?
27　Which Ken has been in Coronation Street from the start?
28　Which soap is the BBC's most watched programme?
29　Which southern hemisphere country did Kathy go to when she left Albert Square?
30　In which city is Brookside set?

Answers

Pot Luck 18 (see Quiz 38, page 46)
1 Fishermen. 2 Doctor. 3 Nothing. 4 Siam. 5 H. 6 Scorpio. 7 Bones. 8 In your mouth. 9 Paul Young. 10 You spoil the child. 11 Violin. 12 A backbone or spinal column. 13 Bean. 14 Queen of Sheba. 15 John Prescott. 16 J.R.R. Tolkien. 17 The Shannon. 18 30th November. 19 Double bass. 20 Dr Zhivago. 21 Radio 2. 22 The Mall. 23 Islam. 24 Dick Emery. 25 Wiltshire. 26 A thief. 27 Brown. 28 Shakespeare. 29 Knots. 30 A long spoon.

Quiz 38 Pot Luck 18

Answers - see Quiz 37, page 45

LEVEL 1

1 What job was done by Peter and Andrew before they were disciples?
2 Ex MP David Owen previously followed which profession?
3 If you are in your birthday suit, what are you wearing?
4 Thailand was formerly known by what name?
5 Which letter describes a hard leaded pencil?
6 Which Zodiac sign is usually shown as a scorpion?
7 Osteoporosis affects which part of the body?
8 Where would you find an incisor?
9 Whose first UK No. 1 hit was Wherever I Lay My Hat?
10 According to the proverb, what happens if you spare the rod?
11 Stephane Grapelli is associated with which musical instrument?
12 What do vertebrates have that invertebrates do not?
13 Which vegetable can be dwarf, runner and broad?
14 Which Queen made a visit to Solomon in The Bible?
15 Who was Tony Blair's first Deputy PM?
16 Who wrote Lord of the Rings?
17 Which river is the longest in the British Isles?
18 On which date is Saint Andrew's Day?
19 Which is largest - cello, viola or double bass?
20 Which epic film had the theme tune Somewhere My Love?
21 Terry Wogan's daily show is on which radio station?
22 Buckingham Palace is at the end of which famous London road?
23 A muezzin is an official of which religion?
24 Who used the catch phrase, "Ooh, you are awful, but I like you"?
25 In which county is Salisbury Plain?
26 In Cockney rhyming slang, what is a tea leaf?
27 What colour is the skin of a kiwi fruit?
28 What does 'S' stand for in RSC?
29 What can be granny, sheepshank and bowline?
30 What do you need to sup with the devil, according to the proverb?

TV: Soaps (see Quiz 37, page 45)
1 Rita. 2 Australia. 3 EastEnders. 4 Family Affairs. 5 Coronation Street.
6 Emmerdale. 7 The Spice Girls. 8 Coronation Street. 9 Grant. 10 Liverpool.
11 Eco warrior. 12 EastEnders. 13 Brookside. 14 Dallas. 15 Shopping
centre. 16 Emmerdale. 17 Alma Baldwin. 18 EastEnders. 19 Close.
20 7.30 p.m.. 21 Friel. 22 Dot. 23 Oil. 24 Peggy. 25 Mike.
26 Duckworth. 27 Barlow. 28 EastEnders. 29 South Africa. 30 Liverpool.

Answers

Quiz 39 Nature: Living World

LEVEL 1

1 Glaucoma affects which part of the body?
2 Which flightless bird lays the world's largest egg?
3 What is a puffball?
4 What happens to a female butterfly after it has laid its eggs?
5 In what type of environment do most crustaceans live?
6 Which natural disaster is measured on the Richter scale?
7 What is the main ingredient of glass?
8 Does a millipede have more, less or exactly 1,000 feet?
9 An ore is a mineral which contains a what?
10 Is the whale shark a mammal like the whale, or a fish like the shark?
11 Which bird is the symbol of the USA?
12 Are butterflies more colourful in warmer or cooler countries?
13 What sort of rock is lava?
14 Which is larger, the dolphin or the porpoise?
15 Which organ of the body has the aorta?
16 How many bones does a slug have?
17 Are worker ants male or female?
18 Altocumulus is a type of what?
19 What is the main source of energy in our ecosystem?
20 Which name for remains of plants and animals which lived on Earth means 'dug up'?
21 On which continent is the world's largest glacier?
22 Kelp is a type of what?
23 What order of mammals does the gibbon belong to?
24 What is the staple food of over half of the world's population?
25 Which creatures are larvae and pupae before being adults?
26 Are most bats visible at night or by day?
27 Which part of a jellyfish has stinging cells?
28 Natural rubber is obtained from what?
29 What is the mother of all the bees in a colony called?
30 The giant sequoia is the largest living what?

Pot Luck 19 (see Quiz 40, page 48)
Answers

1 Jane MacDonald. 2 Egg whites. 3 Betjeman. 4 Liquid or gas. 5 Motor racing. 6 18. 7 Gabriel. 8 Mods. 9 Drei. 10 Winnie The Pooh. 11 Canute. 12 Victor. 13 Bruce Forsyth. 14 Snap-dragon. 15 Sheffield. 16 Quickly. 17 Fountain pen. 18 Italy. 19 Estimated Time of Arrival. 20 Wine. 21 A-Team. 22 Loch Ness Monster. 23 Seven. 24 The All Blacks. 25 The sparrow. 26 Brazil. 27 James Herriot. 28 Poland. 29 Play. 30 Dallas.

Quiz 40 Pot Luck 19

LEVEL 1

Answers - see Quiz 39, page 47

1. Who appeared on The Cruise and became famous for her singing?
2. What is sugar added to, to make meringues?
3. Which poet laureate Sir John died in 1984?
4. What can pass through something if it is porous?
5. For which sport is Eddie Irvine famous?
6. How old should you be to marry without parental permission?
7. In The Bible, which angel foretold of the birth of Jesus?
8. What youth group took to wearing parkas?
9. What is the German word for the number three?
10. Which children's favourite bear said he had "very little brain"?
11. Which English king reputedly commanded the sea to retreat?
12. What is the letter "V" if A is Alpha and B is Bravo?
13. Whose is famous for saying, "Nice to see you, to see you nice"?
14. What is a popular name for the flower the antirrhinum?
15. Which Yorkshire city were Pulp from?
16. In music what does presto mean?
17. What object was invented by Lewis Waterman in 1884?
18. Tuscany is in which European country?
19. In the world of flying, what do the initials ETA stand for?
20. What is retsina?
21. Which Team featured Hannibal Smith?
22. Which monster first hit the headlines in 1933?
23. How many edges are there around a 20 pence coin?
24. What are the New Zealand rugby union team called?
25. According to the rhyme, who killed Cock Robin?
26. The Samba originated in which South American country?
27. Who wrote It Shouldn't Happen to a Vet?
28. The port of Gdansk is in which country?
29. Would you eat, play or sit on a sitar?
30. Which TV series included Sue Ellen and Miss Ellie?

Answers

Nature: Living World (see Quiz 39, page 47)
1 Eyes. 2 Ostrich. 3 Fungus. 4 It dies. 5 Water. 6 Earthquake. 7 Sand.
8 Less. 9 Metal. 10 Fish. 11 Eagle. 12 Warmer. 13 Volcanic rock.
14 Dolphin. 15 Heart. 16 None. 17 Female. 18 Cloud. 19 Sun.
20 Fossil. 21 Antarctica. 22 Seaweed. 23 Primates (also accept apes). 24 Rice. 25 Insects. 26 At night. 27 Tentacles. 28 Rubber Tree. 29 Queen.
30 Tree.

Quiz 41 The Movies: Who's Who?

Answers - see Quiz 42, page 50

1 Which ex James Bond has 'Scotland Forever' tattooed on his arm?
2 Which Jools starred in Spiceworld: The Movie?
3 Which Irish born 007 starred in Tomorrow Never Dies?
4 Which Grease actor danced with Princess Diana at the White House?
5 Which sleuth did Albert Finney play in Agatha Christie's Murder on the Orient Express?
6 Which Attenborough brother is a film actor and director?
7 Who was the star of Moonwalker after being in The Jackson Five?
8 Which bespectacled US actor/director directed the musical Everyone Says I Love You?
9 What type of hat was Charlie Chaplin most famous for?
10 Who is Emma Forbes' actor/director dad?
11 Who was named after her home town of Winona?
12 Which knighted pop singer wrote the music for The Lion King?
13 Hayley Mills is the daughter of which knighted actor?
14 Who separated from husband Bruce Willis in 1998?
15 Which newspaper magnate bought 20th Century Fox in 1985?
16 Who was Sid played by Gary Oldman in Sid and Nancy?
17 What name usually associated with a schoolbag did Woody Allen give his son?
18 Which Welsh actor Sir Anthony bought part of Mount Snowdon in 1998?
19 Which pop star Tina starred in Mad Max Beyond the Thunderdome?
20 Which Ms Foster swapped her real first name from Alicia?
21 In rhyming slang what financial term is Gregory Peck?
22 Which child star was Shirley MacLaine named after?
23 Who appeared first at Madame Tussaud's, Harrison Ford or Hugh Grant?
24 Who starred as Steed in the film version of The Avengers?
25 Which boxer played himself in The Greatest?
26 Film buff Barry Norman is a member of which club with the same name as a Marx brother?
27 Who sang It's Not Unusual in Mars Attacks!?
28 Which racing driver Moss starred in Casino Royale?
29 Who are Cary, Katharine and James in The Philadelphia Story?
30 Whose real name is James Baumgarner?

Pot Luck 20 (see Quiz 42, page 50)
1 Samantha Janus. 2 Ian Fleming. 3 Cornwall. 4 Skeleton. 5 Oporto.
6 Green. 7 Diamond. 8 Pirates. 9 Deux. 10 August. 11 Wrestling.
12 Buttocks. 13 Antonio Banderas. 14 Spain. 15 Rice. 16 Indianapolis.
17 Sylvester. 18 Dover. 19 Deer. 20 Light. 21 Blair. 22 42. 23 BBC.
24 Delta. 25 Japan. 26 Horse racing. 27 Orange/Yellow. 28 An elephant.
29 Lighthouse Family. 30 Par.

Quiz 42 Pot Luck 20

LEVEL 1

Answers - see Quiz 41, page 49

1   Which actress plays Ruth in the TV comedy Babes In The Wood?
2   Who wrote the novel You Only Live Twice?
3   Which English county has a border with only one other county?
4   What collective name is given to the structure of bones in the body?
5   The drink port takes its name from which town?
6   What colour is normally associated with ecological groups?
7   What is the hardest substance known to man?
8   Which people are associated with the Jolly Roger flag?
9   What is the French word for the number two?
10 Alphabetically, which is the second of the 12 calendar months?
11 With which sport do we associate a half nelson?
12 Which muscle is the largest - heart, biceps or buttocks?
13 Which actor played Che in Evita when Madonna was Eva Peron?
14 Which country did the paso doble dance originate in?
15 What type of food can be pilau?
16 In which American city is a 500 mile motor race run annually?
17 Which cartoon cat never manages to catch Tweetie Pie?
18 What is Britain's busiest ferry passenger port?
19 What kind of animal is a hind?
20 What can pass through something if it is translucent?
21 Which Tony first became MP for Sedgefield in 1983?
22 How many sides do seven hexagons have?
23 Was Crackerjack shown on BBC or ITV?
24 What is the letter "D" if A is Alpha and B is Bravo?
25 Which country does the drink sake come from?
26 For which sport is Pat Eddery famous?
27 What colour is saffron?
28 In children's books and on TV, what kind of animal is Babar?
29 Which group entered the UK charts in 1995 with Lifted?
30 What term is used in golf to indicate the stroke rating for each hole?

The Movies: Who's Who? (see Quiz 41, page 49)

1 Sean Connery. **2** Holland. **3** Pierce Brosnan. **4** John Travolta. **5** Poirot.
6 Richard. **7** Michael Jackson. **8** Woody Allen. **9** Bowler. **10** Bryan Forbes.
11 Winona Ryder. **12** Sir Elton John. **13** Sir John Mills. **14** Demi Moore.
15 Rupert Murdoch. **16** Vicious. **17** Satchel. **18** Hopkins. **19** Turner.
20 Jodie Foster. **21** Cheque. **22** Shirley Temple. **23** Harrison Ford.
24 Ralph Fiennes. **25** Muhammad Ali. **26** Groucho. **27** Tom Jones.
28 Stirling Moss. **29** Grant, Hepburn, Stewart. **30** James Garner.

Quiz 43 Hobbies & Leisure 2

Answers - see Quiz 44, page 52

Answers - see Quiz 44, page 52

LEVEL 1

1 What is a bookmaker's licensed premises called?
2 What shape is the target in archery?
3 Where on a dartboard is the bull?
4 Which cubes are necessary for a game of craps?
5 Which direction do you go if you are abseiling?
6 What sort of Park is at Whipsnade?
7 Which locomotive identification hobby shares its name with a controversial 90s movie?
8 In which game do you aim to call "House!"?
9 Yoga was developed from which nation's religion?
10 Is scuba practised above or below the water's surface?
11 From which part of a vehicle might you sell goods to raise cash?
12 What name is given to a small piece of land rented for growing food?
13 In the UK most Bank Holidays fall on which day of the week?
14 Which commodities would you buy at a PYO centre?
15 What does E stand for in NEC?
16 What colour is the baize on a snooker table?
17 Which word precedes sport to describe killing animals for recreation?
18 What type of weapon is used in fencing?
19 What is the name of a coach trip where few know the destination?
20 If you practised on a pommel horse where would you probably be?
21 The Chamber of Horrors is in which London waxworks museum?
22 Which weekly draw is run by Camelot?
23 Are bonsai trees smaller or larger than average?
24 Which club moved to The Riverside in the 1990s?
25 What sort of establishment is a greasy spoon?
26 Who is a tied house usually tied to?
27 What is the type of billiards played in pubs called?
28 The Summer Bank Holiday takes place in which month in the UK?
29 Which name for an expert in a particular hobby is the same as a padded jacket?
30 What does Y stand for in DIY?

Pot Luck 21 (see Quiz 44, page 52)
1 70s. 2 Middlesborough. 3 Cuba. 4 Springfield. 5 Seven. 6 Toboggan.
7 Goliath. 8 On water - it's a boat. 9 Costner. 10 Elephant. 11 Tower
Bridge. 12 Their gills. 13 Meat. 14 Six. 15 Possession. 16 Green & Yellow.
17 Nephews. 18 Eins. 19 James Herriot. 20 Catherine Wheel. 21 Victoria.
22 Canaveral. 23 Mineral water. 24 Baldrick. 25 Pounds. 26 650.
27 Rome. 28 Yellow. 29 Moses. 30 Six.

Quiz 44 Pot Luck 21

Answers - see Quiz 43, page 51

LEVEL 1

1   Did Britain join the EEC in the 60s, 70s or 80s?
2   At which club did Gazza and Paul Merson play in the same team?
3   The Rumba originated in which country?
4   Where do the cartoon Simpsons live?
5   How many edges are there around a 50 pence coin?
6   What type of vehicle is seen on the Cresta Run?
7   Which Biblical giant was killed by David?
8   Where would you find a useful junk?
9   Which Kevin was Wyatt Earp in the 1994 movie?
10 Which animal does ivory predominantly come from?
11 Which London bridge opens upwards to let tall ships through?
12 Fish breathe through what?
13 What was sold at London's Smithfield market?
14 How many noughts are there in the written number one million?
15 According to the saying, what is "nine points of the law"?
16 What colour is earth in modern three core electric cables?
17 What relation are Huey, Dewey and Louie to Donald Duck?
18 What is the German word for the number one?
19 Who wrote the novel All Creatures Great and Small?
20 Which firework is named after a saint?
21 Which Queen became Empress of India in 1876?
22 From which cape is the American Space Shuttle launched?
23 Vichy is famous for which drink?
24 Which Blackadder character had a fascination for turnips?
25 According to the saying, which money will look after itself?
26 How many centimetres are there in six and a half metres?
27 The Vatican City is within which other capital city?
28 What colour is the shade of jonquil?
29 In The Bible, who was found in the bulrushes?
30 How many points does a snowflake have?

Hobbies & Leisure 2 (see Quiz 43, page 51)
1 Betting shop. 2 Circular. 3 Centre. 4 Dice. 5 Downwards. 6 Animal Park.
7 Trainspotting. 8 Bingo. 9 Indian. 10 Below. 11 Car boot. 12 Allotment.
13 Monday. 14 Fruit and vegetables (Pick Your Own). 15 Exhibition.
16 Green. 17 Blood. 18 Sword. 19 Mystery tour. 20 Gym. 21 Madame
Tussaud's. 22 The National Lottery. 23 Smaller. 24 Middlesbrough. 25 Cafe.
26 Brewery. 27 Bar billiards. 28 August. 29 Anorak. 30 Yourself.

Answers

Quiz 45 Sporting Chance 1

Answers - see Quiz 46, page 54

LEVEL 1

1 Which ice dance pair have the freedom of the city of Nottingham?
2 Which Frank Sinatra classic did Geoff Boycott choose on Desert Island Discs?
3 What sort of animal takes part in a point-to-point?
4 In snooker what colour ball scores least?
5 In which country did sumo wrestling originate?
6 What was the name of Damon Hill's racing driver father?
7 Mike Tyson was suspended for biting off which part of Evander Holyfield?
8 In which sport did Justin Rose become a pro after the '98 British Open?
9 In which Channel does the Admiral's Cup take place?
10 Which Scot Stephen won five successive snooker world championships in the 90s?
11 What do Redgrave and Pinsent race in?
12 Which Walter won the Derby on Lammtara in 1995?
13 In athletics what is the shortest outdoor track race?
14 What is the national sport of Spain known as corrida de toros?
15 How often is the Grand National normally run?
16 What would you ride in a velodrome?
17 Which sport has Australian Rules?
18 Which golfer Jack was known as the Golden Bear?
19 How long does the annual motor race at Le Man last?
20 The 'Golden Gloves' championship is in which sport?
21 The Fastnet Race is competed for on what type of surface?
22 Which youngsters run between the ends of the net during a tennis match ?
23 How does soccer player Dennis Bergkamp refuse to travel?
24 In which sport do you try to play below par?
25 Which Frankie had seven wins at Ascot at odds of 25,095 to 1?
26 How was Sir Garfield St Auburn Sobers known as a player?
27 Which sport do The Barbarians play?
28 Which game can be lawn or crown green?
29 Which two continents compete for the Ryder Cup?
30 Which jockey was jailed in the 80s for tax evasion?

Answers

Pot Luck 22 (see Quiz 46, page 54)
1 Greendale. 2 Bruce Forsyth. 3 25. 4 Hutchence. 5 Banned from British racecourses. 6 Travel agents. 7 Liver. 8 Grasshoppers. 9 Roberts. 10 Oldest university. 11 Great Britain. 12 Heart. 13 Birds. 14 Peter Gabriel. 15 No. 16 Blue. 17 Two. 18 Glasgow. 19 Lancashire. 20 Roxy Music. 21 Stripes. 22 Delilah. 23 Canada. 24 Italy. 25 The Lone Ranger. 26 East. 27 Lewinsky. 28 16. 29 Gallagher. 30 Guernsey.

Quiz 46 Pot Luck 22

Answers - see Quiz 45, page 53

1 Where are you if Mrs Goggins serves you in the post office?
2 Whose catchphrase was, "Didn't they do well"?
3 What percentage is half of a half?
4 Which late Michael was lead singer with INXS?
5 What happens if a bookie is "warned off Newmarket Heath"?
6 ABTA is concerned with which group of people?
7 In the body, which organ secretes bile?
8 In Switzerland, which famous soccer club has an insect name?
9 Which Julia starred as a waitress in Mystic Pizza?
10 What will Harvard University always be in America?
11 Which country was the first to use postage stamps?
12 Which part of his anatomy did Tony Bennett leave in San Francisco?
13 What does Bill Oddie like to go outside to watch?
14 Which Peter made the album Solsbury Hill?
15 Was the great racehorse Red Rum coloured red?
16 Traditionally, what colour is willow pattern?
17 How many members were there in the group The Carpenters?
18 Sauchiehall Street is in which city?
19 Wasim Akram first played County Cricket for which county?
20 Which group was fronted by Bryan Ferry?
21 What is the distinctive pattern on Dennis The Menace's shirt?
22 In The Bible, who cut off Samson's hair?
23 The province of Manitoba is in which country?
24 Was Gazza's first foreign club based in France, Italy or Spain?
25 Which cowboy had a horse named Silver?
26 Is St Andrew's golf course on the east or west coast of Scotland?
27 Which Monica became intimately associated with Bill Clinton?
28 How many sides would four trapezium's have?
29 Which Liam married Patsy Kensit in 1997?
30 St Peter Port is on which island?

Answers

Sporting Chance 1 (see Quiz 45, page 53)
1 Torvill & Dean. 2 My Way. 3 Horse. 4 Red. 5 Japan. 6 Graham.
7 Ear. 8 Golf. 9 English Channel. 10 Hendry. 11 Boat. 12 Swinburn.
13 100m. 14 Bull fighting. 15 Once a year. 16 Bicycle. 17 Football.
18 Nicklaus. 19 24 hours. 20 Boxing. 21 Water. 22 Ballboys/ballgirls.
23 By air. 24 Golf. 25 Dettori. 26 Gary Sobers. 27 Rugby. 28 Bowls.
29 Europe & America. 30 Lester Piggott.

Quiz 47 TV: Famous Faces

Answers - see Quiz 48, page 56

LEVEL 1

1 Who travelled from Pole to Pole and Around the World in 80 Days?

2 Which Newsnight interrogator has the nickname Paxo?

3 Clive James hails from which Commonwealth country?

4 Who was born John Cheese and changed his name by one letter?

5 Which Magnusson was given the first TV interview by Earl Spencer after his sister's death?

6 Which David and Jonathan hosted the 1998 Election coverage?

7 Which Gardener's World presenter wrote a novel Mr MacGregor?

8 Which Kate won an OBE for her reporting in Beijing and the Gulf?

9 Which famous part of her did Friends' Rachel advertise?

10 Anthony Worrall Thompson replaced Michael Barry on which food magazine show?

11 Which Sir David's catchphrase is "Hello, good evening and welcome"?

12 After 25 years at the BBC which football pundit went to Sky in 1998?

13 Which Paula gave interviews on her bed in The Big Breakfast?

14 Which Irishman has presented The Eurovision Song Contest?

15 Which practical joke Jeremy first hosted You've Been Framed?

16 Which 'big name' moved her talk show from ITV to BBC in 1998?

17 Is Paul Ross the brother, son or no relation of Jonathan Ross?

18 Whose catchphrase was 'Awight!'?

19 Which stock cube did Lynda Bellingham advertise?

20 How are TV cooks Clarissa and Jennifer better known?

21 What is Anthea Turner's TV presenter sister called?

22 Who was the footballing team captain on They Think It's All Over?

23 Who is actor Tony Britton's TV presenter daughter?

24 Ian McCaskill retired from presenting what in 1998?

25 Which Gloria presented an Open House on Channel 5?

26 In Ground Force is it Charlie or Tommy who has long red hair?

27 What are the first names of Reeves and Mortimer?

28 Which Judith did Anthea Turner replace on Wish You Were Here?

29 Which Match of the Day presenter took on a Radio 2 show in 1998?

30 What is Prime Suspect actress star Helen Mironoff's real name?

Pot Luck 23 (see Quiz 48, page 56)
1 Wherever I Lay My Hat. 2 13. 3 Hip. 4 Black Sea. 5 Carbon dioxide.
6 Hamlet. 7 Basketball. 8 Richard Branson. 9 Mary Poppins. 10 Seven.
11 June. 12 Gideons. 13 Shakespeare. 14 Member (of the Order) of the
British Empire. 15 Country. 16 Jonah. 17 Motorcycling. 18 Louis
Armstrong. 19 Primer. 20 Ludo. 21 Truro. 22 Anatomy. 23 Farming &
Agriculture. 24 Time. 25 West Sussex. 26 Sherry. 27 Actual Bodily Harm.
28 Matador. 29 House of Commons. 30 Funf.

1 What was Paul Young's only UK No. 1 hit in 1983?
2 How many players are on a cricket field during normal play?
3 What fruit comes from the rose?
4 The River Danube flows out into which Sea?
5 Which gas puts the bubbles into bottled fizzy drinks?
6 Which Shakespeare character gave the "To be or not to be" speech?
7 The Harlem Globe Trotters are famous in which sport?
8 Who is older Richard Branson or William Hague?
9 "Supercalifragilisticexpialidocious" comes from which Disney movie?
10 How many noughts are there in the written number ten million?
11 Which month of the year in Britain includes the longest day?
12 Copies of The Bible are left in hotel rooms by which religious organisation?
13 Who wrote the play A Winter's Tale?
14 What do the initials M.B.E. stand for?
15 What have you betrayed if you commit treason?
16 Who was swallowed by a whale in The Bible?
17 For which sport is Mick Doohan famous?
18 Which musician had the nickname 'Satchmo'?
19 When decorating what name is given to the first coat?
20 What is the children's version of backgammon called?
21 What is the administrative headquarters of the county of Cornwall?
22 Which scientific word deals with the structure of the body?
23 The Royal Smithfield Show is connected to which industry?
24 What does a chronometer measure?
25 Chichester is the county town of which county?
26 Jerez in Spain is famous for which alcoholic drink?
27 In crime what do the initials A.B.H. stand for?
28 In a bull fight, what name is given to the person who kills the bull?
29 Which is the Lower House in British politics?
30 What is the German word for the number five?

Answers

TV: Famous Faces (see Quiz 47, page 55)
1 Michael Palin. 2 Jeremy Paxman. 3 Australia. 4 John Cleese. 5 Sally.
6 Dimbleby. 7 Alan Titchmarsh. 8 Adie. 9 Hair. 10 Food & Drink.
11 Frost. 12 Jimmy Hill. 13 Yates. 14 Terry Wogan. 15 Beadle.
16 Vanessa. 17 Brother. 18 Michael Barrymore. 19 Oxo. 20 Two Fat
Ladies. 21 Wendy. 22 Gary Lineker. 23 Fern Britton. 24 Weather
forecasting. 25 Hunniford. 26 Charlie. 27 Vic & Bob. 28 Chalmers.
29 Desmond Lynam. 30 Helen Mirren.

Quiz 49 Celebs

Answers - see Quiz 50, page 58

Answers - see Quiz 50, page 58

LEVEL 1

1 Which pop band did Geri Halliwell leave in Spring 1998?
2 What is the married name of Cherie Booth QC?
3 Who was the fiancee of Michael Hutchence at the time of his death?
4 What is Caroline Aherne's showbiz pensioner persona?
5 Which London store did Mohammed Al-Fayed buy in 1985?
6 What is the first name of politician turned author Lord Archer?
7 Who is the man behind the Virgin group?
8 What type of adviser was subsequent bankrupt John Bryan to Fergie?
9 Which footballer married Sheryl and had a son called Regan?
10 Which Tory politician did Ffion Jenkins marry?
11 Which rock star did Texan model Jerry Hall marry in 1990?
12 In which country was Ulrika Jonsson born?
13 Which radio DJ has his own company, Ginger Productions?
14 Who left husband Peter Powell for Grant Bovey in 1998?
15 How is former Royal girlfriend Kathleen Stark better known?
16 Who founded the London nightclub Stringfellow's?
17 Which country did Earl Spencer move to in the mid 1990s?
18 Which Royal was Lord Snowdon married to?
19 What was Liz Hurley's infamous Versace dress held together with?
20 Which millionairess cook is a director of Norwich City Football Club?
21 Which chain of cosmetics shops did Anita Roddick found?
22 What was the sporting profession of Jemima Khan's husband?
23 What is Camilla Shand's married name?
24 What is Simon Le Bon's model wife called?
25 Which celebrity actor Grant's middle name is Mungo?
26 Which nightclub was named after Lady Annabel Goldsmith?
27 What does John Galliano design?
28 Which Nigel writes about celebs in his Daily Mail diary?
29 Which Foreign Secretary did Gaynor Regan marry in 1998?
30 What is the first name of PR man Mr Clifford?

Answers

Pot Luck 24 (see Quiz 50, page 58)
1 Athletics. 2 Champion. 3 James Herriot. 4 Joseph. 5 Grievous Bodily Harm. 6 Like a lamb. 7 Snow White & the Seven Dwarfs. 8 Five. 9 Caribbean. 10 India. 11 Growing of crops. 12 Mae West. 13 On the shoulder. 14 King Charles. 15 Military policeman. 16 Animal. 17 Boutique. 18 Member of the European Parliament. 19 Grand National. 20 Mg. 21 2000. 22 December. 23 David. 24 Leather. 25 Five. 26 John Lennon. 27 Democrats & Republicans. 28 Trowbridge. 29 Dix. 30 Harry Corbett.

Quiz 50 Pot Luck 24

Answers - see Quiz 49, page 57

1   For which sport is Paula Radcliffe famous?
2   In the TV song, who was the 'Wonder Horse'?
3   Who wrote the novel "Let Sleeping Vets Lie"?
4   Which of Jacob's sons had a coat of many colours, in The Bible?
5   In crime what do the initials G.B.H. stand for?
6   According to the saying, how will March go out if it comes in like a lion?
7   Which Disney movie includes the song Whistle While You Work?
8   After how many years must an election be held in Britain?
9   Jamaica is in which sea?
10 Which country does the musical instrument the sitar come from?
11 Which kind of farming is arable farming?
12 Which famous film star gave her name to a life jacket?
13 Where would you wear an epaulette?
14 Which kind of spaniel was named after a king?
15 In the army what is an MP?
16 Is a jellyfish a mineral, vegetable or animal?
17 In the Sixties what was Biba?
18 In politics, what do the initials M.E.P. stand for?
19 In 1993, which horse race was made void after a false start?
20 Which two letters form the symbol for the element magnesium?
21 How many centimetres are there in twenty metres?
22 Which month of the year in Britain includes the shortest day?
23 Who killed the giant Goliath?
24 What is prepared in a tannery?
25 How many lines are there in a limerick?
26 Which member of the Beatles sang Imagine?
27 Which are the two main political parties in America?
28 What is the administrative headquarters of the county of Wiltshire?
29 What is the French word for the number ten?
30 Did Harry Corbett, Harry H Corbett or Ronnie Corbett work with Sooty?

Answers

Celebs (see Quiz 49, page 57)
1 The Spice Girls. 2 Blair. 3 Paula Yates. 4 Mrs Merton. 5 Harrods.
6 Jeffrey. 7 Richard Branson. 8 Financial. 9 Paul Gascoigne. 10 William
Hague. 11 Mick Jagger. 12 Sweden. 13 Chris Evans. 14 Anthea Turner.
15 Koo Stark. 16 Peter Stringfellow. 17 South Africa. 18 Princess Margaret.
19 Safety pins. 20 Delia Smith. 21 Body Shop. 22 Cricketer. 23 Parker-
Bowles. 24 Yasmin. 25 Hugh Grant. 26 Annabel's. 27 Clothes.
28 Dempster. 29 Robin Cook. 30 Max.

Quiz 51 Children's TV

Answers - see Quiz 52, page 60

1   What mighty hero did Prince Adam turn into with the aid of Greyskull castle?
2   Where is Grange Hill Comprehensive?
3   What was the follow up to How!?
4   Tom Baker was the longest serving Doctor in which sci fi series?
5   Which children's favourite has the number plate PAT 1?
6   Which Linford presented Record Breakers?
7   Which Engine's friends were Terence the Tractor and Bertie the Bus?
8   Does Tom or Jerry have the furrier coat?
9   What cuddly creatures are Uncle Bulgaria and Orinoco?
10 What was Worzel Gummidge?
11 Are Smurfs blue or orange?
12 Which Street teaches about letters and numbers?
13 What sort of creature is Pingu?
14 Which family is headed by Homer?
15 What colour is Teletubby Laa Laa?
16 Which Bear was found in a London railway station?
17 What is Popeye's occupation?
18 What sort of creature is Children's BBC's Otis?
19 What is the most number of presenters Blue Peter has at once?
20 Matthew Corbett said goodbye to which puppet companion in 1998?
21 What sort of animal was Huckleberry?
22 Which Grove is a children's drama series?
23 Who is Dastardly's canine sidekick?
24 On Your Marks and Art Attack are about what subject?
25 Spot is chiefly what colour?
26 Which heroic earth organisation fought Spectra in Battle of the Planets?
27 What sort of animal is Garfield?
28 What is Casper?
29 What Sentinels were Mercury, Hercules and Astria?
30 What kind of prehistoric creature is Dink?

Answers

Pot Luck 25 (see Quiz 52, page 60)
1 Butterfly. 2 Two. 3 The eye. 4 Red rose. 5 Jamaica. 6 Tom Hanks.
7 Lisa Riley. 8 Alcohol. 9 Trois. 10 Animal. 11 Motor racing. 12 Fire.
13 Reveille. 14 Limerick. 15 John Smith. 16 Max Bygraves. 17 K.
18 Greece. 19 Mrs Laurence. 20 A brush. 21 El Salvador. 22 Etc.
23 A jellyfish. 24 Zoos. 25 A Tap. 26 U. 27 Tom. 28 Ulrika Jonsson.
29 Not speaking to them. 30 Three.

Quiz 52 Pot Luck 25

Answers - see Quiz 51, page 59

1 Which swimming stroke was introduced in the 1956 Olympics?
2 What's the greatest number of consecutive calendar months with 31 days?
3 What name is given to the calm area at the centre of a hurricane?
4 Which flower is the symbol of the Labour Party in Britain?
5 Kingston is the capital of which island nation?
6 Who played Forrest in the 1994 film Forrest Gump?
7 Who replaced Jeremy Beadle to present You've Been Framed!?
8 Complete the Oasis song title "Cigarettes and ....?
9 What is the French word for the number three?
10 Are sponges mineral, vegetable or animal?
11 For which sport is Jean Alesi famous?
12 According to the proverb, there's no smoke without what?
13 Which army bugle call is played to wake up the troops?
14 Which Irish town gives its name to a five line humorous verse?
15 Who preceded Tony Blair as Labour Party leader?
16 Who is renowned for saying, "I wanna tell you a story"?
17 Which letter of the alphabet is used as a measure of the size of a computer's memory?
18 Which country produces the pine scented wine called retsina?
19 What is the Princess Royal's married name?
20 What name is given to a fox's tail?
21 San Salvador is in which country?
22 Which abbreviation means "and so on"?
23 What is a Portuguese Man-o'-War?
24 What do Whipsnade, Chessington and London have in common?
25 What is the English equivalent of the American 'faucet'?
26 Alphabetically, which letter is the last of the vowels?
27 Which name links golfers Kite and Watson?
28 Who presents Gladiators with Jeremy Guscott?
29 What are we not doing if we send someone to Coventry?
30 How many balls are used in billiards?

Answers

Children's TV (see Quiz 51, page 59)
1 He-Man. 2 London. 3 How 2. 4 Doctor Who. 5 Postman Pat.
6 Christie. 7 Thomas the Tank Engine. 8 Tom. 9 Wombles. 10 Scarecrow.
11 Blue. 12 Sesame Street. 13 Penguin. 14 The Simpsons. 15 Yellow.
16 Paddington. 17 Sailor. 18 Aardvark. 19 Four. 20 Sooty. 21 Hound.
22 Byker Grove. 23 Muttley. 24 Art & crafts. 25 Yellow. 26 G-Force. 27
Cat. 28 Ghost. 29 The Space Sentinels. 30 Dinosaur.

Quiz 53 Leisure: Food & Drink 2

Answers - see Quiz 54, page 62

1 Tikka is a dish in which country's cookery?
2 A strudel is usually filled with which fruit?
3 What relation is Albert to fellow chef and restaurateur Michel Roux?
4 Which pasta sauce originated in Bologna in Italy?
5 What is a frankfurter?
6 How are eggs usually cooked in the breakfast dish bacon and eggs?
7 What is fromage frais a soft type of?
8 Does an Italian risotto contain rice or pasta?
9 Over what would you normally pour a vinaigrette dressing?
10 Rick Stein's restaurant and cooking specialises in what?
11 What colour wine is a Valpolicella?
12 In which country did Chianti originate?
13 What is the main filling ingredient of a quiche?
14 Is a poppadum crisp or soft?
15 What sort of drink is espresso?
16 Is brioche a type of bread or a fruit?
17 What shape is the pasta used to make lasagne?
18 What is mozzarella?
19 What colour is fudge?
20 Which north of England county is famous for its hotpot?
21 Do you eat or drink a loyal toast?
22 What type of meat is found in a cock-a-leekie soup?
23 Which food links Gary Lineker and The Spice Girls?
24 What is the alcoholic ingredient of Gaelic coffee?
25 Which fruit is usually used in marmalade?
26 At what age can you legally drink alcohol in an pub?
27 What does G stand for in G and T?
28 What are the two main colours of liquorice Allsorts?
29 Would you eat or drink schnapps?
30 A Conference is what type of fruit?

Pot Luck 26 (see Quiz 54, page 62)
1 The mice. 2 Sport's trophy (golf). 3 American Indians. 4 Queen Mother.
5 Spanish. 6 1997. 7 Perry Como. 8 Six. 9 Advent. 10 A kimono. 11 Mount
Sinai. 12 Worzel Gummidge. 13 Althorp Park. 14 Quotient. 15 Hiroshima.
16 Tottenham Hotspur. 17 Tomorrows World. 18 Germany. 19 Boxing.
20 Neuf. 21 Tiger. 22 Tuxedo. 23 Battle of Hastings. 24 Rabbit. 25 Terry
Waite. 26 Yellow. 27 Victory in Europe. 28 168. 29 The eye. 30 Anne Frank.

61

Quiz 54 Pot Luck 26

1　According to the proverb, what plays when the cat's away?
2　Did Harry Vardon give his name to a disease, a sport's trophy or a fruit?
3　Which people wore moccasins originally?
4　Which Royal was born in 1900?
5　What is the main spoken language in Mexico?
6　In which year did Hong Kong revert to being part of China?
7　Who had hits with Magic Moments and Catch a Falling Star?
8　How many noughts are there in the written number fifty two million?
9　Which season comes just before Christmas in the Christian calendar?
10　Which long dress is traditionally worn by Japanese women?
11　In The Bible, on which mountain was Moses told the commandments?
12　Actor John Pertwee played which TV scarecrow?
13　At which Park is Princess Diana buried?
14　What does the Q stand for in IQ?
15　Where was the first atomic bomb dropped on 6th August 1945?
16　White Hart Lane is home to which football club?
17　Philippa Forrester and Peter Snow co-hosted which science based TV programme?
18　Hanover, Westphalia and Bavaria are all parts of which country?
19　For which sport is Chris Eubank famous?
20　What is the French word for the number nine?
21　Which animal in the poem by Blake was described as "burning bright"?
22　What do Americans call a dinner jacket?
23　In which battle was King Harold killed?
24　What type of animal can be Dutch, Angora and Chinchilla?
25　Who was a Beirut hostage with John McCarthy and Brian Keenan ?
26　What colour was the "itsy bitsy teeny weeny bikini" in the pop song?
27　What do the initials VE stand for in VE Day?
28　How many hours are there in a week?
29　Which part of the body can suffer from an astigmatism?
30　Which Jewish girl kept a diary whilst hidden in Amsterdam in 1942?

Answers

Leisure: Food & Drink 2 (see Quiz 53, page 61)
1 India. 2 Apple. 3 Brothers. 4 Bolognaise. 5 Sausage. 6 Fried.
7 Cheese. 8 Rice. 9 Salad. 10 Fish. 11 Red. 12 Italy. 13 Eggs.
14 Crisp. 15 Coffee. 16 Bread. 17 Rectangular. 18 Cheese. 19 Light
brown. 20 Lancashire. 21 Drink (toast to the queen). 22 Chicken.
23 Walker's crisps. 24 Whiskey. 25 Oranges. 26 18. 27 Gin. 28 Black
and white. 29 Drink. 30 Pear.

Quiz 55 The Movies: Greats

Answers - see Quiz 56, page 64

LEVEL 1

1 Which great screen dancer is on the cover of Sgt Pepper?
2 Which wartime classic starred Ingrid Bergman and Humphrey Bogart?
3 Who is Jamie Lee Curtis's actor father?
4 Cary Grant was born in which west country port?
5 Was Rita Hayworth a blonde or a redhead?
6 Was it Bob Hope or Bing Crosby who was born in south London?
7 Which monster was arguably Boris Karloff's most famous role?
8 How was dancer Eugene Curran Kelly better known?
9 Who was the original Candle in the Wind dedicated to?
10 Which Anthony starred as the lead character in Psycho?
11 Which Sir Alec starred in, and had a share of the profits of, Star Wars?
12 Who was taller, Rock Hudson or Mickey Rooney?
13 Which James starred in Harvey and The Philadelphia Story?
14 Which Italian born actor is best known for silent movies such as The Sheikh?
15 Which Citizen was the subject of Orson Welles' first film?
16 Lauren Bacall was the wife of which Humphrey?
17 Tough guy Frank J Cooper adopted which first name?
18 Which Joan starred in Whatever Happened to Baby Jane?
19 How was Ruth Elizabeth Davis better known?
20 Which Charlie was a founder of the film studio United Artists?
21 Bing Crosby had just finished a round of which game when he died?
22 William Claude Dunkenfield used his first two initials to become who?
23 Jane and Peter are the children of which screen great Henry?
24 Which Katharine enjoyed a long on and off screen relationship with Spencer Tracy?
25 Which Doris enjoyed popularity in films with Rock Hudson?
26 He was born John Uhler Lemmon III but how is he known in films?
27 Who is Michael Douglas's famous actor father?
28 In which German capital was Marlene Dietrich born?
29 Did Clark Gable die during his last film in the 40s, 50s or 60s?
30 Greta Garbo was born in which Scandinavian capital?

Pot Luck 27 (see Quiz 56, page 64)

1 Italy. 2 An ill wind. 3 Aladdin. 4 Beef cattle. 5 Windsor. 6 Runnymede.
7 Washington. 8 Around your waist. 9 Neun. 10 Egypt. 11 J. 12 Jack.
13 Origami. 14 Circus. 15 Dutch. 16 Krypton. 17 Trousers. 18 The
teeth. 19 Spain. 20 900. 21 Jennifer Aniston. 22 Computer Languages.
23 Cavalier. 24 Easter. 25 Pink. 26 France. 27 Arachnophobia. 28 The
skin. 29 Horses. 30 Rugby League.

Quiz 56 Pot Luck 27

Answers - see Quiz 55, page 63

1. Sicily, Lombardy and Tuscany are all parts of which country?
2. What kind of wind blows no good according to the proverb?
3. Which Disney movie includes the song A Whole New World?
4. What type of animal can be Charolais, Galloway and Simmental?
5. Which is the largest castle in Britain?
6. Where did King John sign the Magna Carta?
7. In which capital is the Capitol Building?
8. Where would you wear a cummerbund?
9. What is the German word for the number nine?
10. Which country had eleven kings called Rameses?
11. What appears most as the initial letter in calendar month names?
12. According to the rhyme, who fixed his head with vinegar and brown paper?
13. What name is given to the Japanese craft of paper folding?
14. Billy Smart and Chipperfields provided what type of entertainment?
15. What was the nationality of diarist Anne Frank?
16. What was the name of Superman's home planet?
17. Who or what are Oxford Bags?
18. What part of your body is covered by orthodontics?
19. Paella is a traditional dish from which country?
20. How many seconds are in a quarter of an hour?
21. Which Friends star has advertised L'Oreal?
22. What are COBOL, FORTRAN and ALGOL?
23. What type of person was Laughing in the famous portrait?
24. Which festival follows Lent in the Christian calendar?
25. What colour is the Financial Times?
26. Brittany and Picardy are parts of which country?
27. Which phobia describes the fear of spiders?
28. In medicine, what does a dermatologist specialise in?
29. Suffolk Punch, Shires and Clydesdales are all types of what?
30. For which sport are Robbie and Henry Paul famous?

Answers

The Movies: Greats (see Quiz 55, page 63)
1 Fred Astaire. 2 Casablanca. 3 Tony Curtis. 4 Bristol. 5 Redhead.
6 Bob Hope. 7 Frankenstein. 8 Gene Kelly. 9 Marilyn Monroe. 10 Perkins.
11 Guinness. 12 Rock Hudson. 13 Stewart. 14 Rudolph Valentino.
15 Citizen Kane. 16 Bogart. 17 Gary. 18 Crawford. 19 Bette Davis.
20 Chaplin. 21 Golf. 22 W.C.Fields. 23 Fonda. 24 Hepburn. 25 Day.
26 Jack Lemmon. 27 Kirk Douglas. 28 Berlin. 29 60s. 30 Stockholm.

Quiz 57 Geography: Euro Tour

Answers - see Quiz 58, page 66

Answers - see Quiz 58, page 66

1 In which country would you find Jerez?
2 How would you travel if you left for France from a hoverport?
3 Eurostar trains run from London to which Belgian city?
4 In which country is Cologne?
5 Does London or Rome have the higher population?
6 The province of Flanders is in which country?
7 Which landlocked country is divided into cantons?
8 In which city would you find the Parthenon?
9 Bohemia is part of which Republic, formerly part of Czechoslovakia?
10 Is Schiphol an airport or a river in the Netherlands?
11 In which country is Estoril?
12 Where is the Black Forest?
13 What type of country is Monaco?
14 Andorra lies between France and which other country?
15 In which Sea does Cyprus lie?
16 Belarus and Ukraine were formerly part of which huge republic?
17 What is the English name for the city known to Italians as Venezia?
18 Is Sweden a kingdom or a republic?
19 Vienna lies on which river?
20 Is Ibiza part of the Canaries or the Balearics?
21 In which Circle does about a third of Finland lie?
22 The Hague is the seat of government of which country?
23 Crete and Corfu belong to which country?
24 Which Scandinavian country is opposite Norway and Sweden?
25 Is Europe the second largest or the second smallest continent?
26 Which country marks the most westerly point of mainland Europe?
27 The Iberian Peninsula consists of Portugal and which other country?
28 Which French city is Europe's largest?
29 What are the Balkans, the Apennines and the Pyrenees?
30 Which island is known to the French as Corse?

Answers

Pot Luck 28 (see Quiz 58, page 65)

1 Film. 2 Born. 3 Brian Johnston. 4 Reed. 5 60s. 6 Muslim. 7 Michael Heseltine. 8 Enfield. 9 Bees. 10 Four. 11 Falk. 12 Golf. 13 Provence. 14 Devon. 15 Greek gods. 16 Flint. 17 John Le Mesurier. 18 Irish. 19 Noddy. 20 Triangular. 21 England. 22 Furniture. 23 Witch. 24 Harmonica. 25 Sport. 26 Keystone. 27 Forty. 28 Meat Loaf. 29 Celtic. 30 Dog.

Quiz 58 Pot Luck 28

Answers - see Quiz 57, page 65

1   Which came first the film or stage show of Phantom Of The Opera?
2   In Bruce Springsteen songs what goes before In The USA and To Run?
3   Which famous cricket commentator died of a heart attack in January 1994?
4   Which Lou wrote and sang A Perfect Day?
5   Was Liz Hurley born in the 50s, 60, or 70s?
6   Which religion has people called to prayer by a muezzin?
7   Which Tory MP earned the name Goldilocks?
8   Which Harry created the character of Frank Doberman?
9   Which insects include drones, queens and workers?
10 Has a violin four, six or eight strings?
11 Which actor Peter played crumple coated cop Columbo?
12 Fuzzy Zoeller was linked with which sport?
13 Where did Peter Mayle spend a year of his life?
14 In which county was the Plymouth Brethren founded?
15 Athena, Nike and Zeus were all what?
16 Which Keith is lead singer with the Prodigy?
17 As what name did John Elton Halliley act in Dad's Army?
18 Which Derby is run at the Curragh?
19 Who had a best friend with the politically incorrect name of Big Ears?
20 A lateen sail is what shape?
21 Revie, Robson, and Taylor have all managed which team?
22 Which valuable things were made by Thomas Sheraton?
23 On TV, Sabrina is the name of the Teenage... what?
24 Which musical instrument does Larry Adler play?
25 Tony Banks was Minister for what in Tony Blair's first Cabinet?
26 What type of crazy cops were created by Mack Sennett?
27 What do XL stand for in Roman numerals?
28 What's the foodie stage name of sizeable singer Marvin Lee Aday?
29 Brady, Macari and Stein have managed which Scottish soccer club?
30 What kind of animal is a fox terrier?

Geography: Euro Tour (see Quiz 57, page 65)
1 Spain. 2 Hovercraft. 3 Brussels. 4 Germany. 5 London. 6 Belgium.
7 Switzerland. 8 Athens. 9 Czech Republic. 10 Airport. 11 Portugal. 12
Germany. 13 Principality. 14 Spain. 15 Mediterranean. 16 USSR.
17 Venice. 18 Kingdom. 19 Danube. 20 Balearics. 21 Arctic Circle.
22 Netherlands. 23 Greece. 24 Denmark. 25 Second smallest.
26 Portugal. 27 Spain. 28 Paris. 29 Mountain ranges. 30 Corsica.

Answers

Quiz 59 Nature: Plant World

Answers - see Quiz 60, page 68

LEVEL 1

1   Where is water stored in a cactus plant?
2   Are most conifers evergreen or deciduous?
3   Ceps and chanterelles are types of what?
4   Flax is grown to produce which fabric?
5   Which drug is obtained from the coca plant?
6   Bamboo is the tallest type of what?
7   Which Mexican drink comes from the agave plant?
8   Is it true or false that laurel has poisonous leaves?
9   The petiole is on which part of a plant?
10 What colour is cuckoo spit?
11 Juniper is the flavouring in which drink?
12 What colour are oil seed rape flowers?
13 What goes before lavender and holly to make another plant's name?
14 What can be obtained from the cassava plant which would have gone in a typical school dinner pudding?
15 Harebells are usually what colour?
16 Does a polyanthus have a single or several blooms?
17 Which ingredient in tonic water comes from the bark of the cinchona?
18 Which plants would a viticulturist grow?
19 Wild cornflowers are usually what colour?
20 Which paintbrush cleaner is found in the resin of a conifer?
21 Which pear has the most protein?
22 In the garden what would you use secateurs for?
23 Do peanuts grow on trees or low plants?
24 What colour is chlorophyll?
25 In which Gardens is the Princess of Wales Conservatory?
26 Cacti are native to which continent?
27 What would you find in an arboretum?
28 Which fast grower is nicknamed the mile-a-minute vine?
29 Which yellow flower is nicknamed the Lent lily?
30 Which trees carry their seeds in cones?

Pot Luck 29 (see Quiz 60, page 68)

Answers
1 A will. 2 Four. 3 Warwick. 4 Lewis Collins. 5 Zwanzig. 6 Bryan Adams.
7 A cactus. 8 Brazil. 9 Street-Porter. 10 Australia. 11 Eight. 12 Black.
13 Landscape Gardening. 14 A size of paper. 15 Edward Woodward. 16 A herb. 17 River Niagara. 18 Snow White. 19 Horse racing. 20 Beef. 21 Purple.
22 Three. 23 Alaska. 24 Val Doonican. 25 Simple Simon. 26 Luke and Matt Goss. 27 A kind of plum. 28 Fourteen. 29 Lizzie. 30 Flattery.

Quiz 60 Pot Luck 29

Answers - see Quiz 59, page 68

1   If you die intestate you have not made what?
2   What's the least number of Mondays that can occur in July?
3   Which Derek partnered John Cleland at the Vauxhall Touring Cars Team?
4   In the TV series The Professionals, who played Bodie?
5   What is the German word for the number twenty?
6   Who had a No. 1 UK hit with Everything I do, I do it for You?
7   What is a prickly pear?
8   Romario starred in the 1994 World Cup for which country?
9   Media person Janet Bull changed her last name to what in her search for 'yoof'?
10 Bob Hawke was prime minister of which country?
11 How many coins does Great Britain have?
12 What colour is sable in heraldry?
13 For what was Capability Brown famous?
14 What is foolscap?
15 On TV who played the Equaliser?
16 What kind of plant is marjoram?
17 On which River are the Niagara Falls?
18 Which Disney movie includes the song Heigh-Ho?
19 For which sport is Willie Carson famous?
20 Sirloin, Rump and Topside are all joints of which meat?
21 What colour is Tinky Winky in the Teletubbies?
22 How many leaves are on a shamrock?
23 Which American state is the largest in area?
24 Which singer was associated with a rocking chair?
25 According to the nursery rhyme, who met a pieman going to the fair?
26 Which two brothers made up the group Bros?
27 What is a bullace?
28 How many lines are in a sonnet?
29 A Model T Ford was nicknamed Tin what?
30 According to the proverb, imitation is the sincerest form of what?

Answers

Nature: Plant World (see Quiz 59, page 67)
1 Stem. 2 Evergreen. 3 Fungi. 4 Linen. 5 Cocaine. 6 Grass. 7 Tequila.
8 True. 9 Leaf stalk. 10 White. 11 Gin. 12 Yellow. 13 Sea. 14 Tapioca.
15 Blue. 16 Several. 17 Quinine. 18 Vines. 19 Blue. 20 Turpentine.
21 Avocado. 22 Cutting, pruning. 23 Low plants. 24 Green. 25 Kew.
26 America. 27 Trees. 28 Russian Vine. 29 Daffodil. 30 Conifers.

Quiz 61 Sporting Chance 2

Answers - see Quiz 62, page 70

LEVEL 1

1 What type of sport is eventing?
2 Which international side did Diego Maradona play for?
3 Phidippides was the first runner of which 26 mile race?
4 Which Stephen was the then youngest ever winner of a professional snooker title in 1987?
5 Did Evander Holyfield box at heavyweight or welterweight?
6 Which country did Virginia Leng represent at the Olympic Games?
7 FC Porto play football in which country?
8 At the USA PGA Championships, what game is played?
9 If you saw Benny the Dip win, what would you be watching?
10 At which sport might you see the American Williams sisters play?
11 Does the Le Mans 24 hour race take place in summer or winter?
12 In swimming, is freestyle usually performed on the back or front?
13 Which country won the first 25 America's Cup trophies in yachting?
14 In which sport is there a Foil discipline?
15 How was boxer Rocco Francis Marchegiano better known?
16 Caber tossing is native to which country?
17 What is the slowest swimming stroke?
18 For which national rugby side did Gavin Hastings play?
19 Magic Johnson found fame at which US sport?
20 Which horse race is sometimes called just The National?
21 What was tennis's Billie Jean Moffitt's married name?
22 Which Jackie's record of Grand Prix wins did Alain Prost pass in '87?
23 Which heavyweight Mike knocked out 15 of his first 25 pro opponents in the first round?
24 Which first name is shared by jockeys Carson and Shoemaker?
25 In which sport is a ball hit through a hoop with a mallet?
26 What is Scottish long distance runner Liz Lynch's married name?
27 What does the first F in FIFA stand for?
28 F1 driver Jacques Villeneuve is from which country?
29 Which winter sport can be alpine or Nordic?
30 Is the Oaks a race for colts or fillies?

Pot Luck 30 (see Quiz 62, page 70)

Answers

1 Two. 2 Mean. 3 Lettuce. 4 A flag. 5 An even number. 6 Fan-dabi-dozi. 7 Avocado pear. 8 The mirror. 9 Half a pound of tuppenny rice. 10 Eight. 11 A Watermelon. 12 Penny Black. 13 Judas. 14 Half a crown. 15 Zulu. 16 One. 17 The Alps. 18 Gold. 19 Pepper. 20 Westminster Abbey. 21 A knot. 22 Coffee. 23 Victory. 24 Bread. 25 Green. 26 The harp. 27 Blue. 28 White Star Line. 29 An element. 30 Queen Victoria.

Quiz 62 Pot Luck 30

Answers - see Quiz 61, page 69

1 How many people perform a pas de deux in a ballet?
2 If T is time what is M in G.M.T.?
3 Cos and Iceberg are varieties of which salad plant?
4 As well as being a TV programme, what is a Blue Peter?
5 What type of number will you always get if you add two odd numbers together?
6 What was the phrase associated with the duo the Krankies?
7 Which pear is usually served as a starter and is not sweet?
8 Who told the Queen that Snow White was the "fairest of them all"?
9 What is mixed with half a pound of treacle in Pop goes the Weasel?
10 How many furlongs are there in a mile?
11 Which melon has black pips and red juicy flesh?
12 What was the common name for the first postage stamp?
13 Which biblical character had the second name Iscariot?
14 What was the name for two shillings and sixpence?
15 What is the letter "Z" if A is Alpha and B is Bravo?
16 How many hooks do you use for crochet?
17 The Matterhorn is in which European mountain range?
18 What did Fort Knox originally store?
19 Steak au poivre is steak covered in what?
20 Where did the Queen's Coronation take place?
21 If you asked a Scout to make a sheep-shank, what would he make?
22 What drink is the main export from Brazil?
23 What was the name of Admiral Nelson's ship?
24 Chapatti is a kind of Indian what?
25 What colour is the door of the pub the Rovers Return?
26 Which stringed instrument has the most strings in an orchestra?
27 What colour is connected with the River Danube?
28 Which shipping line did Titanic belong to?
29 What is the name of the glowing curly wire in a light bulb?
30 At the start of the 20th century who was Queen of England?

Answers

Sporting Chance 2 (see Quiz 61, page 69)
1 Equestrian. 2 Argentina. 3 Marathon. 4 Hendry. 5 Heavyweight.
6 Great Britain. 7 Portugal. 8 Golf. 9 Horse racing. 10 Tennis.
11 Summer. 12 Front. 13 USA. 14 Fencing. 15 Rocky Marciano.
16 Scotland. 17 Breast stroke. 18 Scotland. 19 Basketball. 20 Grand
National. 21 King. 22 Stewart. 23 Tyson. 24 Willie. 25 Croquet.
26 McColgan. 27 Federation. 28 Canada. 29 Skiing. 30 Fillies.

Quiz 63 Pop: Karaoke

Answers - see Quiz 64, page 72

LEVEL 1

1 Which Grease classic begins "I got chills, they're multiplyin'"?
2 What's the title of The Spice Girls hit which begins "I'll tell you what I want, what I really really want"?
3 What is the first line of Nessun Dorma?
4 What did Tina Turner sing after "Do I love you my oh my"?
5 What follows the Beatles "will you still need me, will you still feed me"?
6 Which song begins, "I feel it in my fingers, I feel it in my toes"?
7 In Candle in the Wind 98 " how are England's hills described?
8 How many times is "submarine" sung in the chorus of Yellow Submarine?
9 Which hit began "Oh my love, my darlin', I hunger for your touch"?
10 Which song's second line is "and so I face the final curtain"?
11 Which song begins "First I was afraid I was petrified?
12 In which song did Tammy Wynette bemoan "Sometime it's hard to be a woman"?
13 Which Slade Xmas hit has the line "Everybody's having fun"?
14 In the Titanic song what follows, "Near, far, wherever you are, I believe..."?
15 What follows Bryan Adams "Everything I do"?
16 Which Dire Straits hit begins "Here comes Johnny"?
17 What follows "Two little boys had two little....."?
18 Which charity hit has the line "Feed the world"?
19 What follows The Spice Girls "swing it, shake it, move it, make it"?
20 Which Abba hit states "I was defeated you won the war"?
21 What do neighbours become in the Neighbours theme song?
22 What follows "I believe for every drop of rain that falls"?
23 Which football anthem speaks of "Jules Rimet still leaming"?
24 Which song's second line is "I just called to say I care"?
25 Which Evita song begins, "It won't be easy, you'll think it strange"?
26 What did Boy George sing after singing karma five times?
27 Which Lion King song began "From the day we arrive on the planet"?
28 Which Simon & Garfunkel hit begins "When you're weary, feeling small"?
29 Which traditional song has the line, "The pipes, the pipes are calling"?
30 What are the last three words of Queen's We Are the Champions?

Answers

Pot Luck 31 (see Quiz 64, page 72)
1 The Peril. 2 Jennifer Paige. 3 Mint. 4 Soldier Sailor. 5 Calais. 6 Horse racing. 7 August. 8 Berkshire. 9 Trombone. 10 Tuesday. 11 VAT. 12 Bulb. 13 Yellow. 14 Cricket. 15 Andrew Lloyd Webber. 16 A constellation or galaxy. 17 Minestrone. 18 Champagne. 19 Little girls. 20 Patience. 21 They are poisonous. 22 Silver. 23 Ganges. 24 Tannic/Tannin. 25 Boots. 26 A house. 27 Please. 28 Red. 29 Norfolk. 30 Sherry.

Quiz 64 Pot Luck 31

LEVEL 1

Answers - see Quiz 63, page 71

1   If Dennis is the Menace what is Beryl?
2   Who had a huge UK hit in September 1998 with Crush?
3   Which sweet flavoured herb is often used to accompany roast lamb?
4   According to the rhyme, which two characters followed Tinker Tailor?
5   Which French port is closest to Britain?
6   To see which sport could you go to Towcester?
7   Lammas Day is in which month?
8   In which county is the Royal Military Academy at Sandhurst?
9   Which brass instrument has a sliding, adjustable tube?
10 Which day's child is "full of grace" according to the traditional rhyme?
11 Which current day tax replaced Purchase tax in 1973?
12 Is a snowdrop grown from a bulb or seed?
13 What colour is Laa Laa in the Teletubbies?
14 For which sport is David Gower famous?
15 Who composed the music for Cats?
16 What do we call a group of stars?
17 Which soup is made from a variety of vegetables and pasta?
18 What sort of drink is Moet & Chandon?
19 Maurice Chevalier "thanked heaven" for what?
20 Which has smaller cards, an ordinary pack or a patience pack?
21 What gives cause for concern about the seeds of a laburnum tree?
22 What colour is argent in heraldry?
23 The city of Calcutta stands on which river?
24 Tea contains which acid?
25 Which High Street chemists shop opened its first store in 1877?
26 What are you probably buying if you are gazumped?
27 What does the Italian "per favore" mean?
28 What colour, together with yellow, is the Spanish flag?
29 In which county was Lord Nelson born?
30 What kind of drink can be Bristol Cream?

Answers

Pop: Karaoke (see Quiz 63, page 70)
1 You're the One That I Want. 2 Wannabe. 3 Nessun dorma, nessun dorma.
4 River deep mountain high. 5 When I'm sixty four. 6 Love Is All Around.
7 Greenest. 8 Six. 9 Unchained Melody. 10 My Way. 11 I Will Survive. 12 Stand
By Your Man. 13 Merry Christmas Everybody. 14 That the heart does go on. 15 I do it
for you. 16 Walk of Life. 17 Toys. 18 Do They Know It's Christmas? 19 Who do you
think you are?. 20 Waterloo. 21 Good friends. 22 A flower grows. 23 Three Lions. 24 I
Just Called to Say I Love You. 25 Don't Cry For Me Argentina. 26 Chameleon. 27
Circle of Life. 28 Bridge Over Troubled Water. 29 Danny Boy. 30 Of the world.

Quiz 65 TV Times 1

Answers - see Quiz 66, page 74

LEVEL 1

1 Which is the female half of Mulder and Scully?
2 What is the profession of TV's Two Fat Ladies?
3 What is the subject of the Channel 4 show Hooked?
4 Football Focus is a part of which Saturday sports programme?
5 What colour is Channel 5's logo?
6 Which Ally is a zany US TV lawyer?
7 What would Peter Cockcroft talk about on TV?
8 Who took over Gardener's World from the late Geoff Hamilton?
9 Which Australian co presents Animal Hospital?
10 Maureen Rees found TV fame at what type of School?
11 GMTV is usually seen at what time of day?
12 Which letters does TV's Kavanagh have after his name?
13 What sex is the audience of Chris Tarrant's show Man O Man?
14 Who presents the celebrity version of Ready Steady Cook?
15 Which TV presenter is Johnny Ball's daughter?
16 Which Mary founded the Clean Up TV campaign in 1964?
17 Which female pop quintet launched Channel 5?
18 Does Food & Drink's Oz Clarke specialise in food or drink?
19 Which Jerry hosts a controversial talk show?
20 In which work location was the series The Hello Girls set?
21 Which Carol took over from Anne Robinson on Points of View?
22 What links Terry Wogan, Les Dawson and Lily Savage?
23 Which part of the country is served by Anglia Television?
24 Ground Force offered a viewer a makeover in which part of the home?
25 Who is presenter Julia Carling's ex-husband?
26 'It's good to talk' was the ad slogan of which phone company?
27 Who is taller, Michael Barrymore or Ronnie Corbett?
28 Which broadcasting corporation is known as Auntie?
29 On which channel is Panorama broadcast?
30 Who is the human half of Wallace and Gromit?

Pot Luck 32 (see Quiz 66, page 74)
1 Darts. 2 The farmer's wife. 3 Organ. 4 Diamonds. 5 Broken. 6 All Saints. 7 1984. 8 Apples. 9 Rutland. 10 Lady and the Tramp. 11 Blue Peter. 12 Hops. 13 Pears. 14 Saviour's Day. 15 Paul Merton. 16 White. 17 He was married. 18 Torvill & Dean. 19 Eight. 20 Dance steps. 21 A plant. 22 Richard. 23 Red. 24 Birmingham. 25 Three. 26 Bank of England. 27 Goodwood. 28 Champagne. 29 A bulb. 30 New York.

Quiz 66 Pot Luck 32

LEVEL 1

Answers - see Quiz 65, page 73

1 For which sport is Eric Bristow famous?
2 According to the nursery rhyme, who cut off the three mice tails?
3 Which is the largest musical instrument which has a keyboard?
4 What is mined at Kimberley in South Africa?
5 What does a German mean if he says something is "kaput"?
6 Who had a No. 1 UK hit in September 1998 with Bootie Call?
7 Which George Orwell novel has a year as its title?
8 Cider is made from which fruit?
9 What was the smallest county in England until 1974?
10 Which Disney movie includes the song He's A Tramp?
11 Which children's TV series was forty years old in October 1998?
12 What is dried in Kentish oast houses?
13 Which fruit can be served Belle Helene?
14 Which Day gave Cliff Richard a No. 1 for Christmas 1990?
15 Who is older Paul Merson or Paul Merton?
16 What colour along with red and blue is the Luxembourg flag?
17 What happened to Solomon Grundy on Wednesday, according to the rhyme?
18 Which Olympic ice skating duo danced to Ravel's Bolero?
19 On the Union Jack, how many blue triangles are there?
20 What does a choreographer plan?
21 What is a yucca?
22 In pop music, who is Jagger's long time writing partner?
23 What colour is Po in the Teletubbies?
24 Crossroads was set near which major city?
25 How many people are in a boat in a rowing coxed pair race?
26 What is sometimes called the 'Old Lady of Threadneedle Street'?
27 Which race meeting is known as 'Glorious'?
28 What was invented by Dom Peter Perignon, a French monk?
29 Is a tulip grown from seed or a bulb?
30 Which American city has the Yankees and Mets baseball teams?

Answers

TV Times (see Quiz 65, page 73)
1 Scully. 2 Cooks. 3 Fishing. 4 Grandstand. 5 Yellow. 6 McBeal. 7 Weather. 8 Alan Titchmarsh. 9 Rolf Harris. 10 Driving School. 11 Morning. 12 QC. 13 Female. 14 Fern Britton. 15 Zoe Ball. 16 Whitehouse. 17 The Spice Girls. 18 Drink. 19 Springer. 20 Telephone Exchange. 21 Vorderman. 22 Blankety Blank. 23 East Anglia. 24 Garden. 25 Will Carling. 26 BT. 27 Michael Barrymore. 28 BBC. 29 BBC 1. 30 Wallace.

Quiz 67 Sporting Chance 3

Answers - see Quiz 68, page 76

LEVEL 1

1   What is the surname of German F1 drivers Ralph and Michael?
2   Which jump event did Carl Lewis specialise in as well as sprinting?
3   What colour is the cover of the Rothman's Football Yearbook?
4   Is professional badminton an indoor or outdoor game or both?
5   What was the professional name of boxer Joe Louis Barrow?
6   Who won the European Cup-winner's Cup in 1998?
7   Of the 197 teams invited to the 1996 Olympics, how many accepted?
8   At which sport did suspended Irish Olympic gold medal winner Michelle de Bruin compete?
9   Which horned animal name does Leeds' Rugby Super League team have?
10 In which sport might you hit another living thing with a crop?
11 Peter O'Sullevan commentated on which sport?
12 Which Rugby side shares its name with stinging insects?
13 Which red flower is the emblem of the England Rugby Union team?
14 In which country is the golfing venue Valderrama?
15 Which motoring Grand Prix is held at the Hungaroring?
16 What's the highest score in darts from three different doubles?
17 In which country is the oldest football league in the world?
18 Which area of New York has a Globetrotters basketball team?
19 Which Bin was introduced for Rugby League players in 1983?
20 How many disciplines are there in a biathlon?
21 In which Sheffield theatre were the World Snooker Championships first held in 1977?
22 In which country was judo coincidentally added to the Olympic programme?
23 In badminton what were goose feathers used for?
24 What is the usual surface of the lane in ten pin bowling?
25 Which German Men's Wimbledon champion was born on Billie Jean King's 23rd birthday?
26 Which positive statement did Magic Johnson make prior to temporary retirement?
27 On what surface is curling played?
28 Which animal is on top of Rugby's Calcutta Cup?
29 In which sport would you wear a judogi?
30 What type of sporting event was The Rumble in the Jungle?

Pot Luck 33 (see Quiz 68, page 76)
1 Red. 2 A hat. 3 Liver. 4 Julie Walters. 5 The Severn Estuary. 6 Music.
7 Swimming. 8 Tower of London. 9 Peter Sellers. 10 New York. 11 A
beetle. 12 Isle of Dogs. 13 Hastings. 14 African. 15 Dudley Moore.
16 Robson and Jerome. 17 Antelope. 18 Linen. 19 Red. 20 The Bill.
21 Saddam Hussein. 22 Spitting Image. 23 Vauxhall. 24 A bull. 25 Four.
26 Sheffield. 27 Chippendale. 28 None. 29 Trotters. 30 Australia.

Answers

Quiz 68 Pot Luck 33

Answers - see Quiz 67, page 75

LEVEL 1

1   What colour is Michael Aspel's book on This is your Life?
2   What is a tam-o'-shanter?
3   Which organ is particularly affected by hepatitis?
4   Who played the title role in the film Educating Rita?
5   On which river estuary does Swansea stand?
6   The letters F.R.A.M. mean a Fellow of which Royal Academy?
7   For which sport was Duncan Goodhew famous?
8   The raven is traditionally associated with which Tower?
9   Who played Inspector Clouseau in the Pink Panther films?
10 In which country is the Big Apple?
11 What is a cockchafer?
12 Which animal isle is in the River Thames?
13 Where did a famous battle take place in 1066?
14 Which elephants are the largest - African or Indian?
15 Which English musician and comedian married Tuesday Weld?
16 Who released I Believe coupled with Up On The Roof?
17 What kind of mammal is a chamois?
18 Which fabric is produced from flax?
19 Does coq au vin contain red or white wine?
20 Which TV series is set in Sun Hill police station?
21 During the Gulf War, who was the leader of Iraq?
22 Which TV puppet programme makes fun of politicians?
23 Which car maker has the same name as a London bridge?
24 Which animal should you take by the horns, according to the proverb?
25 How many pins are in the back row of a ten pin bowling triangle?
26 Which city is furthest North - Bristol or Sheffield?
27 Which of Chippendale, Ming and Wedgwood is not a type of pottery?
28 How much gold is there in a one pound coin?
29 What are a pig's feet called?
30 Of which country's coast is the world's largest coral reef?

Answers

Sporting Chance 3 (see Quiz 67, page 75)
1 Schumacher. 2 Long jump. 3 Blue. 4 Indoor. 5 Joe Louis. 6 Chelsea FC.
7 197. 8 Swimming. 9 Rhinos. 10 Equestrianism. 11 Horse racing.
12 Wasps. 13 Rose. 14 Spain. 15 Hungarian. 16 114. 17 England.
18 Harlem. 19 Sin bin. 20 Two. 21 Crucible. 22 Japan. 23 Shuttlecock.
24 Wood. 25 Boris Becker. 26 First basketball player to say he was HIV
positive. 27 Ice. 28 Elephant. 29 Judo. 30 Boxing match.

Quiz 69 Movies: The Brits

Answers - see Quiz 70, page 78

LEVEL 1

1 What was the Spice Girls' first film?

2 Who with The Shadows starred in The Young Ones?

3 Which movie told of redundant steel workers becoming strippers?

4 The Bridge on the River Kwai prisoners are imprisoned by whom?

5 Nick Hornby's Fever Pitch is about which game?

6 Which Kenneth directed and starred in Hamlet?

7 The Blue Lamp preceded which TV series about PC George Dixon?

8 A BAFTA is a British Award for film and what?

9 What nationality was The...Patient in the 1996 Oscar winner?

10 Which US food expert Loyd is the son in law of David Puttnam?

11 Mrs Blake Edwards won an Oscar for Mary Poppins; who was she?

12 What is the nationality of Sir Anthony Hopkins?

13 In which part of the UK was Trainspotting set?

14 Which British Transport Minister twice won an Oscar?

15 Which Sir Richard directed Chaplin?

16 Which 1994 British hit shot Hugh Grant to superstardom?

17 Which Emma wrote the screenplay for Sense & Sensibility?

18 Jenny Agutter found fame in which movie about an Edwardian family?

19 Is Helena Bonham Carter a British Prime Minister's or a US President's grand daughter?

20 Elizabeth Taylor was twice married to this Welsh actor; who was he?

21 Who was born Maurice Micklewhite but is perhaps best known as Alfie?

22 Which Julie was Oscar nominated in 1998?

23 Which Ewan plays the young Obi Wan Kenobi in Episode I of Star Wars

24 In which film did Tom Conti play Pauline Collins' Greek lover?

25 Which blonde bombshell was born Diana Fluck?

26 Linus Roache's father has played which Coronation Street character since the soap began?

27 Who or what was the film Wilde with Stephen Fry about?

28 In which film did Joanna Lumley play Shirley's old school friend?

29 In which part of the UK was Robert Carlyle born?

30 Hot Chocolate's You Sexy Thing was the theme for which 1997 film?

Pot Luck 34 (see Quiz 70, page 78)

1 France. 2 Windsor Castle. 3 Yogi Bear. 4 Lime. 5 Badminton. 6 Oysters.
7 Norman Watts. 8 Five. 9 Four. 10 Coronation. 11 Flock together.
12 Poet. 13 Ten shilling note. 14 Javelin. 15 Cornwall. 16 A catamaran.
17 Eeyore. 18 L. S. 19 An apple. 20 Europe, Asia. 21 Elizabeth I.
22 Yachting. 23 Yugoslavia. 24 Goat. 25 Leeds. 26 Peppermint.
27 The humming bird. 28 Cricket. 29 Michael & Janet. 30 Bottom.

Answers

Quiz 70 Pot Luck 34

LEVEL 1

1 The Dauphin was heir to which European throne?
2 Which castle was partly damaged by fire in 1992?
3 Which bear had a friend called Boo Boo?
4 What is the another name for a linden tree?
5 Which sport is named after a place which is famous for horse trials?
6 The precious stone, a pearl, can be found in what?
7 What is Curly's proper character name in Coronation Street?
8 How many senior titles (excluding over 35 events) are contested each Wimbledon?
9 How many passenger terminals does Heathrow Airport have?
10 At which ceremony is a Monarch given their crown?
11 According to the saying, what do birds of a feather do?
12 Was Ted Hughes a dancer, painter or poet?
13 Which British bank note stopped being available in 1970?
14 For which sport is Tessa Sanderson famous?
15 Prince Charles is Duke of which English county?
16 What is a yacht with two hulls called?
17 Which character from Winnie The Pooh lost his tail?
18 What two initials did northern artist Lowry have?
19 What did William Tell shoot from his son's head with a crossbow?
20 Which continents are separated by the Urals?
21 Who was England's Queen when Shakespeare was alive?
22 Cowes on the Isle of Wight is famous for which sport?
23 Which country was formerly ruled by President Tito?
24 Which animal's milk is used to make cheese called Chevre?
25 Which city is furthest North – Lincoln or Leeds?
26 What flavour is Kendal's most famous cake?
27 Which is the only bird that can fly backwards?
28 What is John Major's favourite sport?
29 Which Jacksons recorded Scream?
30 Which part of your body is a character in Shakespeare's A Midsummer Night's Dream?

Answers

Movies: The Brits (see Quiz 69, page 77)
1 Spiceworld The Movie. 2 Cliff Richard. 3 The Full Monty. 4 Japanese.
5 Football. 6 Branagh. 7 Dixon of Dock Green. 8 Television. 9 English.
10 Grossman. 11 Julie Andrews. 12 Welsh. 13 Scotland. 14 Glenda Jackson.
15 Attenborough. 16 Four Weddings and a Funeral. 17 Thompson. 18 The
Railway Children. 19 British Prime Minister's. 20 Richard Burton. 21 Michael
Caine. 22 Christie. 23 McGregor. 24 Shirley Valentine. 25 Diana Dors. 26 Ken
Barlow. 27 Oscar Wilde. 28 Shirley Valentine. 29 Scotland. 30 The Full Monty.

Quiz 71 Leisure: Home & D-I-Y

Answers - see Quiz 72, page 80

LEVEL 1

1   What sort of security device is a Chubb?
2   An Entryphone would normally be found at the entrance to what?
3   What in the bedroom would have a TOG rating?
4   What colour is Copydex adhesive?
5   What is the abbreviation for volt?
6   Is pine a soft or hard wood?
7   Which machine tool is used for turning wood?
8   Do weft fibres run across the width or the length of a fabric?
9   What goes between a nut and the surface to protect it?
10 Soldering joins two pieces of what?
11 Cushions, curtains etc. are referred to as what sort of furnishings?
12 Should silk be washed in hot or cool water?
13 Which tool can be band, hand or hack?
14 E numbers refer to additives to what?
15 Is an emery cloth rough or smooth?
16 Which device turns off an appliance when a temperature is reached?
17 A rasp is a type of what?
18 Is Araldite a strong or light glue?
19 In which sort of bank would you deposit waste glass?
20 Canning, bottling and freezing are types of what?
21 What would a bradawl produce in wood?
22 Batik is a type of dyeing on what?
23 What would you normally make in a percolator?
24 Where is the door on a chest freezer?
25 A bedsit usually consists of how many rooms?
26 What type of electrical devices are 'white goods'?
27 Is a kilogram less or more than two pounds in weight?
28 What colour does silver turn when it is tarnished?
29 Which wood is darker, mahogany or ash?
30 What does the ply of a yarn refer to?

Answers

Pot Luck 35 (see Quiz 72, page 80)
1 George Bush. 2 Sheffield. 3 Dock. 4 North Sea. 5 Angela Lansbury.
6 China. 7 Lines of longitude. 8 Scotland. 9 Glasgow. 10 Furniture.
11 Buttons. 12 Red Rum. 13 Daisy. 14 De Lorean. 15 Blubber. 16 Red.
17 Bob Dylan. 18 Birds of a Feather. 19 Chocolate. 20 Roy Rogers.
21 Decathlon. 22 King John. 23 Scotland. 24 Erasure. 25 A crop.
26 White. 27 At the beginning. 28 Sand. 29 Four. 30 Train.

Quiz 72 Pot Luck 35

Answers - see Quiz 71, page 79

LEVEL 1

1   Who was the last President of the USA elected in the 1980s?
2   Which city is furthest North – Cardiff or Sheffield?
3   Which plant helps to take away the sting of a stinging nettle?
4   The River Forth flows into which Sea?
5   Which actress plays Jessica Fletcher in Murder She Wrote?
6   Which country was ruled by Chairman Mao?
7   What name is given to the imaginary lines drawn from north to south on a map?
8   Where in Britain can you spend paper £1 notes?
9   What is Rab C. Nesbitt's city?
10 Thomas Sheraton was a designer and manufacturer of what?
11 Which came first, zips, velcro or buttons?
12 Which horse named after a drink won the Grand National three times?
13 What was the name of Donald Duck's girlfriend?
14 What make of car was featured in the movie Back to the Future?
15 What is the fat of a whale called?
16 Which is the warmest sea in the world, The Red, Med or Dead?
17 Who wrote the pop anthem Knockin' On Heaven's Door?
18 Who or what flock together according to the saying?
19 What is the flavour of a Devil's Food Cake?
20 Which cowboy had a horse called Trigger?
21 For which sport is Daley Thompson famous?
22 Which King put his seal on the Magna Carta?
23 Which is nearest to Ireland, England, Scotland or Wales?
24 Abba-Esque wasn't a No. 1 for Abba, but it was for which group?
25 What is a horse rider's whip called?
26 What colour balls were used at Wimbledon before yellow balls?
27 Where would you expect to hear the prologue in a play?
28 Which of the following will not dissolve in water, salt, sugar or sand?
29 How many teats does a cow have normally?
30 Was the Flying Fortress a plane or a train?

Answers

Leisure: Home & D-I-Y (see Quiz 71, page 79)
1 Lock. 2 Block of flats. 3 Duvet. 4 White. 5 V. 6 Soft. 7 Lathe.
8 Width. 9 Washer. 10 Metal. 11 Soft furnishings. 12 Cool. 13 Saw.
14 Food. 15 Rough. 16 Thermostat. 17 File. 18 Strong. 19 Bottle bank.
20 Preserving. 21 Hole. 22 Fabric. 23 Coffee. 24 Top. 25 One.
26 Large kitchen appliances, such as freezers and washing machines. 27 More.
28 Black. 29 Mahogany. 30 Its thickness.

Quiz 73 Pop: The 90s

Answers - see Quiz 74, page 82

LEVEL 1

1 Which football anthem was co written by Skinner and Baddiel?
2 What is the surname of Oasis brothers Noel and Liam?
3 Who was Candle in the Wind 1997 dedicated to?
4 Which Zoo sang Spaceman in 1996?
5 In which drama series did chart toppers Robson & Jerome find fame?
6 Isaac, Taylor and Zac make up which boy band?
7 Who said 'Eh Oh' on the their first smash hit?
8 Whose album of Urban Hymns hit the top spot?
9 Which 90s band were named after an area of London?
10 Knockin' On Heaven's Door was released after which 1996 tragedy?
11 Which single was released by Robson & Jerome and two years later by The Three Tenors?
12 Who was 'Older' in the 90s after a long running battle with Sony?
13 Who were Back For Good in 1995 before disbanding altogether?
14 Whose death propelled Bohemian Rhapsody back to the charts?
15 Which Peter had a No 1 with Flava?
16 Who had a No 1 with Nilsson's Without You?
17 Who backed Katrina on her 1997 Eurovision winner?
18 Which Damon fronted Blur?
19 Who starred in and sang on the soundtrack of The Bodyguard?
20 In September '98 Celine Dion released an album in which language?
21 Which toy provided Aqua with a No 1?
22 Which country singer John died flying his plane in 1997?
23 Who had a daughter Lourdes Maria in 1996?
24 Which band's name is a US emergency number?
25 Dana International won Eurovision 98 for which Middle East country?
26 Oasis were formed in which UK city?
27 Who had a huge hit with Drop Dead Gorgeous?
28 Which Darren appeared in the 90s version of Summer Holiday?
29 In which county were Blur formed?
30 My Heart Will Go On came from which smash hit film?

Pot Luck 36 (see Quiz 74, page 82)
1 Tasmania. 2 Balsawood. 3 Tennis. 4 The candlestick maker. 5 Up.
6 Roald Dahl. 7 Hindu. 8 St. David. 9 USA. 10 1940s. 11 Davy Crockett.
12 Polo. 13 Shoes. 14 South Pacific. 15 George Bush. 16 Silver. 17 A stone. 18 Sweets. 19 St Ives. 20 240. 21 Four. 22 Jacobites. 23 Touché.
24 Rainbow. 25 Avon. 26 Boots. 27 Black and yellow. 28 Javelin.
29 One. 30 Chester.

Quiz 74 Pot Luck 36

Answers - see Quiz 73, page 81

LEVEL 1

1 Which Australian state is named after its discoverer Abel Tasman?

2 Which very soft wood is popular with model makers?

3 Which sport was played by Gabriela Sabatini?

4 According to the nursery rhyme, who joined the butcher and baker?

5 Do bananas grow pointing up or down?

6 Who wrote Charlie and the Chocolate Factory?

7 The River Ganges is sacred to the people of which religion?

8 Which Saint is the patron saint of Wales?

9 Which country was the 1994 football World Cup Final played in?

10 Was Terry Venables born in the 1940s, 1950s or the 1960s?

11 Which American hero wore a hat with a racoon tail hanging from the back?

12 Which sport is played on the largest pitch: cricket, football or polo?

13 What are or were winkle pickers?

14 Which part of an ocean shares its name with a musical?

15 Who was American president immediately before Bill Clinton?

16 Which metal is the FA Cup made from?

17 What did David throw from his sling to kill Goliath?

18 What do American children mean if they ask for candy?

19 Where was the person going, who met a man with seven wives?

20 Electricity comes into our homes at how many volts?

21 In the neck of a violin how many tuning pegs are there?

22 What were supporters of James II and his Stuart descendants called?

23 What is shouted by people when they make contact in fencing?

24 Which children's TV programme featured Bungle and Zippy?

25 Which English county shares its name with a beauty products range?

26 Which is the largest chain of chemist shops in the world?

27 What colour is Rupert the Bear's scarf?

28 For which sport was Fatima Whitbread famous?

29 How many players take part in a game of patience at any one time?

30 Which city is furthest north – Bristol or Chester?

Answers

Pop: The 90s (see Quiz 73, page 81)
1 Three Lions. 2 Gallagher. 3 Diana, Princess of Wales. 4 Babylon Zoo.
5 Soldier Soldier. 6 Hanson. 7 Teletubbies. 8 The Verve. 9 East 17.
10 Dunblane. 11 You'll Never Walk Alone. 12 George Michael. 13 Take
That. 14 Freddie Mercury. 15 Andre. 16 Mariah Carey. 17 The Waves.
18 Albarn. 19 Whitney Houston. 20 French. 21 Barbie. 22 Denver.
23 Madonna. 24 911. 25 Israel. 26 Manchester. 27 Republica. 28 Day.
29 Essex. 30 Titanic.

Quiz 75 People & Places

Answers - see Quiz 76, page 84

LEVEL 1

1   In which World War was the Home Guard founded?

2   In which country were the Borgias a powerful family?

3   Benazir Bhutto was Prime Minister of which Muslim state?

4   Which Al was crime boss of Chicago during the Prohibition?

5   Which South African shared the Nobel Peace Prize with FW de Klerk in 1993?

6   What was President John F Kennedy's wife called?

7   What did Anthony Wedgwood Benn become known as?

8   In which country was Terry Waite imprisoned?

9   Roman Emperor Hadrian gave his name to what in Britain?

10   Which animals did Hannibal use to frighten the Romans?

11   Hirohito was Emperor of which country during WWII?

12   Which Russian word for Caesar was used by Russian monarchs?

13   Where was T.E. Lawrence involved in an independence struggle?

14   Which Russian revolutionary took his name from the River Lena?

15   When did Columbus discover America?

16   Which 11thC Scottish king was the subject of a Shakespeare play?

17   In which country of the UK was David Livingstone born?

18   Which British admiral Horatio was born in Norfolk?

19   Where is Botany Bay?

20   Which country put the first woman in space?

21   Which journalist John was imprisoned in Beirut with Brian Keenan?

22   What was Argentinean vice president Eva Duarte's married name?

23   Ho Chi Minh founded the Communist Party in which country?

24   Which English Quaker founded the colony of Pennsylvania?

25   Which African country was bombed on the orders of Ronald Reagan in 1986?

26   In which country was Joan of Arc born?

27   Where was the tomb of Tutankhamun discovered in 1922?

28   Which famous Indian monument was built by Shah Jahan?

29   Zulu leader Buthelezi became a government minister where?

30   Which nurse is famous for her work during the Crimean War?

Answers

Pot Luck 37 (see Quiz 76, page 84)

1 Golf. 2 Marzipan. 3 Rural England. 4 Two. 5 22. 6 Putty. 7 Roger Bannister. 8 Ballet. 9 Glasgow. 10 Eleven. 11 Des O'Connor. 12 A skateboard. 13 Carrot. 14 Gymnasts. 15 Billy Butlin. 16 The sea. 17 A fiddle. 18 Cookery. 19 Canada. 20 19th. 21 Collar bone. 22 Victoria. 23 The service. 24 Forget. 25 Grass. 26 Kill You. 27 A Swiss cheese. 28 Spain. 29 The knight. 30 Red and black.

Quiz 76 Pot Luck 37

Answers - see Quiz 75, page 83

LEVEL 1

1 Which sport is Sandy Lyle famous for playing?
2 What name is given to the almond coating often on a Christmas cake?
3 C.P.R.E. is the Council for the Protection of what?
4 How many Bank Holidays are there in May?
5 How many yards are there between the wickets in cricket?
6 What sticky paste usually holds glass in a window?
7 Who was the first person to run a mile in under four minutes?
8 What is performed by the Russian Bolshoi company?
9 Which Scottish city has the biggest population?
10 How many players can a team have on the field in American football?
11 Who invites contestants on the TV programme to Take Your Pick?
12 What has a kicktail and four wheels?
13 Which vegetable, high in vitamin A, is said to be good for the eyes?
14 What kind of athletes perform a flic-flac?
15 Who set up England's biggest chain of holiday camps?
16 Neptune was the god of what?
17 According to the saying, which instrument can you be as fit as?
18 What type of TV programmes are presented by Keith Floyd?
19 Which is biggest – the USA, Germany or Canada?
20 Was basketball developed in the 17th, 18th or 19th century?
21 What is the common name for the clavicle?
22 Africa's biggest lake is named after which British queen?
23 What is the name given to the first hit in a game of tennis?
24 What do elephants never do according to the saying?
25 Bamboo is a very large variety of what?
26 What will too much love do, according to Brian May?
27 What is Emmenthal?
28 In which country were the 1992 Summer Olympic Games held?
29 Which chess piece is shaped like a horse's head?
30 What two colours are Dennis the Menace's sweater?

Answers

People & Places (see Quiz 75, page 83)
1 Second. 2 Italy. 3 Pakistan. 4 Capone. 5 Nelson Mandela. 6 Jackie.
7 Tony Benn. 8 Lebanon. 9 Hadrian's Wall. 10 Elephants. 11 Japan.
12 Tsar. 13 Arabia. 14 Lenin. 15 1492. 16 Macbeth. 17 Scotland.
18 Nelson. 19 Australia. 20 USSR. 21 McCarthy. 22 Peron.
23 Vietnam. 24 Penn. 25 Libya. 26 France. 27 Egypt. 28 Taj Mahal.
29 South Africa. 30 Florence Nightingale

Quiz 77 TV Times 2

Answers - see Quiz 78, page 86

LEVEL 1

1 On which type of show is Ainsley Harriott most likely to appear?
2 Which Carol was the first presenter of Changing Rooms?
3 Which washing up liquid did Nanette Newman famously advertise?
4 Which programme is often referred to simply as Corrie?
5 Which Zoe succeeded Gaby Roslin on The Big Breakfast?
6 Which impersonator Rory starred in Who Else?
7 Who is Mrs Richard Madely who appears on This Morning?
8 Which Fiona succeeded Anthea Turner on GMTV's morning sofa?
9 In which country is Ballykissangel set?
10 Scriptwriter Carla Lane is famous for campaigning on whose behalf?
11 Who was the BT housewife in the ads as played by Maureen Lipman?
12 In which show did David Jason call Nicholas Lyndhurst a plonker?
13 Which Rik was involved in a quad bike accident in 1998?
14 Which Have I Got News For You? star's real name is Paul Martin?
15 Which Helen appeared nude on the cover of Radio Times to celebrate her 50th birthday?
16 Who was the taller in the Peter Cook and Dudley Moore partnership?
17 Did Bob Monkhouse celebrate his 60th, 70th or 80th birthday in a TV special in 1998?
18 Who is Paul O'Grady's blonde, cigarette smoking alter ego?
19 What is the occupation of Bramwell in the TV series?
20 Who was the regular presenter of The Cook Report?
21 Who is Reeves' TV comedy partner?
22 In which show would you see the neighbour-from-hell Dorien Green?
23 Which TV cook went on tour on The Rhodes Show?
24 What is the first name of Prime Suspect writer La Plante?
25 Which morning show did Chris Evans and Gaby Roslin present?
26 Which TV astronomer was born Patrick Caldwell-Moore?
27 What is the surname of sister presenters Anthea and Wendy?
28 Who presented The Full Wax?
29 Which Victorian drama series has a hospital called The Thrift?
30 Laurence Lllewelyn-Bowen is a TV expert on what?

Answers

Pot Luck 38 (see Quiz 78, page 86)
1 Hovercraft. 2 Three. 3 A mole. 4 Makepeace. 5 Jersey. 6 George Graham. 7 Rats. 8 The Bermuda Triangle. 9 Wheel clamps. 10 Maple. 11 Guinevere. 12 Newcastle. 13 Hiawatha. 14 A gas. 15 Four. 16 Peacocks. 17 Enid Blyton. 18 A harmonica. 19 Debbie McGee. 20 The bully-off. 21 Yellow. 22 Coca-Cola. 23 Golf. 24 A river. 25 Roller skates. 26 Boxing. 27 Squirrel. 28 Brown. 29 Three. 30 The Muppets.

Quiz 78 Pot Luck 38

LEVEL 1

1   In 1959, what kind of vehicle crossed the Channel for the first time?
2   How many minutes are there per round in professional boxing?
3   Which animal built the hill that William III's horse stumbled on?
4   Which is female, Dempsey or Makepeace?
5   Which Channel Isle is famous for very creamy milk?
6   Which soccer boss left Arsenal following 'bung' allegations?
7   Which animals do sailors say desert a sinking ship?
8   Which triangle are ships and planes said to disappear in?
9   What were used on illegally parked cars for the first time in 1983?
10 The leaf from which tree is a logo for Air Canada?
11 Who was the legendary King Arthur's wife?
12 The TV series Byker Grove is set in which city?
13 Which Red Indian married Laughing Water?
14 What does a liquid turn into if it is heated up?
15 How many people take part in each heat of Blind Date?
16 A muster is a collection of what type of birds?
17 Who wrote about Noddy and Big Ears?
18 What is the proper name for a mouth organ?
19 Who is Paul Daniel's wife?
20 What is the start of a hockey match called?
21 What colour was Bobby Shafto's hair in the nursery rhyme?
22 Which popular drink was invented by Dr John Pemberton?
23 Which sport did Sam Snead play?
24 What is the Tigris?
25 In Starlight Express what do the performers wear on their feet?
26 Which sport is featured in the Rocky movies?
27 Which animal family do chipmunks belong to?
28 What colour is umber?
29 How many of Henry VIII's wives were called Catherine?
30 Which puppet show has two old men called Statler and Waldorf?

Answers

TV Times 2 (see Quiz 77, page 85)
1 Cookery. 2 Smillie. 3 Fairy liquid. 4 Coronation Street. 5 Ball. 6 Bremner.
7 Judy Finnegan. 8 Phillips. 9 Ireland. 10 Animals. 11 Beattie. 12 Only
Fools and Horses. 13 Mayall. 14 Paul Merton. 15 Mirren. 16 Peter Cook.
17 70th. 18 Lily Savage. 19 Doctor. 20 Roger Cook. 21 Mortimer. 22 Birds
of a Feather. 23 Gary Rhodes. 24 Lynda. 25 The Big Breakfast. 26 Patrick
Moore. 27 Turner. 28 Ruby Wax. 29 Bramwell. 30 Home decorating.

Quiz 79 Summer Sports

Answers - see Quiz 80, page 88

LEVEL 1

1   Which sport are the Lord's Taverners famous for playing?
2   Which Denise won European gold in the heptathlon in '98?
3   Who was the last British Wimbledon champion?
4   Sergey Bubka has set a world record in which field event over 30 times?
5   Which British tennis star reached the Wimbledon semi finals in 1998?
6   Which summer sport did Kerry Packer revolutionise in the 70s?
7   Who has won moreMajor golf titles than any other player?
8   Chris Boardman suffered an accident riding what in summer 1998?
9   Which country staged the summer Olympics in 1984 and 1996?
10 Between 1990 and 1998 all Ladies Wimbledon Singles champions were born in which continent?
11 The summer Olympics are held every how many years?
12 In cricket, what must a ball not do to score six runs?
13 Jonathan Edwards specialises in what type of jump?
14 For which international side did Shane Warne play cricket?
15 Which golfer is known as the Great White Shark?
16 Which Martina did Martinez beat in the 1994 Wimbledon final?
17 Which Tour is the world's premier cycling event?
18 Which German tennis player's father Peter was jailed for tax fraud?
19 Sonia O'Sullivan races for which country?
20 How many runners are there in the 400m relay team?
21 Which Jana won Wimbledon 98 after her third final?
22 You would do a Fosbury flop in which athletics event?
23 Which country has the oldest cricket competition in the world?
24 How many balls an over are there in cricket?
25 Who told a Wimbledon umpire "You cannot be serious!"?
26 Which West Indian cricketer was called Vivian?
27 Who shattered Roger Maris's all-time Baseball home run record in '98
28 Which Jimmy won Wimbledon doubles with Ilie Nastase?
29 What was the nationality of tennis pin up Gabriela Sabatini?
30 Which team competes against America in the Ryder Cup?

Pot Luck 39 (see Quiz 80, page 88)

Answers

1 Wrestling. 2 Stirrups. 3 Dogger Bank. 4 Nine. 5 US President.
6 Perception. 7 Scandinavia. 8 One. 9 He was bald. 10 Animated cartoons.
11 A reservoir. 12 A spider. 13 The 1812 Overture. 14 14th February.
15 Hundred Acres Wood. 16 Victoria. 17 Four. 18 Moses. 19 The Pacific
Ocean. 20 Teeth. 21 Harvey. 22 The maiden all forlorn. 23 Arms. 24 Show
jumping. 25 Worms. 26 Four. 27 Jade. 28 Four. 29 A collage. 30 Sixpence.

Quiz 80 Pot Luck 39

LEVEL 1

Answers - see Quiz 79, page 87

1 With which sport is Hulk Hogan associated?
2 What are the metal loops that you place your feet in when horse riding?
3 Which bank is a dangerous sand bar in the North Sea?
4 How many players are there in a rounders team?
5 Whose official plane is Air Force One?
6 What does the letter P stand for in ESP?
7 Which group of countries did the Vikings come from?
8 How many Popes have been English – one, two or three?
9 What colour was Kojak's hair?
10 What kind of programmes are Hanna and Barbara famous for?
11 What is a man-made lake in which water is stored called?
12 What type of creature is a Black Widow?
13 Which overture has a date in its title and includes cannons and bells?
14 On what date did the St. Valentine's Day Massacre take place?
15 Winnie the Pooh lived in which wood?
16 Melbourne is the capital of which Australian State?
17 How many walls surround a squash court?
18 In The Bible, who parted the sea?
19 Fiji is in which ocean?
20 Which part of your body has a coating of enamel?
21 Which Mr Goldsmith promotes rock concerts?
22 Who milked the cow with the crumpled horn, in the rhyme?
23 Which part of the Venus de Milo's body are missing?
24 In which sport are Michael and John Whitaker famous?
25 Would a vermicide be used to kill worms or mice?
26 How many presidents' faces are carved into Mount Rushmore?
27 Which green stone was buried by the Chinese with their dead?
28 How many New Testament Gospels are there?
29 What word describes a picture made from sticking scraps onto a background?
30 Which English coin was nicknamed the tanner?

Summer Sports (see Quiz 79, page 87)

Answers
1 Cricket. 2 Lewis. 3 Fred Perry. 4 Pole vault. 5 Tim Henman. 6 Cricket. 7 Jack Nicklaus. 8 Bicycle. 9 USA. 10 Europe. 11 Four. 12 Bounce. 13 Triple jump. 14 Australia. 15 Greg Norman. 16 Navratilova. 17 Tour de France. 18 Steffi Graf. 19 Ireland. 20 Four. 21 Novotna. 22 High jump. 23 England. 24 Six. 25 John McEnroe. 26 Viv Richards. 27 Mark McGwire. 28 Connors. 29 Argentinean. 30 Europe.

Quiz 81 Science & Nature: Space

Answers - see Quiz 82, page 90

1   What force makes the Earth orbit the Sun?
2   What colour is the Great Spot on Jupiter?
3   Is Jupiter larger or smaller than Earth?
4   Which gas is present in the Earth's atmosphere which is not present on any other planet?
5   A solar eclipse occurs when the Moon gets between Earth and what?
6   Which is the seventh planet from the Sun?
7   What is the layer around the Earth called?
8   What is the name given to matter so dense that even light cannot escape its pull?
9   Which planet's name comes nearest the end of the alphabet?
10 Herschel planned to name Uranus after the King; which one?
11 What would you find on a celestial map?
12 Is the science of celestial bodies, astrology or astronomy?
13 Which colour in the rainbow has the shortest name?
14 Which TV programme called space The Final Frontier?
15 Were the first US Shuttle flights in the 50s, 60s, or 80s?
16 Which show with Reeves & Mortimer shares its name with another term for meteors?
17 What is a group of stars which make a recognisable pattern called?
18 What does 'S' stand for in NASA?
19 In which decade was the US's first satellite launched?
20 What is the English name for the lunar sea Mare Tranquillitas?
21 Castor and Pollux are two stars in which constellation?
22 John Young ate which item of fast food in space in 1968?
23 Was Apollo a US or USSR space programme?
24 Prior to being an astronaut was John Glenn in the Air Force or the Marines?
25 How long does it take the Earth to orbit the Sun?
26 Mishka, the 1980 Olympic mascot was the first of which toy in space?
27 How is Ursa Major better known?
28 How many times did Gagarin orbit the Earth on his first space flight?
29 What travels at 186,272 miles per second?
30 Edward White was the first American to walk where?

Pot Luck 40 (see Quiz 82, page 90)

1 Nora Batty. 2 Green. 3 An earthquake. 4 Tennis. 5 Monday. 6 Barber.
7 Peron. 8 A sword. 9 West Ham. 10 Oxford. 11 Boxing Day. 12 Nine.
13 A bird (falcon). 14 Mo Mowlam. 15 Blue and White.
16 Boyzone. 17 Clint Eastwood. 18 A cherry. 19 Chess. 20 Nuclear.
21 Methane. 22 Nick Leeson. 23 Cain. 24 BSkyB. 25 Ena Sharples.
26 Annie. 27 Venice. 28 Eight. 29 Eiffel Tower. 30 Strawberry.

Quiz 82 Pot Luck 40

Answers - see Quiz 81, page 89

1 In Last of the Summer Wine, which part was played by Kathy Staff?
2 What colour is Dipsy in the Teletubbies?
3 An aftershock can sometimes follow what natural disaster?
4 For which sport was Sue Barker famous?
5 Which day's child is "fair of face" according to the traditional rhyme?
6 Which tradesman from Seville is featured in the title of an opera?
7 Which Argentinean president had wives called Eva and Maria Estela?
8 In legend, who or what was Excalibur?
9 Which London club did soccer's Ian Wright join from Arsenal?
10 Which university is the oldest in England?
11 St Stephen's Day is generally known by what other name?
12 How many players are in a baseball team?
13 What is a peregrine?
14 Who was Tony Blair's first Northern Ireland Minister?
15 What are the two main colours of the Argentinean flag?
16 Who had a No. 1 UK hit in September 1998 with No Matter What?
17 Which actor links Play Misty For Me and Pale Rider?
18 What type of fruit is a morello?
19 With which board game are Karpov and Kasparov associated?
20 Sizewell in Suffolk is associated with which form of power?
21 Which gas is the full name for marsh gas?
22 Who was Lisa Leeson's notorious husband?
23 In The Bible, who was Adam and Eve's firstborn son?
24 Which company acquired Manchester United Football Club in September 1998?
25 Which character in Coronation Street was played by Violet Carson?
26 The song Tomorrow comes from which musical?
27 In which Italian city is the Rialto Bridge?
28 How many noughts are in the written number one hundred million?
29 What is the most lasting symbol of the French Exhibition of 1889?
30 Royal Sovereign is a type of which soft fruit?

Science & Nature: Space (see Quiz 81, page 89)
Answers
1 Gravity. 2 Red. 3 Larger. 4 Oxygen. 5 The Sun. 6 Uranus.
7 Atmosphere. 8 Black Hole. 9 Venus. 10 George. 11 Stars.
12 Astronomy. 13 Red. 14 Star Trek. 15 80s. 16 Shooting Stars.
17 Constellation. 18 Space. 19 1950s. 20 Sea of Tranquillity. 21 Gemini.
22 Burger. 23 USA. 24 Marines. 25 A year. 26 Teddy bear. 27 Great
Bear. 28 Once. 29 Light. 30 Space.

Quiz 83 The Movies: The Oscars

Answers - see Quiz 84, page 92

1 Which Oscar winner became a Labour MP?
2 Which sea disaster movie swept the Oscars at the 1998 ceremony?
3 Which Plasticine pair had six Oscar nominations by 1998?
4 Which Kevin won Best Director and starred in Dances With Wolves?
5 Braveheart was set in which country?
6 Who won Best Actor for The Silence of the Lambs?
7 Who directed Schindler's List?
8 Which British actor Jeremy was a winner with Reversal of Fortune?
9 Was it Tom Hanks or Tom Cruise who won in 1993 and again in '94?
10 Sonny's ex wife won Best Actress in Moonstruck; who was she?
11 Which Susan won for Dead Man Walking?
12 Which foot is named in the title of the movie with Daniel-Day Lewis?
13 Was Clint Eastwood Best Actor or Best Director for Unforgiven?
14 How often are the Oscars presented?
15 Which keyboard instrument gave its name to a film with Holly Hunter?
16 Kathy Bates won with Misery based on which Stephen's novel?
17 Which Kate was Oscar-nominated for Titanic?
18 Did Madonna receive one, two or no nominations for Evita?
19 What was Best Picture when Tom Hanks won Best Actor for Forrest Gump?
20 Which Al was Best Actor for Scent of a Woman?
21 Which Shirley won an Oscar at the age of five?
22 For which film did James Cameron win a 1997 Oscar?
23 Which British movie about the 1924 Olympics was an 80s winner?
24 Which Oscar winner based in India holds the record for most extras?
25 Which son of Kirk Douglas won for Wall Street?
26 Platoon was about which Asian war?
27 Which Ralph was an English Patient winner?
28 Talk To The Animals came from which movie about a Doctor?
29 When did the English Patient win Best Picture?
30 Dances With Wolves was the first film of what type to win Best Picture for 60 years?

Answers

Pot Luck 41 (see Quiz 84, page 92)
1 Lean. 2 Anglesey. 3 A hop, a step and a leap. 4 Gondolas. 5 Canaries.
6 Greece. 7 Red. 8 Milky Way. 9 Motor racing. 10 Green (the Incredible
Hulk). 11 Six. 12 Its age. 13 A flower. 14 A fish. 15 Table tennis. 16 High
jumping. 17 Universe. 18 A monkey. 19 Beatrix Potter. 20 Spain. 21 In your
bones. 22 Apple trees. 23 The Flintstones. 24 A Christmas Carol. 25 Falkland
Islands. 26 White. 27 Ireland. 28 Dick Turpin. 29 Scotland. 30 Six.

Quiz 84 Pot Luck 41

LEVEL 1

1   Which David directed the epic movie Lawrence of Arabia?
2   Which island is off the north-western tip of Wales?
3   The triple jump involves a run and then which three movements?
4   Which black boats sail along the canals of Venice?
5   Which bird was taken to work by miners to test for gas?
6   Mount Olympus is in which European country?
7   What colour hat is worn by Papa Smurf?
8   Which chocolate sweet bar is named after our galaxy?
9   For which sport was Gilles Villeneuve famous?
10 What colour did Dr. Banner become when he got angry?
11 How many legs does a fully grown insect have?
12 What can be discovered by counting the rings in a tree trunk?
13 Who or what is Sweet William?
14 What kind of creature is an anchovy?
15 What game are you playing if you hold a bat in a penholder grip?
16 In which sport would you see a Fosbury Flop?
17 Which word collectively describes all the stars and planets?
18 Which has the longer tail, a monkey or ape?
19 Who wrote the Peter Rabbit novels?
20 Which country produces Valencia oranges?
21 Where in your body would you find marrow?
22 Which tree does mistletoe grow on?
23 Who live at 342 Greasepit Terrace, Bedrock?
24 In which Dickens' novel does Jacob Marley's ghost appear?
25 Which islands were invaded in 1982 by the Argentineans?
26 What colour are the stars on the American flag?
27 In which country would you visit to kiss the Blarney Stone?
28 Which highwayman had a horse called Black Bess?
29 The TV series Take the High Road is set in which country?
30 How many strings are there on a Spanish guitar?

The Movies: The Oscars (see Quiz 83, page 91)
1 Glenda Jackson. 2 Titanic. 3 Wallace & Gromit. 4 Costner. 5 Scotland.
6 Anthony Hopkins. 7 Steven Spielberg. 8 Irons. 9 Hanks. 10 Cher.
11 Sarandon. 12 Left Foot. 13 Director. 14 Once a year. 15 The Piano.
16 King. 17 Winslet. 18 None. 19 Forrest Gump. 20 Pacino. 21 Temple.
22 Titanic. 23 Chariots of Fire. 24 Gandhi. 25 Michael. 26 Vietnam.
27 Fiennes. 28 Doolittle. 29 1996. 30 Western.

Answers

Quiz 85 Geography: On the Map

LEVEL 1

Answers - see Quiz 86, page 94

1 Which language other than English is an official language of the Channel Islands?
2 Which Tsar changed Russia's capital from Moscow to St Petersburg?
3 You would find Delphi on a map of which country?
4 What is farther north, Clacton or Brighton?
5 Which continent has an Ivory Coast?
6 On which island would you find the Giant's Causeway?
7 If you were on a French autoroute what type of road would you be on?
8 Which Gulf lies between Saudi Arabia and Iran?
9 Lake Superior is on the border of the USA and which other country?
10 Which tiny European landlocked state is a Grand Duchy?
11 Macedonia was formerly a part of which communist republic?
12 Which Himalayan kingdom has been called the world's highest rubbish dump because of waste left behind by climbers?
13 Which Australasian capital shares its name with a Duke and a boot?
14 Which river which flows through Germany is Europe's dirtiest?
15 Where would you be if you saw Nippon on the map?
16 Whose address is often referred to as Number Ten?
17 Which motorway goes past Stoke On Trent?
18 On which continent is the Basque country?
19 The Home Counties surround which city?
20 Malta is to the south of which island to the south of Italy?
21 The Ural Mountains mark the eastern frontier to which continent?
22 How is the London Orbital Motorway better known?
23 Is Moldova in Europe or Africa?
24 Which island republic lies to the north west of the UK?
25 Miami is a port in which US state?
26 Kew Gardens are next to which London river?
27 Which country has Lakes Garda, Maggiore and Como?
28 Is Madagascar an island or is it an African peninsula?
29 In which city is Red Square?
30 Which country's official languages are Hebrew and Arabic?

Pot Luck 42 (see Quiz 86, page 94)

1 Gaz. 2 Rosary. 3 Sewing Machine. 4 University. 5 Herod. 6 Duffy.
7 Celine Dion. 8 Cat. 9 M. 10 Salmon. 11 Petrol. 12 Finland.
13 Badminton. 14 Walking distance. 15 12. 16 Gas. 17 100. 18 Tim Henman. 19 Huit. 20 Notting Hill. 21 Blue. 22 Squirrel. 23 Five.
24 Germany. 25 Golf. 26 Deadly nightshade. 27 Cilla Black. 28 Mars.
29 Supper. 30 Blue.

Answers

93

Quiz 86 Pot Luck 42

Answers - see Quiz 85, page 93

LEVEL 1

1 Actor Robert Carlyle led The Full Monty as which character?
2 What does a Catholic call the string of beads used when praying?
3 In 1851, what was invented by Isaac Singer?
4 In what type of educational establishment was Educating Rita set?
5 In The Bible, which King tried to get the baby Jesus put to death?
6 Which nurse returned to Casualty in the autumn 1998 series?
7 Who had a hit with the Titanic theme song My Heart Will Go On?
8 In cartoons, what type of animal is Sylvester?
9 Which letter represents 007's boss?
10 Which fish leap up river to get to their spawning grounds?
11 What do Americans usually mean by gas?
12 In which country did saunas originate?
13 A shuttlecock is used in which game?
14 What is measured by a pedometer?
15 How many creatures give their names to Chinese years?
16 Which domestic fuel has its charges calculated in therms?
17 How many decades are there in a millennium?
18 Who was disqualified from Wimbledon in 1995 after accidentally hitting a ball-girl?
19 What is the French word for the number eight?
20 In which part of London is there an annual famous carnival?
21 If put in an alkaline solution, what colour does litmus paper become?
22 Which animal lives in a drey?
23 If Dec 1st is a Tuesday, how many Wednesdays are in the month?
24 Did Beethoven come from Austria, Germany or Holland?
25 For which sport is Sam Torrance famous?
26 Belladonna is also known by which Deadly name?
27 Who hosts the TV entertainment programme The Moment of Truth?
28 The month March is named after which Roman god?
29 Leonardo da Vinci's religious painting featured The Last... what?
30 What colour is connected to neutral in modern three core electric cable?

Geography: On the Map (see Quiz 85, page 93)

Answers
1 French. 2 Peter the Great. 3 Greece. 4 Clacton. 5 Africa. 6 Ireland.
7 Motorway. 8 Persian Gulf. 9 Canada. 10 Luxembourg. 11 Yugoslavia.
12 Nepal. 13 Wellington. 14 Rhine. 15 Japan. 16 Prime Minister.
17 M6. 18 Europe. 19 London. 20 Sicily. 21 Europe. 22 M25.
23 Europe. 24 Iceland. 25 Florida. 26 Thames. 27 Italy. 28 Island.
29 Moscow. 30 Israel.

Quiz 87 Hobbies & Leisure 3

LEVEL 1

Answers - see Quiz 88, page 96

1 What is normally the first Bank Holiday after Christmas Day?
2 Which sport would you watch at Aintree?
3 Are there more chairs at the start or end of a game of musical chairs?
4 What links a novice's ski slope and a garden centre?
5 What name is given to the promotional scheme to save points for cheaper plane travel?
6 Are boys or girls cubs?
7 What colour would a Sloane Ranger's wellies be?
8 The initials RSVP come from a request in which language ?
9 What colour are most road signs on UK motorways?
10 In which UK county might you holiday on the Broads?
11 Are Open University courses usually followed by mature students or school leavers?
12 In which city is the exhibition centre Olympia?
13 What would you hire at Moss Bros?
14 Butlin's was the first type of what?
15 What is the flower shaped ribbon awarded at gymkhanas called?
16 What is a less formal name for a turf accountant?
17 Which magazine's title is the French word for 'she'?
18 On which summer bank holiday is the Notting Hill Carnival held?
19 Which public track can be used for horses but not traffic?
20 On which date in May was May Day traditionally?
21 Does a busker entertain indoors or out of doors?
22 In which month would you celebrate Hogmanay?
23 In golf, what is usually meant by the nineteenth hole?
24 What is a horse chestnut called when it's used in a children's game?
25 Which Scottish city hosts an annual arts festival?
26 What colour uniform do Guides wear?
27 Are seats in the circle of a theatre on the ground or first floor?
28 Where would a shopper be if they went to M&S?
29 If you wore jodhpurs you'd probably be about to do what?
30 On which ground in north west England do you watch Test cricket?

Pot Luck 43 (see Quiz 88, page 96)
Answers
1 Queen Elizabeth II. 2 Wales. 3 The species. 4 England. 5 Skinner. 6 Hair. 7 Cleo Laine. 8 The Teletubbies. 9 Shaken but not stirred. 10 Hadlee. 11 (West) Germany. 12 Raspberry. 13 Oskar. 14 Brazil. 15 Sunday. 16 Scarlet. 17 Isle of Wight. 18 Pet Shop Boys. 19 Dean. 20 Cat. 21 McGrath. 22 Andre Agassi. 23 Skier. 24 Jackson. 25 Salt. 26 Medieval. 27 John Major's son James. 28 Barbie. 29 Dorset. 30 Rugby Union.

Quiz 88 Pot Luck 43

Answers - see Quiz 87, page 95

1 Who described 1992 as an 'annus horribilis'?
2 In which country would you see the Great and Little Orme?
3 According to Rudyard Kipling the female of what is deadlier than the male?
4 Which country hosted soccer's 1966 World Cup?
5 In EastEnders which Ethel had a dog called Willie?
6 What falls out if you have alopecia?
7 Which singer is Mrs Johnny Dankworth?
8 Who lives at Home Hill?
9 How does James Bond like his Martini served?
10 Which Richard was the first knighted New Zealand cricketer?
11 Europe's first motorway was built in which country?
12 What rude noise is the English equivalent of a Bronx Cheer?
13 What was Schindler's first name in the film Schindler's List?
14 In which South American country was Ayrton Senna born?
15 If January 1st was on a Thursday what day would February 1st be?
16 What colour was The Pimpernel created by Baroness Orczy?
17 Shanklin and Sandown are on which Isle?
18 Which Boys had a No.1 in the 1980s with Always On My Mind?
19 Who was the male half of the Torvill and Dean partnership?
20 What kind of animal was Korky from the Dandy comic?
21 Which Rory appeared with Gary Lineker in They Think It's All Over?
22 Which US tennis player married Brooke Shields?
23 Is Alberto Tomba a skier, a track athlete or an ice hockey player?
24 Which singer Michael had a No 1 with Earth Song?
25 Sodium chloride is better known as which condiment?
26 Was Brother Cadfael a fictional medieval or Victorian detective?
27 Which Prime Minister's son did Emma Noble become engaged to?
28 Which doll has a boyfriend called Ken?
29 According to The Comic Strip, in which county did Five Go Mad?
30 If Lions are playing Wallabies what sport are you watching?

Answers

Hobbies & Leisure 3 (see Quiz 87, page 95)

1 Boxing Day. 2 Horse racing. 3 Beginning. 4 Nursery. 5 Air miles.
6 Boys. 7 Green. 8 French. 9 Blue. 10 Norfolk. 11 Mature students.
12 London. 13 Formal dress. 14 Holiday camp. 15 Rosette. 16 Bookie.
17 Elle. 18 August Bank Holiday. 19 Bridleway. 20 First. 21 Out of
doors. 22 December. 23 The club-house bar. 24 Conker. 25 Edinburgh. 26
Blue. 27 First floor. 28 Marks & Spencer. 29 Horse riding. 30 Old Trafford.

Quiz 89 TV Times 3

Answers - see Quiz 90, page 98

Answers - see Quiz 90, page 98

LEVEL 1

1   Which day follows TFI on Chris Evans' show?
2   Who was the host of the variety show Lenny Goes To Town?
3   Which medical drama takes place in Holby's A & E department?
4   The Jerry Springer Show comes from which country?
5   At what time of day is Richard & Judy's magazine programme?
6   What is presented to the 'victim' at the end of This Is Your Life?
7   In ER, what is ER?
8   Which comedian John does LibDem Party Political Broadcasts?
9   How many rooms are changed in Changing Rooms?
10   Newsround is aimed at which group of viewers?
11   In which series set in Ireland did barmaid Assumpta meet a sad end?
12   Which near silent walking disaster was created by Rowan Atkinson?
13   Who is Mel Smith's TV comedy partner?
14   Which Geoff gardened at Barnsdale?
15   Which series was dubbed 'Barewatch' and 'Boobwatch'?
16   Which charity campaign has Pudsey Bear as its mascot?
17   Which Michael's 70s chat show was revived in 1998?
18   In which Practice have doctors Kerruish, Glover and Attwood worked?
19   Which was broadcast later, Newsnight or News at Ten?
20   Who is the host of GMTV's Lorraine Live?
21   Which phone number is the name of a series with Michael Buerk?
22   What follows Police, Camera..., in the show about awful drivers?
23   In which city is The Cosby Show set?
24   Which drama series where Robson and Jerome found fame is about army life?
25   On which day of the week does the so called God slot take place?
26   Which talent show features, 'Tonight Matthew I'm going to be....'?
27   Which Cilla Black series made dreams come true?
28   Which motor magazine now with Jeremy Clarkson began in 1978?
29   What is the hair link between Chris Evans and Nicholas Witchell?
30   Which Files feature Mulder and Scully?

Pot Luck 44 (see Quiz 90, page 97)

Pot Luck 44 (see Quiz 90, page 97)
1 Eagle. 2 Wales. 3 Stairway To Heaven. 4 Faraday. 5 Paint. 6 Lyon.
7 Nicey. 8 Bell shaped. 9 Cycling. 10 Hood. 11 Water. 12 Les Battersby.
13 Metronome. 14 Before. 15 South Africa. 16 A3. 17 Slade.
18 Atmosphere. 19 Belgium. 20 Mars. 21 Carter. 22 Ear. 23 Medusa.
24 Cricket. 25 Dick. 26 1940s. 27 Normandy. 28 George Michael.
29 Zimbabwe. 30 Sally.

Answers

Quiz 90 Pot Luck 44

Answers - see Quiz 89, page 97

1   Which comic did Dan Dare first appear in?
2   Golfer Ian Woosnam comes from which country?
3   Which song links Rolf Harris and Led Zeppelin?
4   Which inventor Michael is on a £20 note?
5   Gouache is a type of what?
6   The notorious Klaus Barbie was the Butcher of where in France?
7   Who is the mate of spoof DJ Smashy?
8   What shape is something if it is campanulate?
9   Boardman and Obree could clash in which sport?
10 Which Robin was the spoof film Men In Tights about?
11 Which word can go in front of BISCUIT, CLOSET and COLOUR?
12 As which character was Coronation Street actor Bruce Jones the neighbour from hell?
13 Which ticking instrument keeps perfect time for a musician?
14 Was the Automobile Association founded before or after World War I?
15 Which nation came back to international rugby in 1993?
16 Which is bigger A3 or A4 paper?
17 Which band featured Noddy Holder and Dave Hill?
18 The mesosphere and the stratosphere are layers of what?
19 With which country are Walloons associated?
20 What links a chocolate bar, a planet and a god of war?
21 Which Kevin was in the title of a hit for the Manic Street Preachers?
22 In which part of the body are the smallest bones?
23 In Greek legend, who had a bad hair day with snakes on her head?
24 Gubby Allen was linked with which sport?
25 What was the first name of Wacky Racer Mr Dastardly?
26 Was Chris Tarrant born in the 1940s or the 1960s?
27 Operation Overlord was the codename for the 1944 Allied invasion of where?
28 Who took a Careless Whisper to No. 1 in the 1980s?
29 Which country do golfers Nick Price and Mark McNulty come from?
30 What name is shared by actress Whittaker and the Webster she played in Corrie?

Answers

TV Times 3 (see Quiz 89, page 97)
1 Friday. 2 Lenny Henry. 3 Casualty. 4 USA. 5 Morning. 6 Book.
7 Emergency Room. 8 Cleese. 9 Two. 10 Children. 11 Ballykissangel.
12 Mr Bean. 13 Griff Rhys Jones. 14 Hamilton. 15 Baywatch. 16 Children in
Need. 17 Parkinson. 18 Peak Practice. 19 Newsnight. 20 Lorraine Kelly. 21
999. 22 Action. 23 New York. 24 Soldier Soldier. 25 Sunday. 26 Stars In
Their Eyes. 27 Surprise Surprise. 28 Top Gear. 29 Red hair. 30 The X Files.

1 Who sang a Barcelona duet with Freddy Mercury?
2 Which composer wrote the Four Seasons?
3 Which branch of performing is Michael Flatley famous for?
4 In which country was the Halle Orchestra founded?
5 Which dancer Wayne toured in 1998 to mark his 50th birthday?
6 Which instrument did Stephane Grapelli play?
7 Which writers of comic opera are referred to as G&S?
8 Which playwright was known as the Bard of Avon?
9 Billy Smart was associated with what type of entertainment?
10 In which country is an eisteddfod held?
11 Which Circle is a professional association of conjurors?
12 Which charity gala with many different performers is held in November and attended by the Royal Family?
13 Which Lord Andrew wrote the musical Whistle Down the Wind?
14 In Rodgers and Hammerstein who wrote the music?
15 In which country was the Bolshoi Ballet founded?
16 Which Vanessa is a famous young violinist?
17 Which London theatre shares its name with a half human, half fish mythical creature?
18 At what time of year would you go and watch a nativity play?
19 When faced with an orchestra, what does Sir Simon Rattle do?
20 The Last Night of the Proms takes place in which month?
21 A person playing a pantomime dame is usually which sex?
22 What type of singing made Maria Callas famous?
23 What was the surname of US musical composers George and Ira?
24 What is the final concert at the Promenade Concerts called?
25 Two out of the Three Tenors are which nationality?
26 Which Sir Noel wrote and starred in his plays and musicals?
27 What is the first name of Scarborough-based playwright Ayckbourn?
28 Opera singer Lesley Garrett is from which county?
29 Do you stand or sit for the Hallelujah Chorus from The Messiah?
30 In panto how do you respond to ' Oh yes it is!'?

Answers

Pot Luck 45 (see Quiz 92, page 100)
1 Fawlty Towers. 2 Middlesbrough. 3 Bill Wyman. 4 H.G. 5 Felicity.
6 The Young Ones. 7 Pottery. 8 Long haired. 9 James Bond. 10 Scarlett.
11 Wok. 12 The Archers. 13 Beef. 14 Horse. 15 Spoons. 16 Hello. 17 Nigel. 18 King Edward. 19 Crawford. 20 Arkansas. 21 Canada. 22 Etna. 23 Smoking. 24 Deer. 25 Outside. 26 Two (South Australia & New South Wales). 27 Moonlight Serenade. 28 New Testament. 29 Jeroboam. 30 Bronx.

Quiz 92 Pot Luck 45

Answers - see Quiz 91, page 99

LEVEL 1

1 Where did Polly work for Basil and Sybil?
2 Which English soccer side did Gazza make his debut for in a Wembley final?
3 Who is older Bill Wyman or the Prince of Wales?
4 What are the two initials of early 20th Century sci fi writer Wells?
5 Which Kendall starred in the sitcom Solo?
6 On which anarchic TV series did Neil, Mike, Rik and Vyvyan appear?
7 What did Clarice Cliff make?
8 Is an Afghan hound short haired or long haired?
9 Which secret agent was created by Ian Fleming?
10 Which Captain fought against the Mysterons?
11 What is a round bottomed Chinese cooking pan called?
12 In which radio series is there a pub called The Bull?
13 What sort of meat is usually in a hamburger?
14 What type of animal is a palomino?
15 What is Uri Geller famous for bending?
16 Would you say Bonjour to a French person when you say hello or goodbye?
17 Violinist Kennedy chose to drop which first name professionally?
18 Which monarch gave his name to a type of potato?
19 Which Michael created the Phantom in Lloyd Webber's musical?
20 Is Bill Clinton's home state Arkansas or Arizona?
21 In which country is Hudson Bay?
22 Which Sicilian mountain is Europe's highest volcano?
23 ASH is a pressure group against what?
24 Which animal might be fallow or red?
25 Would you find a gazebo inside or outside your home?
26 How many Australian states have South in their names?
27 Was Glenn Miller's theme tune Moonlight Sonata or Moonlight Serenade?
28 Is the book of Jude in the Old or New Testament?
29 Which is larger a magnum of champagne or a Jeroboam?
30 Which tough area of New York gives its name to a gin, vermouth and orange cocktail?

Leisure: Performing Arts (see Quiz 91, page 99)
1 Monserrat Caballe. 2 Vivaldi. 3 Dance. 4 UK. 5 Sleep. 6 Violin. 7 Gilbert & Sullivan. 8 William Shakespeare. 9 Circus. 10 Wales. 11 Magic Circle. 12 Royal Variety Show. 13 Lloyd Webber. 14 Rodgers. 15 Russia. 16 Mae. 17 Mermaid. 18 Christmas. 19 Conduct. 20 September. 21 Male. 22 Opera. 23 Gershwin. 24 Last Night of the Proms. 25 Spanish. 26 Coward. 27 Alan. 28 Yorkshire. 29 Stand. 30 "Oh no it isn't!".

Quiz 93 Sport: World Cup Fever

Answers - see Quiz 94, page 102

LEVEL 1

1   How often is the World Cup held?
2   Did Jimmy Greaves ever play in a World Cup Final?
3   Who won the last World Cup of the 20th century?
4   What colour shirts were England wearing when they won in 1966?
5   Who became known sarcastically as The Hand of God?
6   Who was sent off in France 98 and fled to Posh Spice in New York?
7   Which side from Great Britain did not make France 98?
8   Which 1966 World Cup veteran resigned as Eire manager in 1995?
9   Which British side did Brazil play in the first match of France 98?
10 Which European country did Berti Vogts manage?
11 Which TV pundit Jimmy spoke about every World Cup from 1966?
12 Who were beaten finalists in the last World Cup of the 20th century?
13 In France 98 which Caribbean side were called the Reggae Boys?
14 Who was axed from the England side in 98 after reports of kebab binges?
15 Was Sainsbury's or Tesco the official World Cup supermarket?
16 Is it true or false that Norway beat Germany in the 1995 World Cup?
17 In France 98 who did Suker play for?
18 Who was the only Englishman to lift the World Cup before 2000?
19 Which central American country was the first to host the World Cup twice, in 1986?
20 Which ex World Cup manager's autobiography is An Englishman Abroad?
21 What colour are Brazil's shirts?
22 Who were the only non Europeans to win the World Cup in the 90s?
23 Who was England's youngest player in France 98?
24 What colour coded hair was seen on the Nigerian team in France 98?
25 Which Gary was top scorer in the 1986 World Cup?
26 In which month did France 98 finish?
27 Which Scandinavian side was third in the 1994 US tournament?
28 Which South American side knocked England out of France 98?
29 In which city did France 98 begin and end?
30 On Top of the World was which country's World Cup anthem?

Pot Luck 46 (see Quiz 94, page 102)

Answers

1 Lancashire. 2 L.B.. 3 Kent. 4 Rum. 5 Locum. 6 Argentina. 7 Dog.
8 Northamptonshire. 9 D H Lawrence. 10 Apple. 11 Germany. 12 Italy.
13 Mel B (Scary Spice). 14 Gunnell. 15 London. 16 China. 17 Harrison.
18 Potter. 19 Holly. 20 Surrey. 21 Cuckoo. 22 Tenor. 23 Bit.
24 Addams. 25 Chris de Burgh. 26 Tennis. 27 Alice (in Wonderland).
28 Sleeve. 29 Celine Dion. 30 Perambulator.

Quiz 94 Pot Luck 46

LEVEL 1

Answers - see Quiz 93, page 101

1 Mike Atherton plays for which county cricket club?
2 Which were the initials of US President Johnson?
3 In which county is Ashford International station?
4 Does a Pina Colada contain rum or gin?
5 Which word for a duty doctor is a Latin name for place holder?
6 Which country's Rugby Union side are the Pumas?
7 Is a Dandie Dinmont, a dog, a cat or a horse?
8 In which county is the stately home of Althorp?
9 Which controversial author used the initials for his first names David Herbert?
10 What sort of fruit flavour does Calvados have?
11 In which country were BMW's first made?
12 St Francis of Assisi is patron saint of which country?
13 Who was the first Spice Girl to marry?
14 Which Sally was British women's team captain in the 1996 Olympics?
15 In which city is MP Diane Abbott's constituency?
16 Which country was once called Cathay?
17 Which Mr Ford starred in the 1990 movie Presumed Innocent?
18 Which Dennis created The Singing Detective?
19 Which Buddy did Alvin Stardust sing about?
20 Alec Stewart plays cricket for which English county?
21 Which bird lays its eggs in the nests of other birds?
22 Was the singer Mario Lanza a bass, baritone or tenor?
23 What name is given to the part of the bridle in a horse's mouth?
24 Wednesday and Pugsley are part of which family?
25 Christopher Davidson found fame as a singer as which Chris?
26 Maria Bueno was famous for which sport?
27 In fiction, which girl swam in a pool of her own tears?
28 A raglan forms which part of a garment?
29 Who had a huge 1995 hit with Think Twice?
30 Pram is an abbreviation of which word?

Sport: World Cup Fever (see Quiz 93, page 101)
1 Every four years. 2 No. 3 France. 4 Red. 5 Diego Maradonna. 6 David Beckham. 7 Wales. 8 Jack Charlton. 9 Scotland. 10 Germany. 11 Hill. 12 Brazil. 13 Jamaica. 14 Paul Gascoigne. 15 Sainsbury's. 16 True – Women's World Cup. 17 Croatia. 18 Bobby Moore. 19 Mexico. 20 Bobby Robson. 21 Yellow. 22 Brazil. 23 Michael Owen. 24 Green. 25 Lineker. 26 July. 27 Sweden. 28 Argentina. 29 Paris. 30 England's.

Answers

1 Which Yasser founded the PLO?
2 Which Kennedy announced he was running for President in 1960?
3 Nikita Krushchev was head of state of which Union?
4 In which Italian city were the 1960 summer Olympics held?
5 Whose Lover was the subject of a court case in book form?
6 The USSR sent its first man where in April 1960?
7 Which Russian dancer Rudolph defected to the West?
8 Across which former European capital was a Wall built?
9 Which drug taken by pregnant mothers caused abnormalities in babies?
10 Which Harold became Labour leader in 1963?
11 Of where did Neil Armstrong say, "The surface is like fine powder"?
12 What were mailbags containing over £1 million stolen from?
13 Caroline was the name of Britain's first off shore pirate what?
14 Which British WWII leader died in 1965?
15 What sort of champion was Arkle?
16 Which communist country had its famous Red Guards?
17 Which knighted soccer star retired aged 50?
18 Who launched the Queen Elizabeth II - QE2 - on Clydebank?
19 Which model Jean was called The Shrimp?
20 Which homeless charity was set up after TV's Cathy Come Home?
21 What product was banned from TV advertising on health grounds?
22 Which Rolling Stone singer was best man at David Bailey's wedding?
23 Which notorious East End gangland twins were jailed for murder?
24 Which rock star married Patricia Beaulieu?
25 Which capital was said to Swing in the 60s?
26 Which Martin famously gave his 'I have a dream' speech?
27 If Mods rode scooters, who rode motorbikes?
28 LBJ was President of which country?
29 How were Ian Brady and Myra Hindley known?
30 Which actress Marilyn was found dead in her bungalow near Hollywood?

Answers

Pot Luck 47 (see Quiz 96, page 104)
1 Thaw. 2 Florin. 3 Smokie. 4 Chris Evans. 5 1980. 6 Bluto. 7 Yes.
8 Liverpool. 9 Portuguese. 10 Culkin. 11 Mile. 12 Harman. 13 Cyrus.
14 26. 15 The Kinks. 16 Greek gods. 17 Tony. 18 Borzoi. 19 Nissan.
20 Tompkinson. 21 Fox. 22 Cyrillic. 23 British Prime Ministers.
24 Champion. 25 Mick Hucknall. 26 Penicillin. 27 Bishop. 28 Golf.
29 Duck. 30 McCartney.

Quiz 96 Pot Luck 47

Answers - see Quiz 95, page 103

LEVEL 1

1   Which John married actress Sheila Hancock?
2   Which pre decimal coin had the value of two shillings?
3   Which group revived a previous hit in the 90s with the help of Roy 'Chubby' Brown?
4   Which TV presenter's shows have had Toothbrush and Breakfast in their titles?
5   Were the Olympic Games last held in Russia in 1960, 1980 or 1988?
6   Who is Popeye's rival?
7   Was Sir Walter Scott Scottish?
8   Which English soccer side was managed by the late Bob Paisley?
9   What is the main language in Brazil?
10 Which Macaulay starred in the cartoon and live action film The Pagemaster?
11 Which is greater in distance a mile or a kilometre?
12 Which MP Harriet was axed in Tony Blair's first Cabinet reshuffle?
13 Which Billy Ray's Achy Breaky Heart helped establish line dancing?
14 How many red cards are there in a standard pack of cards?
15 Ray Davies was writer and singer with which band?
16 Adonis, Apollo and Poseidon were all what?
17 Who shares a flat with Gary in Men Behaving Badly?
18 Which dog is larger a borzoi or a corgi?
19 The Micra was made by which car company?
20 Which Stephen has been the TV partner of Dervla Kirwan?
21 A vixen is the female of which animal?
22 Which alphabet is used by Muscovites?
23 What links the names Chamberlain, Heath and Wilson?
24 Which jockey Bob fought back from cancer to win the Grand National?
25 Who is Simply Red's lead singer?
26 Which was the first antibiotic to be discovered?
27 Ian Smith played which Harold in Neighbours?
28 For which sport is Sunningdale famous?
29 A Muscovy is what type of bird?
30 Which musical Paul got involved with frogs and Rupert Bear?

Past Times: The 60s (see Quiz 95, page 103)
1 Arafat. 2 John. 3 Soviet. 4 Rome. 5 Lady Chatterley's. 6 Space.
7 Nureyev. 8 Berlin. 9 Thalidomide. 10 Wilson. 11 The Moon. 12 Train.
13 Radio station. 14 Churchill. 15 Horse. 16 China. 17 Sir Stanley
Matthews. 18 Queen Elizabeth II. 19 Jean Shrimpton. 20 Shelter.
21 Cigarettes. 22 Mick Jagger. 23 Kray twins. 24 Elvis Presley. 25 London.
26 Luther King. 27 Rockers. 28 USA. 29 Moors murderers. 30 Monroe.

Answers

Quiz 97 The Movies: Tough Guys

LEVEL 1

Answers - see Quiz 98, page 106

1   Which actor was nicknamed 'Bogey'?
2   Which actor Marlon was paid $18 million for nine minutes in Superman in 1978?
3   Which western star John first acted as Duke Morrison?
4   Which Samuel starred as a gangster in Pulp Fiction?
5   Which Bruce starred in The Jackal?
6   Which soccer side does Evita actor Jimmy Nail support?
7   Tough guy Robert de Niro sang about New York in which film?
8   Which lager did Crocodile Dundee star Paul Hogan advertise?
9   Which Vietnam veteran Oliver directed Platoon?
10 Which star of The Godfather bought an island called Tetiaroa?
11 Which Martin was assigned to assassinate Brando in Apocalypse Now?
12 What did George C. Scott refuse to do about his Oscar for Patton?
13 Gene Hackman played cop Popeye Doyle in which classic thriller?
14 Which tough English actor Sean is the son of a former Dr. Who?
15 Which famous US family did Arnold Schwarzenegger marry into?
16 Was Charles Bronson one of ten or fifteen children?
17 Is Bruce Willis a cop or a soldier in the Die Hard movies?
18 Which hell raiser Oliver released a single Lonely For a Girl in 1965?
19 Lee Marvin headed a Dirty cast of how many in the 1967 movie?
20 Which singer who died in 1998 was the tough guy captain in Von Ryan's Express?
21 How many gunfighters were hired in The Magnificent film of 1960?
22 On what vehicle did Steve McQueen try to flee in The Great Escape?
23 Which Sylvester starred in Judge Dredd?
24 What is the first name of Reservoir Dogs director Tarantino?
25 Which tough guy Arnold has appeared on a postage stamp of Mali?
26 Which Mel starred in the Lethal Weapon series of films?
27 Which bare-headed actor was in The Magnificent Seven and The King and I?
28 Which Clint got the part in Dirty Harry when Sinatra pulled out?
29 Which James Bond has an actor son called Jason?
30 Was The Untouchables with Kevin Costner set in the 20s, 40s or 60s?

Pot Luck 48 (see Quiz 98, page 106)

1 Tennis. 2 Heart. 3 Chris Tarrant. 4 Australia. 5 Frog. 6 Bertie Bassett.
7 Rot away. 8 Five. 9 Ten. 10 Aberdeen. 11 Boyzone. 12 Belgium. 13
Black Bess. 14 Purdy. 15 Eric Clapton. 16 Marylebone Cricket Club. 17
Bahamas. 18 The Taming of the Shrew. 19 Margaret Thatcher. 20 Henry. 21
Violin. 22 Cornwall. 23 George Cole. 24 British Prime Minister. 25
Vauxhall Vectra. 26 Vingt. 27 Aircraft. 28 Wizzard. 29 Blue. 30 France.

Quiz 98 Pot Luck 48

LEVEL 1

1   For which sport is Billie-Jean King famous?
2   According to the proverb, absence makes which organ grow fonder?
3   Who hosted ITVs Who Wants to be a Millionaire?
4   In which country is Ayer's Rock?
5   Which species of creature includes the most poisonous animal in the world?
6   Which figure advertised Bassetts Liquorice Allsorts?
7   If something is biodegradable, what will it do?
8   How many noughts are in the written number two hundred thousand?
9   Every how many years is a National Census taken in Britain?
10 Where are you if you visit the Granite City?
11 Which group had a No. 1 album in 1998 with Where We Belong?
12 In which country is the town of Spa?
13 What was the name of Dick Turpin's horse?
14 In the New Avengers, which character was played by Joanna Lumley?
15 Which guitarist is nicknamed 'Slowhand'?
16 In cricket, what does the initial M stand for in MCC?
17 Nassau is the capital of which group of islands?
18 In which Shakespeare play does Kate marry Petruchio?
19 Who was Tory leader immediately before John Major?
20 Which Lenny was the first genuinely black member of the Black and White Minstrel Show?
21 Which musical instrument does Tasmin Little play?
22 Which English county boasts the longest coastline?
23 In the TV series Minder, who played Arthur Daly?
24 Eden, Heath and Macdonald have all held which important position?
25 To the nearest mile, how long is the London Marathon?
26 What is the French word for the number twenty?
27 What are DC-10s and 747s?
28 See My Baby Jive was a 70s No 1 for which magic-sounding group?
29 What colour is azure in heraldry?
30 Which country is immediately south of Belgium?

The Movies: Tough Guys (see Quiz 97, page 105)
1 Humphrey Bogart. 2 Brando. 3 John Wayne. 4 Jackson. 5 Willis. 6 Newcastle Utd. 7 New York, New York. 8 Fosters. 9 Stone. 10 Marlon Brando. 11 Sheen. 12 Accept it. 13 French Connection. 14 Pertwee. 15 Kennedy. 16 Fifteen. 17 Cop. 18 Reed. 19 Dozen. 20 Frank Sinatra. 21 Seven. 22 Motorcycle. 23 Stallone. 24 Quentin. 25 Schwarzenegger. 26 Gibson. 27 Yul Brynner. 28 Eastwood. 29 Sean Connery. 30 20s.

Answers - see Quiz 100, page 108

LEVEL 1

1 In which country did black activist Steve Biko die in 1977?
2 Which US President was brought down by the Watergate scandal?
3 What did a policeman use to hide a streaker's embarrassment in a famous incident at Twickenham in 1974?
4 Which London born comic Charlie was knighted?
5 Which tree population was decimated by a Dutch disease?
6 Did Skytrain provide cut price tickets by air or rail?
7 Who succeeded John Paul I as Pope?
8 The New English version of which Book was published in 1970?
9 Which Czech tennis star Martina defected to the West?
10 In which country did Pol Pot conduct a reign of terror?
11 Which Sebastian was a record breaking middle distance runner?
12 Which father of twins was the husband of the British PM?
13 Which princess was sportswoman of the year in 1971?
14 The Queen celebrated how many years on the throne in her Jubilee?
15 Which Lord disappeared after his nanny was murdered?
16 Who beat four male candidates to become Tory leader in 1975?
17 Which war ended with the fall of Saigon in 1975?
18 Which country's athletes were murdered at the 1972 Olympics?
19 John Curry won Olympic gold on what surface?
20 In which county did a Ripper carry out horrific murders?
21 Which Lord and Royal uncle was murdered off Ireland?
22 Which Mother won a Nobel Peace Prize?
23 Charles de Gaulle died after being president of which country?
24 Were Sunderland in the first or second division when they won the FA Cup in 1973?
25 Where was the monarchy restored after the death of Franco?
26 In 1971 the first British soldier was killed in which British province?
27 Evonne Goolagong from which country won Wimbledon in 1971?
28 Which Chris was Jimmy Connors' fiancee when he first won Wimbledon?
29 Which James succeeded Harold Wilson as Prime Minister?
30 David Steel became leader of which political party in 1976?

Answers

Pot Luck 49 (see Quiz 100, page 108)
1 Orange. 2 Jennifer Saunders. 3 Madonna. 4 London & Birmingham.
5 Lancashire. 6 Wren. 7 18. 8 Martin. 9 Cricket. 10 1940s. 11 Enya.
12 Red Indian tribes. 13 Take That. 14 White. 15 Four. 16 Matchstick Men.
17 Alfred Hitchcock. 18 Five. 19 Charles Dickens. 20 Hutch. 21 Soprano.
22 Northumberland. 23 MW. 24 Green. 25 A king. 26 Yorkshire.
27 Food. 28 Angostura Bitters. 29 Garland. 30 Queensland.

Quiz 100 Pot Luck 49

LEVEL 1

Answers - see Quiz 99, page 107

1   In international soccer, what is the main colour of Holland's shirts?
2   Who is older – Ruby Wax or Jennifer Saunders?
3   Into The Groove gave a first UK No. 1 for which singer?
4   Which two cities were linked by the M1 when it first opened?
5   Which ex-Corrie actress Sarah shares her surname with an English county?
6   What is Britain's smallest bird?
7   How many sides are there in a pair of nonagons?
8   Which George was the main producer of The Beatles' hits?
9   E W Swanton wrote about which sport?
10 Was Joanna Lumley born in the 1940s,50s or 60s?
11 How is Eithne Ni Bhraonain better known in the music world?
12 Mohawk, Seminole and Sioux are all names of what?
13 Which star group was Jason Orange a member of?
14 Is Riesling a red or white wine?
15 How many Teletubbies are there?
16 What type of men gave Status Quo their first hit?
17 Who links the films Rebecca, Psycho and Vertigo?
18 What's the most number of Sundays that could occur in December?
19 Which author created the reclusive character Miss Havisham?
20 On TV, did David Soul play Starsky or Hutch?
21 What type of voice does opera star Lesley Garrett have?
22 What is England's most north easterly county?
23 Is Radio 5 Live broadcast on MW or FM?
24 What colour is verdigris which appears on copper or brass?
25 Who is killed if regicide is committed?
26 Ridings used to divide which county?
27 Is Robert Carrier linked with food, theatre or sport?
28 Pink gin is gin flavoured with what?
29 Which Judy starred in Meet Me In St Louis?
30 Brisbane is the capital of which Australian state?

Answers

Past Times: The 70s (see Quiz 99, page 107)
1 South Africa. 2 Nixon. 3 His helmet. 4 Chaplin. 5 Elm. 6 Air. 7 John Paul II. 8 Bible. 9 Navratilova. 10 Cambodia. 11 Coe. 12 Denis Thatcher. 13 Anne. 14 25. 15 Lucan. 16 Margaret Thatcher. 17 Vietnam. 18 Israel. 19 Ice. 20 Yorkshire. 21 Mountbatten. 22 Teresa. 23 France. 24 Second. 25 Spain. 26 Northern Ireland. 27 Australia. 28 Evert. 29 Callaghan. 30 Liberal.

Quiz 101 Science: Technology

LEVEL 1

1 What type of energy is generated by PowerGen?
2 What type of company can be found in Silicon Glen in Scotland?
3 In a car, what might be disc or drum?
4 Was the first modern cassette made in the 40s, 60s or 70s?
5 Which type of transport has rubber skirts?
6 A rotor propels what type of aircraft?
7 Did early TV have 405 or 625 lines?
8 The Manhattan Project in the early 40s was developing what?
9 Which substance, recently found to be dangerous, is called 'woolly rock'?
10 What is the lowest number on the Beaufort Scale?
11 Apples and Apricots were what in the technological world?
12 Is coal obtained from decayed animal or plant matter?
13 What produces bubbles in the making of champagne?
14 Is the empennage of a plane at the front or the tail?
15 William Morris, Lord Nuffield was the first UK manufacturer of mass produced what?
16 What does 'P' stand for in DTP?
17 Entrepreneur Ted Turner is a big name in which industry?
18 What ill-fated personal transport was invented by Sir Clive Sinclair?
19 Which letter is farthest left on a computer keyboard?
20 Which country is the world's largest exporter of grain?
21 Which metal is used thermometers?
22 Which colour identifies an ordinary diesel pump at a service station?
23 Nylon took its name from which two cities?
24 Which underground weapon did Whitehead develop in 1866?
25 Which boom is produced by breaking the sound barrier?
26 C-Curity was the first type of which fastener?
27 What does 'C' stand for in ASCII?
28 What sort of factory did Joseph Rowntree found?
29 What does a pluviometer measure?
30 Bournville was established for the workers of which company?

Answers

Pot Luck 50 (see Quiz 102, page 110)

1 Austria. 2 Simon & Garfunkel. 3 Claustrophobia. 4 Palm Sunday. 5 Sunday. 6 September. 7 Fossils. 8 Bambi. 9 David. 10 Harry Houdini. 11 York. 12 Esther Rantzen. 13 Iron. 14 Pratchett. 15 Warwickshire. 16 American football. 17 Budgie. 18 Scotland. 19 Red Dwarf. 20 Eyre. 21 Dvorak. 22 Terry Wogan. 23 London. 24 Ireland. 25 Filbert. 26 The Archies. 27 Party. 28 Drew. 29 Independent. 30 Computer.

Quiz 102 Pot Luck 50

Answers - see Quiz 101, page 109

LEVEL 1

1   Racing driver Niki Lauda was born in which country?
2   Which duo had hits with Mrs Robinson and America?
3   What is the fear of enclosed spaces called?
4   Which Sunday comes before Easter Day?
5   On TV, which night featured a show from the London Palladium?
6   Alphabetically, which is the last of the calendar months?
7   What would a palaeontologist study?
8   Which Disney creature nickname was given to Tony Blair?
9   What is the first name of New Baywatch star Hasselhoff?
10 When Eric Weiss escaped from his name he was known as who?
11 Which race course hosts the Ebor Handicap?
12 Which female presenter fronted the long running That's Life?
13 Which metal has the chemical symbol Fe?
14 Which Terry writes the best selling sci fi Discworld novels?
15 Which English county did Brian Lara first play for?
16 What's the sport if the Chicago Bears take on the Miami Dolphins?
17 What is the name of Sarah Ferguson's little helicopter?
18 In which country did golf originate?
19 Holly the computer appeared on which TV sci fi comedy?
20 Which is Australia's largest lake?
21 Who composed the New World Symphony?
22 Who presents Auntie's Sporting Bloomers on TV?
23 In which city does The Last Night of the Proms take place?
24 Vocalist Enya hails from which country?
25 Which Street is home for Leicester City?
26 Sugar Sugar was a one off number 1 for which group?
27 Which word can go in after BIRTHDAY, HEN, LABOUR and STAG?
28 Which Barrymore was in E.T. and Batman Forever?
29 What does the I stand for in ITV?
30 What would you be using if you needed a mouse mat?

Science: Technology (see Quiz 101, page 109)
1 Electricity. **2** Computer firms. **3** Brakes. **4** 60s. **5** Hovercraft. **6** Helicopter. **7** 405. **8** Atomic bomb. **9** Asbestos. **10** 0. **11** Computers. **12** Plant. **13** Carbon dioxide. **14** Tail. **15** Cars. **16** Publishing. **17** Broadcasting. **18** C5. **19** Q. **20** USA. **21** Mercury. **22** Black. **23** New York, London. **24** Torpedo. **25** Sonic boom. **26** Zip. **27** Code. **28** Cocoa. **29** Rainfall. **30** Cadbury's.

Quiz 103 TV Gold

Answers - see Quiz 104, page 112

LEVEL 1

1 Who was head of the family in Till Death Us Do Part?
2 Which house was Revisited in the classic 80s drama?
3 Where was the BBC's 1992 ill fated soap set?
4 On which weekend evening was Jim'll Fix It broadcast?
5 In Tenko the women were imprisoned by whom?
6 What was Lovejoy's occupation?
7 Which series was about a Mobile Army Surgical Hospital in Korea?
8 Which Michael played the hapless Frank Spencer?
9 What was unusual about Hopkirk in the Randall and Hopkirk agency?
10 What institution was Please Sir set in?
11 What was the rank of Phil Silvers' Bilko?
12 Who were the US TV equivalent of the Beatles?
13 Which Leonard Rossiter sitcom sounds like a problem with old houses?
14 How was Arthur Fonzerelli known in Happy Days?
15 Which animals did Barbara Woodhouse work with?
16 Who was June in Terry and June?
17 What sort of animal was Grizzly Adams?
18 What was Torquay's most famous hotel run by Basil and Sybil?
19 Jewel in the Crown was set in wartime where?
20 In which county was All Creatures Great and Small set?
21 What sort of performers were in Spitting Image?
22 Which father of Paula Yates presented Stars on Sunday?
23 What was the profession of Albert Steptoe and son Harold?
24 Which hero was "Riding through the glen, With his band of Men"?
25 Which classic sci fi series began in the 23rd century?
26 In which country was Van der Valk set?
27 What sort of statesman was Alan B'Stard?
28 Which Eric played Hattie Jacques' brother?
29 Was it Mork or Mindy who came from the planet Ork?
30 What sort of Men were Bill and Ben?

Past Times: The 80s (see Quiz 104, page 112)
1 Margaret Thatcher. 2 London. 3 Eggs. 4 Johnson. 5 North Sea. 6 King's Cross. 7 Neil Kinnock. 8 Duchess of Windsor. 9 Zeebrugge. 10 Philippines. 11 South Africa. 12 Prince Andrew. 13 Runner. 14 Wembley. 15 Morecambe. 16 Parkinson. 17 Bradford. 18 Liberal Democrats. 19 In space. 20 Greenham. 21 Harrods. 22 Bjorn Borg. 23 Car accident. 24 Dallas. 25 Falklands. 26 Tyson. 27 Champion. 28 Reagan. 29 New York. 30 Kindergarten.

Quiz 104 Past Times: The 80s

Answers - see Quiz 103, page 111

LEVEL 1

1   Which serving British PM survived an assassination attempt?
2   In which city did the SAS storm the Iranian embassy?
3   Edwina Currie resigned over a what type of farm food?
4   Which Ben was disqualified from the Seoul Olympics for drug taking?
5   In which Sea did the oil rig Piper Alpha catch fire?
6   Which north London Tube station was gutted by fire in 1987?
7   Who was Labour leader when Thatcher had her third election victory?
8   Which late Duchess's jewels were auctioned for over £30 million?
9   The Herald of Free Enterprise sank off which Belgian port?
10 President Marcos was ousted in a rebellion in which island country?
11 Desmond Tutu became an Archbishop in which country?
12 Who was the second of the Queen's sons to marry in the 80s?
13 Was Zola Budd a swimmer, a runner or a gymnast?
14 At which UK stadium was the Live Aid concert held?
15 Which Eric, half of a classic comedy duo died in 1984?
16 Which Tory minister Cecil resigned in a scandal in 1983?
17 In which Yorkshire city's football ground was there a fatal fire in '85?
18 What is the full name of the Lib Dems, formed in 1989?
19 Sally Ride became the USA's first woman where?
20 At which Common was there a camp against cruise missiles?
21 Outside which London store did a bomb explode in December 1983?
22 Which Swedish tennis star retired age 26?
23 In what type of accident was Princess Grace of Monaco killed?
24 Which soap asked the audience asked 'Who shot JR?'
25 Which war in the south Atlantic was Britain involved in?
26 Which Mike became the youngest heavyweight boxing champion?
27 Which Bob rode Aldaniti to a Grand National win in 1981?
28 Which US president was the victim of an assassination attempt?
29 In which city was Beatle John Lennon murdered?
30 Where was Lady Diana Spencer working when photographed in a seemingly see through skirt?

TV Gold (see Quiz 103, page 111)
Answers
1 Alf Garnett. 2 Brideshead. 3 Spain. 4 Saturday. 5 Japanese. 6 Antiques dealer. 7 M*A*S*H. 8 Crawford. 9 He was a ghost. 10 School.
11 Sergeant. 12 The Monkees. 13 Rising Damp. 14 The Fonz/Fonzie.
15 Dogs. 16 June Whitfield. 17 Human. 18 Fawlty Towers. 19 India.
20 Yorkshire. 21 Puppets. 22 Jess Yates. 23 Rag & bone merchants.
24 Robin Hood. 25 Star Trek. 26 Holland. 27 New Statesman. 28 Sykes.
29 Mork. 30 Flowerpot men.

Quiz 105 Pop: Charts

Answers - see Quiz 106, page 114

LEVEL 1

1   Whose album True Blue was No 1 in 28 countries?
2   What was The Spice Girls' first No 1?
3   Whose charity hit included Something About the Way You Look Tonight?
4   Which of Madonna's two hits from Evita got highest in the charts?
5   Which Frank Sinatra hit has spent most weeks in the UK charts?
6   In which decade did the UK singles charts begin?
7   Who as well as The Troggs charted with Love Is All Around?
8   Which wartime song charted with Robson & Jerome's Unchained Melody?
9   Which father and daughter had a No 1 with Somethin' Stupid?
10 How was Roberto Milani known when he had Europe's '96 top seller?
11 Which soccer side charted with Come On You Reds?
12 Whose Release Me spent a record number of weeks in the charts?
13 Was Celine Dion's Power of Love the same as Jennifer Rush's or Frankie Goes to Hollywood's?
14 Who was the first all female band to have three consecutive No 1's?
15 How many weeks did Elvis spend in the charts duetting?
16 Who spent most weeks in the UK charts, the Stones or Status Quo?
17 Which musical did Boyzone's No 1 No Matter What come from?
18 Who is the most successful Australian female to have been in the UK singles charts?
19 Billboard is a list of best selling records where?
20 Which band were in the chart most weeks in 1995 and again in 1996?
21 Which family were at No 1 with Do the Bartman?
22 Which Scandinavian country do chart toppers Aqua come from?
23 Who accompanied Vic Reeves on his No 1 hit Dizzy?
24 Whose 96 No 1s were Firestarter and Breathe?
25 Which Boys' first No 1 was West End Girls?
26 Whose Cigarettes and Alcohol was their highest chart hit at the time?
27 Which solo Briton Cliff has spent most weeks in the UK singles charts?
28 Which female solo star has spent most weeks in the British charts?
29 Love Me For a Reason charted for The Osmonds and which band?
30 Who wrote the series Crocodile Shoes and its chart songs?

Who was Who? (see Quiz 106, page 114)

1 Bill Clinton. 2 Salvation Army. 3 Louis Pasteur. 4 Nobel. 5 Henry VIII.
6 Guy Fawkes. 7 Henry Ford. 8 Second World War. 9 India. 10 Oil.
11 Glenys Kinnock. 12 Charles. 13 Che Guevara. 14 Queen Victoria.
15 Pankhurst. 16 Saddam Hussein. 17 One. 18 American. 19 W.G.Grace.
20 56. 21 Buster Keaton. 22 Mandela. 23 Mao Tse Tung. 24 Groucho. 25
Mary. 26 Miller. 27 Mussolini. 28 Italian. 29 Tony Blair. 30 John F Kennedy.

Answers

LEVEL 1

1   Who became US President in 1992 when Governor of Arkansas?
2   Which religious Army was founded by Catherine and William Booth?
3   Which scientist gave his name to the process of pasteurisation?
4   Who left $9 million to give prizes in five different fields?
5   Which King of England provided his children with most stepmothers?
6   Who lit the fuse for the 1605 Gunpowder Plot?
7   Was it John Ford or Henry Ford who manufactured cars?
8   During which war did Anne Frank write her diary?
9   Indira Gandhi was Prime Minister of which country?
10   John Paul Getty made his millions from which commodity?
11   Who was Labour leader Neil Kinnock's wife who became an MEP?
12   Who was the first 20th century Prince of Wales to be divorced?
13   How was Argentinean Ernesto Guevara de la Serna better known?
14   William Gladstone was Prime Minister under which monarch?
15   What was suffragette leader Emmeline Goulden's married name?
16   Who became President of Iraq in 1979?
17   How many English kings have been called Stephen?
18   What was the nationality of the Duchess of Windsor?
19   Which legendary cricketer had the first names William Gilbert?
20   How old was Hitler when he died, 46, 56 or 66?
21   By which name was silent movie star Joseph Keaton better known?
22   Which Nelson was the first black President of South Africa?
23   How was Mao Zedong also known?
24   Which Marx brother had a moustache, cigar and funny walk?
25   According to The Bible who was the mother of Jesus?
26   Which trombonist Glenn became a famous bandleader?
27   Who was Italian dictator between 1926 and 1943?
28   What was the nationality of inventor Marconi?
29   Which of Queen Elizabeth II's Prime Ministers was not even born when she came to the throne?
30   Who was the youngest US President to die in office?

Answers

Pop: Charts (see Quiz 105, page 113)
1 Madonna. 2 Wannabe. 3 Elton John. 4 Don't Cry For Me Argentina. 5 My Way. 6 50s. 7 Wet Wet Wet. 8 The White Cliffs of Dover. 9 Frank & Nancy Sinatra. 10 Robert Miles. 11 Manchester United. 12 Englebert Humperdinck. 13 Jennifer Rush's. 14 Spice Girls. 15 None. 16 Status Quo. 17 Whistle Down the Wind. 18 Kylie Minogue. 19 USA. 20 Oasis. 21 The Simpsons. 22 Denmark. 23 The Wonder Stuff. 24 Prodigy. 25 Pet Shop. 26 Oasis. 27 Richard. 28 Madonna. 29 Boyzone. 30 Jimmy Nail.

Quiz 107 Pop: Superstars

Answers - see Quiz 108, page 116

LEVEL 1

1 Sir Paul McCartney was awarded the freedom of which city?
2 Which legendary band released The Wall?
3 Which soul star Ray has the nickname The Genius?
4 Which Shirley was dubbed the Tigress from Tiger Bay?
5 Supermodel Rachel Hunter married which superstar Rod?
6 Which ex Police singer founded the Rainforest Foundation in 1988?
7 Who does not use her surname Ciccone?
8 Which brother completes the Gibb trio with Maurice and Robin?
9 Which Billy toured with Elton John in 1998?
10 Which rock superstar was Lisa Marie Presley second husband?
11 Diana Ross is billed as who on her recording of I Will Survive?
12 Montserrat Caballe recorded Barcelona with which rock legend?
13 Which drummer's solo album No Jacket Required was a best seller?
14 Which Rolling Stone did not normally play an instrument on stage?
15 Which group was heard on the soundtrack of Saturday Night Fever?
16 Whose hits range from The Laughing Gnome to Space Oddity?
17 Who sang You Don't Bring Me Flowers with Barbra Streisand?
18 Which Queen of Soul sang the best version of Nessun Dorma according to Pavarotti?
19 Which band would you find The Edge and Bono in?
20 Who lived in a mansion called Graceland?
21 Which boys liked Califrnia Girls?
22 Whose Streets of Philadelphia was his highest hit at the time in 1994?
23 Which Stevie dropped the tag Little and had hits well into adulthood?
24 Which Tina recorded Bond theme Goldeneye?
25 Which superstar founded the Rocket record label?
26 All Lionel Richie's early hits were on which record label?
27 Which Scottish football fan has the first names Roderick David?
28 Which Roy charted with Crying with kd lang four years after his death?
29 Which Barbra did actor James Brolin marry in 1998?
30 Which Barry's song Copacabana became a musical?

Answers

Leisure: The Media (see Quiz 108, page 116)
1 World Service. 2 Magazine. 3 Horse racing. 4 Radio Times. 5 Classic FM. 6 Radio 4. 7 London. 8 Sunday Sport. 9 Five. 10 Manchester. 11 Gossip column. 12 Musical. 13 Men. 14 Saturday. 15 Top shelf. 16 Financial Times. 17 Mail on Sunday. 18 Sunday. 19 BBC. 20 Hello! 21 Murdoch. 22 Three. 23 Independent. 24 Private Eye. 25 Tabloid. 26 England & Scotland. 27 Doctor. 28 Weekly. 29 Edwina Currie 30 Frost.

Quiz 108 Leisure: The Media

Answers - see Quiz 107, page 115

1   Which BBC radio and TV service broadcasts abroad?
2   Is The Spectator a programme to watch or a magazine to read?
3   The Sporting Life devotes itself to which sport?
4   Which radio and TV listings magazine is published by the BBC?
5   Which independent radio station specialises in classical music?
6   Is The Archers on Radio 1 or Radio 4?
7   Where does Capital Radio broadcast to?
8   What is the Sunday version of Daily Sport called?
9   Which BBC Radio station has Live after its number?
10 In which north of England city is Granada TV based?
11 What sort of Column tells of stories and rumours about celebrities?
12 What does M stand for in the pop paper NME?
13 Is GQ for men or women?
14 On which day is Grandstand always broadcast on BBC1?
15 On which shelf would someone buy an 'adult' magazine?
16 What does FT stand for in the name of the financial daily newspaper?
17 What is the Daily Mail's Sunday paper called?
18 On which day of the week is the News of the World published?
19 Which corporation is known as Auntie?
20 Which magazine about celebs is based on the Spanish mag Hola!?
21 Which Rupert founded Sky Television?
22 Which page in a newspaper is famous for its nude photos?
23 What does I stand for in ITV?
24 Which satirical magazine shares its name with the nickname for a detective?
25 Which newspaper is larger, a tabloid or a broadsheet?
26 Border TV serves the borders of which two countries?
27 What professional person would read The Lancet?
28 How often does the magazine Take A Break appear?
29 Which ex MP presented Late Night Currie on Radio 5 Live?
30 Which Sir David co founded LWT and TV-am?

Quiz 109 Pop: Who's Who?

LEVEL 1

Answers - see Quiz 110, page 119

1 Who is Julian Lennon's stepmother?
2 Which pop wife has Liam and a shamrock tattooed on her ankle?
3 Which George did not make a record for five years because of a dispute with Sony?
4 In which Irish city was Sinead O'Connor born?
5 Which Elaine changed her surname from Bickerstaff and went on to star in many West End musicals?
6 Which Stevie led the campaign to commemorate Martin Luther King's birthday in the US?
7 How is Katherine Dawn Lang better known?
8 Bernie Taupin collaborated with which performer for over 20 years?
9 Which Boys were famous for their surfing sound?
10 Whose real name is Charles Edward Anderson Berry?
11 In what type of tragic accident did John Denver meet his death?
12 Which composer of Boyzone's No Matter What appeared with them on Top of the Pops?
13 Andrew Ridgeley was the less famous half of which group?
14 Which band always comes last alphabetically?
15 Which ex Jackson 5 member was 40 in 1998?
16 The Spice Girls recorded their early hits on which label?
17 PJ and Duncan were also known as who?
18 Which soul star did Bryan Ferry name his son Otis after?
19 What are the first names of the Everly Brothers?
20 Was Bryan Adams born in Canada or the USA?
21 Who was left handed, Lennon or McCartney?
22 Which ex husband of Cher died in a skiing accident ?
23 Bjork hails from which country?
24 Who made the album Let's Talk About Love?
25 Which Olivia won a Hayley Mills look alike contest?
26 Who made the album 12 Deadly Cyns?
27 Which Mark co founded Dire Straits?
28 What name links Ant and Faith?
29 Which hit by D:Ream was used in the 97 Labour election campaign?
30 Who changed his name to a symbol?

Answers

Celebs: The Royals (see Quiz 110, page 118)
1 Stark. 2 Brother in law. 3 Some of her dresses. 4 Anne. 5 Edward. 6 Princess Michael of Kent. 7 Margaret. 8 Panorama. 9 Eton. 10 Bulimia. 11 Sarah, Duchess of York. 12 Harry. 13 Andrew. 14 The Queen. 15 Britannia. 16 Miss. 17 Balmoral. 18 Hip. 19 Christmas. 20 Candle in the Wind. 21 Grace Kelly. 22 Grandmother. 23 Westminster. 24 Weight Watchers. 25 Photographer. 26 Paris. 27 Windsor. 28 Queen Victoria. 29 Navy. 30 Anne.

117

Quiz 110 Celebs: The Royals

Answers - see Quiz 109, page 117

1   Which famous actress Koo was romantically linked to Prince Andrew?
2   What relation is Prince Philip to Princess Margaret?
3   What did the Princess of Wales sell at auction in 1997?
4   What is the Princess Royal's real first name?
5   Which Prince's name was linked with PR girl Sophie Rhys-Jones?
6   What is the title of the wife of Prince Michael of Kent?
7   Which Princess was prevented from marrying divorced Peter Townsend in the 50s?
8   On which programme did Princess Diana say her marriage had been "a bit crowded"?
9   Prince Harry followed Prince William to which school in 1998?
10 Which dietary illness did Princess Diana allegedly suffer from?
11 Who is the mother of Princesses Beatrice and Eugenie?
12 Which son of Prince Charles has red hair?
13 Who is older, Prince Andrew or Prince Edward?
14 Which Royal is always referred to as Her Majesty?
15 Which Royal yacht was decommissioned in 1997?
16 Is Princess Anne's daughter a Princess, or a Miss?
17 Where is the Queen's holiday home north of the border?
18 What did the Queen Mother have replaced after a fall in 1997?
19 At which time of year does the Queen always make a TV broadcast?
20 What did Elton John sing at Princess Diana's funeral?
21 Which wife of Prince Rainier of Monaco was an Oscar winner?
22 What relation is the Queen Mother to Prince Charles?
23 In which Abbey did Prince Andrew and Sarah Ferguson marry?
24 Which 'Watchers' organisation did Fergie advertise?
25 Which profession is shared by Lords Snowdon and Lichfield?
26 In which city was Princess Diana tragically killed?
27 Which castle was reopened in 1998 after being damaged by fire?
28 Who was the last British monarch of the 19th century?
29 Before his marriage was Prince Philip in the army or the navy?
30 Which Princess was married to Captain Mark Phillips?

Geography: World Tour (see Quiz 111, page 119)
1 Nile. 2 Pope. 3 West. 4 Canada. 5 Bombay. 6 Abominable.
7 Australia. 8 Southern. 9 India. 10 Peru. 11 Caribbean. 12 Zimbabwe.
13 Suez. 14 Coast. 15 Pacific. 16 South Africa. 17 Abraham Lincoln.
18 Arizona. 19 Australia. 20 Sahara. 21 Monarchy. 22 Africa.
23 Hawaii. 24 Atlantic. 25 Iran. 26 Arctic Circle. 27 Southern. 28 Iraq.
29 China. 30 Canada.

Answers

Quiz 111 Geography: World Tour

 LEVEL 1

Answers - see Quiz 110, page 118

1 Which long river has White and Blue tributaries?
2 Which religious leader is head of state of the Vatican?
3 Is Perth on the west or east coast of Australia?
4 In which country is Calgary?
5 Does Bombay or Tokyo have the higher population?
6 What sort of Snowman is another name for the Himalayan yeti?
7 What is the world's smallest, flattest and driest continent?
8 Is Argentina in the northern or southern half of South America?
9 Pakistan and Bangladesh both border which country?
10 Which country's name is an anagram of PURE?
11 The West Indies lie in which Sea?
12 Zambia is a neighbour of which country which also begins with Z?
13 Which Egyptian canal links the Red Sea and the Mediterranean?
14 Is Ghana on the African coast or wholly inland?
15 Which ocean is the world's deepest?
16 In which country is the homeland of KwaZulu?
17 Who is commemorated at Washington's Lincoln Memorial?
18 Which US state has the zipcode (postcode) AZ?
19 New South Wales is in which country?
20 Which African desert is the world's largest?
21 Is Swaziland a monarchy or a republic?
22 Mount Kilimanjaro is the highest point of which continent?
23 Which US island state has the world's highest annual rainfall?
24 Which ocean lies to the east of South America?
25 Which Islamic Republic used to be called Persia?
26 Two thirds of Greenland lies in which Circle?
27 Is Namibia in northern or southern Africa?
28 Which country's head of state is Saddam Hussein al-Tikriti?
29 Which People's Republic has the world's largest population?
30 Alberta is a province of which country?

Pop: Who's Who? (see Quiz 109, page 117)
Answers
1 Yoko Ono. 2 Patsy Kensit. 3 Michael. 4 Dublin. 5 Paige. 6 Wonder. 7 k d
lang. 8 Elton John. 9 Beach Boys. 10 Chuck Berry. 11 Plane crash.
12 Andrew Lloyd Webber. 13 Wham! 14 ZZ Top. 15 Michael. 16 Virgin.
17 Ant & Dec. 18 Otis Redding. 19 Don & Phil. 20 Canada. 21 McCartney.
22 Sonny. 23 Iceland. 24 Celine Dion. 25 Newton-John. 26 Cyndi Lauper.
27 Knopfler. 28 Adam. 29 Things Can Only Get Better. 30 Prince.

Medium Questions

For the majority of pub quiz situations, these questions are going to be your primarily line of attack. They're tricky enough to make people think about the answer, but they're not so mind-straining that your audience is going to walk off feeling humiliated. And that's important. The majority of folks in the pub are going to know roughly half of the answers to these questions, and where people fall down totally will be in subjects that they know nothing about. If you're setting a quiz for lone contestants, make good use of these questions.

If you're working with teams, you may find that this section is a little on the simple side still. Pick any four people from the bar, and you'll find that between them, they have at least some knowledge of most areas. That means that scores for teams on this sort of material should be around the 75% mark, which leaves plenty of room for doing well or doing badly, but still lets everyone feel good about themselves.

So, either way, use these questions wisely. Rely on their power to help you out of a sticky situation (although that might just be beer on the pub carpet), and you won't go far wrong. They will provide the backbone of your quiz.

Quiz 1 Pot Luck 1

Answers - see Quiz 2, page 122

LEVEL 2

1 Stamp duty is normally paid on the sale of what?
2 Where is the Ceremony of the Keys held every evening?
3 What does a BACS system transfer?
4 Who wears a chasuble?
5 Who or what is your doppelganger?
6 Emphysema affects which part of the body?
7 Which term for school or university is from the Latin meaning 'bounteous mother'?
8 Which salts are hydrated magnesium sulphate?
9 What is the UK equivalent of the US Bureau of Consumer Protection?
10 What did Plaid Cymru add to its name in 1998?
11 Which punctuation mark would an American call a period?
12 At what age does a student now take a GCE exam?
13 Where were the Elgin marbles from originally?
14 Which song starts, "Friday night and the lights are low"?
15 According to legend, what will happen to Gibraltar's ape population if the British leave?
16 Is BST before or behind GMT?
17 What is notable about the staff and patients of the Elizabeth Garrett Anderson Hospital?
18 How many valves does a bugle have?
19 What name is given to the compulsive eating disorder?
20 What is a Blenheim Orange?
21 Which childhood disease is also called varicella?
22 What do citronella candles smell of?
23 Which part of the anatomy shares its name with a punctuation mark?
24 Which tax did council tax immediately replace?
25 Which English archbishop signs his name Ebor?
26 Which saint was born in Lourdes?
27 Which proposal for a single currency shares its name with a bird?
28 Where is the auditory canal?
29 Where is a fresco painted?
30 How long must a person have had to be dead to qualify for a blue plaque?

Sport: Cricket (see Quiz 1, page 121)
1 Geoffrey Boycott. 2 Richie Benaud. 3 Tony Lewis. 4 Trevor McDonald.
5 Terrence. 6 Kapil Dev. 7 Somerset. 8 Denis Compton. 9 Shakoor Rana.
10 Dennis Lillee. 11 Michael Atherton. 12 The Oval. 13 Graham Alan Gooch.
14 Wasim Akram. 15 Headingley. 16 Muthiah Muralitharan. 17 William
Gilbert. 18 David Gower. 19 Leicestershire. 20 Lancashire. 21 Sunglasses.
22 Sunil Gavaskar. 23 Hansie Cronje. 24 Don Bradman. 25 Graeme Hick.
26 Imran Khan. 27 Antigua. 28 The Times. 29 Sri Lanka. 30 Left.

Quiz 2 Sport: Cricket

Answers - see Quiz 1, page 121

LEVEL 2

1 Who did David Gower overtake as England's most prolific run scorer in 1992?
2 Which Australian commentates on BBC TV each summer?
3 Which former test cricketer became President of the MCC in 1998?
4 Which newsreader has written biographies of Viv Richards and Clive Lloyd?
5 What is Ian Botham's middle name?
6 Which Indian was the second bowler to reach 400 Test wickets?
7 Which English county did Viv Richards play for?
8 Which cricketer was the first British sportsman to appear in a major advertising campaign?
9 Which umpire did Gatting publicly argue with in Faisalabad?
10 Which Australian was the first man to take 300 wickets in Test cricket?
11 Who stood in the most tests as England captain?
12 Which is the most southerly of the six regular English Test grounds?
13 Which cricketer's initials are GAG?
14 Who left Lancashire in 1998 to return to Pakistan to clear his name?
15 At which ground did England beat South Africa to clinch the 1998 series?
16 David Lloyd was reprimanded for criticising which Sri Lankan bowler in 1998?
17 What were W.G. Grace's first two names?
18 Whose record did Graham Gooch pass when he became England's leading run scorer?
19 Which county has two two championships in the last three years?
20 Who won the 1998 Nat West Trophy?
21 In 1996 Darren Gough became the first England bowler to bowl wearing what?
22 Which Indian cricketer scored 10,122 runs in 125 matches between 1971 and 1987?
23 Who captained the South Africans on their 1998 England tour?
24 Which cricketer's bat was auctioned for £23,000 in 1997?
25 Which Rhodesian became Zimbabwe's youngest professional at the age of 17 in 1985?
26 Who captained Pakistan in the 1992 World Cup victory?
27 On which island did Brian Lara make his record breaking 375?
28 In which newspaper was it announced that English cricket had died, leading to competition for the Ashes?
29 In which country is Khettarama Stadium?
30 Which hand does David Gower write with?

Pot Luck 1 (see Quiz 1, page 121)

Answers

1 House. 2 Tower of London 3 Money. 4 Priest. 5 Double. 6 Lungs.
7 Alma Mater. 8 Epsom salts. 9 Office of Fair Trading. 10 the Party of Wales.
11 Full stop. 12 18. 13 Greece. 14 Dancing Queen. 15 It will die out.
16 Before. 17 Women. 18 None. 19 Bulimia. 20 Apple. 21 Chicken
pox. 22 Lemons. 23 Colon. 24 Community Charge or Poll Tax. 25 York.
26 Bernadette. 27 EMU. 28 In the ear. 29 On a wall. 30 20 years.

Quiz 3 Pot Luck 2

Answers - see Quiz 4, page 124

LEVEL 2

1   Which Dunfermline East MP has been in the Cabinet in the 90s?
2   Why does a glow worm glow?
3   Who wrote the Kirsty MacColl hit A New England?
4   Princess Margaret was advised against marrying Peter Townsend for what reason?
5   Cambodian leader Saloth Sar was better known by what name?
6   How many holes are most major golf tournaments played over?
7   In the song, what colour rose is linked with Texas?
8   Tokai wine comes from which country?
9   In which month did Samuel Pepys begin his famous diary?
10   Who was Lord Lucan said to have murdered?
11   Mont Blanc stands in France as well as which other country?
12   William Wilkins designed which London gallery?
13   Which city has an American football team called the Cowboys?
14   Which is the world's oldest surviving republic?
15   Which Latin words did H M the Queen use to describe the year 1992?
16   Which cave is the most famous on the Scottish Isle of Staffa?
17   Cars with the international vehicle registration SF come from where?
18   Number 22 in bingo is represented by a pair of little what?
19   What is the core of an ear of maize called?
20   What was the title of the Eurovision winner for Bucks Fizz?
21   In Porterhouse Blue which actor played Skullion?
22   Which country's stamps show the word "Hellas"?
23   Who were the subject of the Cat and Mouse Act of 1913?
24   How many points are scored for a motor racing Grand Prix win?
25   What is the largest structure ever made by living creatures?
26   Papworth Hospital is in which county?
27   Who said, "Float like a butterfly, sting like a bee"?
28   Which magazine was first published in the 1840s and last in the 1990s?
29   Which road is crossed by the horses during the Grand National?
30   Which religious ceremony comes from the Greek word for 'to dip'?

Answers

The Movies: All Action (see Quiz 4, page 124)
1 Goldeneye. 2 Platoon. 3 Jeremy Irons. 4 The Hunt for Red October.
5 Charles Bronson. 6 Jim Carrey. 7 Best Director. 8 Wesley Snipes. 9 Live and Let Die. 10 Faye Dunaway. 11 Donald Pleasance. 12 Die Hard with a Vengeance. 13 Harrison Ford. 14 Marseilles . 15 Apollo 13. 16 Bruce Willis.
17 Popeye Doyle. 18 James Caan. 19 Irish. 20 Brad Pitt. 21 Lost in Space.
22 Phil Collins. 23 Cabbie. 24 Paul & Linda McCartney. 25 JFK. 26 Sean Bean. 27 The China Syndrome. 28 Arnold Schwarzenegger. 29 New York.
30 Leonardo DiCaprio.

Quiz 4 The Movies: All Action

LEVEL 2

Answers - see Quiz 3, page 123

1 Which Bond film shares its name with Ian Fleming's Jamaican home?
2 What was the third of Oliver Stone's films about Vietnam?
3 Which English Oscar winner was the villain in Die Hard III?
4 Patriot Games was the sequel to which film with Alec Baldwin?
5 Who played Bernardo in The Magnificent Seven and Danny Velinski in The Great Escape?
6 Who was The Riddler in Batman Forever?
7 Which Oscar did Kevin Costner win for Dances With Wolves?
8 Who played the defrosted super-villain in Demolition Man?
9 What was Roger Moore's first Bond film in 1973?
10 Who had her first major starring role in Bonnie & Clyde?
11 Who plays the President in Escape From New York?
12 Which was the third Die Hard film?
13 Who played Indiana Jones?
14 Where was French Connection II set?
15 Astronaut Jim Lovell was portrayed by Tom Hanks in which film?
16 Who heads the crew which saves the world in Armageddon?
17 Who did Gene Hackman play in The French Connection?
18 Who played Sonny Corleone in The Godfather and its sequel?
19 What nationality cop did Sean Connery play in The Untouchables?
20 Who co starred with Morgan Freeman in Seven?
21 Which 1998 film of a 60s cult TV series starred Gary Oldman and William Hurt?
22 Who played the train robber of the title role in Buster?
23 What was Mel Gibson's job in the 1997 thriller Conspiracy Theory?
24 Which husband and wife were Oscar nominated for the song from Live And Let Die?
25 Which Oliver Stone movie with Kevin Costner was about events prior to Kennedy's assassination?
26 Which Yorkshireman played the IRA terrorist in Patriot Games?
27 In which '79 movie with Jack Lemmon was Jane Fonda urged to keep quiet about a nuclear accident?
28 Who was the construction worker who had flashbacks in Total Recall?
29 Where does the action of Godzilla take place?
30 Who played two roles in the 90s version of The Man in the Iron Mask?

Answers

Pot Luck 2 (see Quiz 3, page 123)
1 Gordon Brown. 2 To attract mates. 3 Billy Bragg. 4 He was a divorcee.
5 Pol Pot. 6 72. 7 Yellow. 8 Hungary. 9 January. 10 Sandra Rivett.
11 Italy. 12 The National Gallery. 13 Dallas. 14 San Marino. 15 Annus horribilis. 16 Fingal's cave. 17 Finland. 18 Two little ducks. 19 A corncob.
20 Making Your Mind Up. 21 David Jason. 22 Greece. 23 Suffragettes.
24 10. 25. The Great Barrier Reef. 26 Cambridgeshire. 27 Muhammad Ali.
28 Punch. 29 Melling Road. 30 Baptism.

Quiz 5 Pot Luck 3

Answers - see Quiz 6, page 126

LEVEL 2

1   Which U2 member was once the All-Ireland Junior Chess Champion?
2   Who won 100m gold at the 1988 Olympics and was then disqualified?
3   Spy-writer David J. Cornwell writes under which name?
4   What is the unit of measurement for the brightness of stars?
5   Which "-ology" is the study of birds' eggs?
6   Which Dire Straits album included Money for Nothing?
7   Who were Janet, Pam, Barbara, Jack, Peter, George and Colin?
8   In which country would you be to visit Agadir?
9   What name is given to a bell tower not attached to a church?
10 Van Pelt is the surname of which Peanuts character?
11 What is the best hand in a game of poker?
12 The Virgin record label was launched by which instrumental album?
13 Which crab lives in a whelk or winkle shell?
14 In the official conker rules, how many strikes per turn are allowed?
15 Which country celebrated its bicentenary in 1988?
16 What word commonly describes a spasm of the diaphragm?
17 Daniel Carroll found theatrical fame under which name?
18 In pop music, who looked into his father's eyes?
19 Who lit the funeral pyre of Mrs Indira Gandhi?
20 Which country has Jones as its most common name but no J in its alphabet?
21 What name was given to the first antibiotic?
22 According to the advert, which city is home to "probably the best lager in the world"?
23 Switzerland's Mont Cervin is better known by what name?
24 Who wrote the novel Where Eagles Dare?
25 Which England cricket captain had the middle name Dylan?
26 What do the initials CND stand for?
27 What is the collective name for a group of frogs?
28 Who was the first act to have seven consecutive US No 1 singles?
29 Eton school is in which county?
30 Which country was first to host Summer and Winter Olympics in the same year?

Leisure: Food & Drink 1   (see Quiz 6, page 126)

Answers

1 Fish. 2 Kirschwasser. 3 Gin. 4 Sugar. 5 November. 6 Curry powder.
7 Greece. 8 Halal. 9 20. 10 Kiwi fruit. 11 Gelatine. 12 Marty Wilde. 13
Mrs Beeton. 14 Nut. 15 Coca Cola. 16 Elizabeth David. 17 Clarified butter.
18 Carrot. 19 Bloody Mary. 20 Manchester United. 21 Nouvelle cuisine.
2 Aluminium. 23 Jennifer Paterson. 24 Rhodes to Home. 25 Black.
26 Fred Trueman. 27 Poisonous raw. 28 Mushroom. 29 Cherry. 30 Milk.

Quiz 6 Leisure: Food & Drink 1

Answers - see Quiz 5, page 125

1 What type of food is gravadlax?
2 Which type of brandy is made from cherries?
3 Which spirit is Pimm's No 1 based on?
4 Aspartame is an alternative to what when added to food?
5 In which month does Beaujolais Nouveau arrive?
6 Which powder includes turmeric, fenugreek, chillies and cumin?
7 Which country produces more than 70% of the world's olive oil?
8 What name is given to food prepared according to Muslim law?
9 How many standard wine bottles make up a Nebuchadnezzar?
10 Which fruit is also called the Chinese gooseberry?
11 Agar agar is a vegetarian alternative to what?
12 Which 50s pop star's name is cockney rhyming slang for mild?
13 How is cook Isabella Mary Mayson better known?
14 What sort of food is a macadamia?
15 Atlanta is the headquarters of which drinks company?
16 Which pioneering cookery writer wrote Mediterranean Food and French Country Cooking in the 50s?
17 What is ghee?
18 Caraway is related to which family of vegetables?
19 Which queen's nickname is the name of a cocktail?
20 Which football team does Gary Rhodes support?
21 Which term coined in the 70s describes food which does not have rich sauces?
22 What are most beer and soft drinks cans made from?
23 Which of the Two Fat Ladies rides the motorbike?
24 What was Gary Rhodes range of convenience foods called?
25 What colour are fully ripened olives?
26 The Fiery Fred pub was named after whom?
27 Why do cashew nuts have to be roasted to be eaten?
28 What is a morel?
29 What is a morello?
30 Which drink did Bob Geldof advertise?

Answers

Pot Luck 3 (see Quiz 5, page 125)
1 Bono. 2 Ben Johnson. 3 John Le Carre. 4 Magnitude. 5 Oology.
6 Brothers In Arms. 7 The Secret Seven. 8 Morocco. 9 A campanile.
10 Lucy. 11 Royal flush. 12 Tubular Bells. 13 Hermit crab. 14 Three.
15 Australia. 16 Hiccough. 17 Danny La Rue. 18 Eric Clapton. 19 Rajiv Gandhi. 20 Wales. 21 Penicillin. 22 Copenhagen. 23 The Matterhorn.
24 Alistair MacLean. 25 Bob Willis. 26 Campaign for Nuclear Disarmament.
27 An army (or colony). 28 Whitney Houston. 29 Berkshire. 30 France.

LEVEL 2

1 The illness pertussis is more commonly called what?
2 Why do woodpeckers peck at trees?
3 Which rock is the largest monolith in the world?
4 Which Spanish team were the first winners of the European Cup?
5 What type of animal can be Texel and Romney Marsh?
6 Where would you hurt if you were kicked on the tarsus?
7 The Bee Gees were born on which island?
8 What action does a dromophobic fear?
9 In which country is the world's second highest mountain, K2?
10 What nationality is Salman Rushdie?
11 Which Test cricketer played in an FA Cup Final for Arsenal?
12 Which tanker went down on the Seven Stones reef off Land's End?
13 Which large forest is the nearest to London's Liverpool Street Station?
14 Which hit by Judy Collins entered the UK charts on eight occasions?
15 In 1978 how many different Popes were there?
16 In which decade did Constantinople become Istanbul?
17 How many bridesmaids attended Princess Diana?
18 Which poet gave his name to a Cape to the south of Brisbane?
19 Which Russian town produced deformed sheep after a 90s disaster?
20 What is Paul McCartney's first name?
21 Which drug took its name from the Greek god of dreams?
22 Which is the largest borough in the city of New York?
23 Which doll's name gave Aqua a No 1 hit?
24 Which other brook is there on the Grand National course with Becher's?
25 What is examined using an otoscope?
26 What is measured on the Mercalli Scale?
27 Along with Doric and Ionic, what is the third Greek order of architecture?
28 What is lowered by a Beta Blocker?
29 How many pieces does each backgammon player use?
30 A Blue Orpington is a type of what?

Answers

Science & Nature: Animal World (see Quiz 8, page 128)
1 Suffocation. 2 Sett. 3 Velvet. 4 Black. 5 Dachshund. 6 It cannot bark.
7 Afrikaans. 8 Mauritius. 9 Antelope. 10 Snow leopard. 11 Fight.
12 Squirrel. 13 One. 14 Cattle. 15 Hearing. 16 32. 17 Fawn.
18 Hooves. 19 Blood of birds and mammals. 20 Sheep. 21 Pink.
22 White. 23 Japan. 24 Caribou. 25 Lemurs. 26 White / cream.
27 V shape. 28 Elk. 29 Sand. 30 Border collie.

Quiz 8 Nature: Animal World

LEVEL 2

Answers - see Quiz 7, page 127

1   How do the anaconda's victims die?
2   What is the badger's system of burrows called?
3   What is the skin on a deer's antlers called?
4   What colour face does a Suffolk sheep have?
5   Which small breed of dog has a German name meaning badger dog?
6   What is unusual about the sound of the dingo?
7   Aardvark means 'earth pig' in which African language?
8   On which island was the dodo formerly found?
9   What is an impala?
10 What type of leopard is another name for the ounce?
11 Pit bull terriers were bred to do what?
12 To which family does the prairie dog belong?
13 Does the Indian rhinoceros have one or two horns?
14 Bovine Spongiform Encephalitis is a fatal disease of which animals?
15 Tinnitus affects which of the senses?
16 How many teeth do human adults have?
17 What is the most common colour of a Great Dane?
18 What does an ungulate animal have?
19 What do vampire bats feed on?
20 Lanolin is a by product of which domestic animal?
21 If a mammal has albinism what colour are its eyes?
22 What colour are dalmatians when they are born?
23 The tosa is a dog native to which country?
24 What is the reindeer of North America called?
25 Which group of primates are found only on Madagascar?
26 What colour is the coat of a samoyed?
27 What shaped mark does an adder have on its head?
28 What is another name for the wapiti?
29 What do alligators lay their eggs in?
30 Which dog do shepherds now most commonly use for herding sheep?

Pot Luck 4 (see Quiz 7, page 127)

Answers
1 Whooping cough. **2** To catch insects. **3** Ayers Rock. **4** Real Madrid.
5 Sheep. **6** Ankle. **7** Isle of Man. **8** Crossing the road. **9** Pakistan.
10 British. **11** Denis Compton. **12** Torrey Canyon. **13** Epping Forest. **14**
Amazing Grace. **15** Three. **16** 1930s. **17** Five. **18** Byron. **19** Chernobyl.
20 James. **21** Morphine. **22** Queens. **23** Barbie. **24** Valentine's. **25** Ear.
26 Earthquakes. **27** Corinthian. **28** Blood pressure. **29** 15. **30** Chicken.

Quiz 9 Pot Luck 5

Answers - see Quiz 10, page 130

LEVEL 2

1　In which US state is Death Valley?
2　Which Sea does the River Jordan flow into?
3　Who was Speaker of the House after Bernard Weatherill?
4　Who had Top Ten hits with All Night Long and I Surrender?
5　Which BBC magazine was launched in 1929?
6　What did Captain Cook call the Islands of Tonga?
7　Which celebrity was murdered in 1980 outside New York's Dakota Building?
8　Who played Lennie Godber in the TV series Porridge?
9　Which naval base is situated in Hampshire?
10　Which TV actress links EastEnders with The Hello Girls?
11　What is Marc Bolan's son's Christian name?
12　Which war is the first for which there are photographic records?
13　Writer Mary Westmacott is better known by what name?
14　Who or what was a ducat?
15　Which day is the last quarter day in a calendar year in England?
16　Which actor links The Charmer with Dangerfield?
17　In The Bible, who was Jacob's youngest son?
18　What was suffragette Mrs Pankhurst's Christian name?
19　In which sport is the Plunkett Shield competed for?
20　Which animal has breeds called Roscommon, Kerry Hill, Ryedale?
21　Which two countries was the Cod War of the 70s between?
22　What colour are Rupert Bear's trousers?
23　Who is Gary Lineker's sidekick on They Think It's All Over?
24　Which animal can be red, arctic, bat-eared and fennec?
25　Newman Noggs appears in which Charles Dickens novel?
26　What name is given to the base of your spine?
27　Who did Sandy Powell ask "Can You Hear Me, ..?"
28　Which actress links the films Ghostbusters and Alien?
29　Who had hits with Do You Feel My Love and Electric Avenue?
30　Which word describes both a blunt sword and a very thin sheet of metal?

Geography: The UK　(see Quiz 10, page 130)
1　Brighton. 2　Melinda Messenger. 3　South Kensington. 4　Stoke Mandeville.
5　Suffolk. 6　Severn Tunnel. 7　Newgate. 8　Canary Wharf (Isle of Dogs).
9　Salopian. 10　Army exercises. 11　Essex & Suffolk. 12　Bristol. 13　M6.
14　Glastonbury. 15　Big Ben. 16　Fruit, vegetables & flowers. 17　Windscale.
18　Horses. 19　Clyde. 20　Nottingham. 21　Wiltshire. 22　Edinburgh.
23　Petticoat Lane. 24　Papworth. 25　Hyde Park. 26　Aberdeen. 27　Bath.
28　Straits of Dover. 29　Swansea. 30　Bristol.

Quiz 10 Geography: The UK

Answers - see Quiz 9, page 129

LEVEL 2

1   Which seaside resort has Lanes and a nudist beach?
2   Which Page Three blonde is Swindon's most famous export?
3   In which part of London is the Natural History Museum?
4   Where is the National Spinal Injuries Unit?
5   In which county is Sizewell nuclear power station?
6   What is Britain's longest tunnel?
7   The Old Bailey is on the site of which former prison?
8   Where in London would a Canary sit on Dogs?
9   What is a native of Shropshire called?
10 What is Sailsbury Plain primarily used for?
11 In which two counties is Constable Country?
12 Where is the Clifton Suspension Bridge?
13 Spaghetti Junction is on which road?
14 Which Somerset town is said to be the burial place of King Arthur?
15 Which bell was named after Benjamin Hall?
16 What is sold at Spitalfields market?
17 What was the former name of Sellafield?
18 Which animals are kept in the Royal Mews near Buckingham Palace?
19 Holy Loch is an inlet of which river?
20 Which city has an annual Goose Fair?
21 In which English county is Europe's largest stone circle?
22 Which castle is at the west end of the Royal Mile?
23 How is the Sunday market in London's Middlesex Street better known?
24 Which Cambridgeshire hospital is famous for its transplant surgery?
25 Speaker's Corner is on the corner of what?
26 Where is the administrative headquarters of the Grampian region?
27 Which city has a famous Royal Crescent?
28 The Goodwin Sands are at the entrance to which straits?
29 Where is the DVLC?
30 Where is Temple Meads railway station?

Pot Luck 5 (see Quiz 9, page 129)
Answers
1 California. **2** Dead Sea. **3** Betty Boothroyd. **4** Rainbow. **5** The Listener.
6 The Friendly Islands. **7** John Lennon. **8** Richard Beckinsale. **9** Gosport.
10 Letitia Dean. **11** Roland Bolan. **12** Crimean. **13** Agatha Christie. **14** A
coin. **15** Christmas Day. **16** Nigel Havers. **17** Benjamin. **18** Emmeline.
19 Cricket. **20** Sheep. **21** Iceland and Britain. **22** Yellow. **23** Rory
McGrath. **24** Fox. **25** Nicholas Nickleby. **26** Coccyx. **27** Mother.
28 Sigourney Weaver. **29** Eddy Grant. **30** Foil.

Quiz 11 TV: Adverts

Answers - see Quiz 12, page 132

LEVEL 2

1   Carol Vorderman was sacked from Tomorrow's World for advertising what?
2   Which credit card did Rowan Atkinson publicise by not having one?
3   Which opera singer has sung on Kenco Coffee and Renault car ads?
4   Who played the jilted lover in the 80s VW commercial?
5   Which 'pensioner' advertised British Gas with her 'son' Malcolm?
6   For which supermarket did Wood & Walters push their trolleys round country lanes?
7   Which Blankety Blank presenter did Polly Peck hire to advertise their tights?
8   Which soap powder did Shane Richie promote in his doorstep raids?
9   Who advertised Cinzano with Leonard Rossiter?
10 Which juice did Fergie advertise in the US?
11 Lynda Bellingham first found fame advertising what?
12 Which supermarket did John Cleese promote in a loud checked suit?
13 Which company had the slogan 'It's good to talk'?
14 Which cat put its paw in the tine of cat food?
15 Which soap star appeared in a BT ad digging his allotment?
16 Which star of Brushstrokes can be found cleaning bathrooms and kitchens in TV ads?
17 In the Renault ad did Nicole marry Reeves or Mortimer?
18 What type of coffee did Gareth Hunt and Diane Keen enjoy?
19 Which star of Friends uses L'Oreal "Because I'm worth it!"?
20 Which song accompanies Ian McCaskill's BT ad?
21 Emma Forbes' mother advertised which washing up liquid?
22 Which margarine did 'Victor Meldrew' encourage us to eat?
23 Who cried when his Walkers Crisps were taken from him?
24 Ironically Julie Peasgood advertised which product?
25 Which fast food chain did soccer stars Waddle, Pearce and Southgate promote?
26 Which breakfast cereal was Jackie Charlton seen eating with his grandson?
27 Messrs Venables, Robson and Taylor collectively promoted which book?
28 Geoffrey Palmer from As Time Goes By advised to "slam in" what ?
29 Bruce Forsyth dresses up as a judge to advertise what product?
30 Which supermarket did Michael Barrymore advertise in the autumn of 1998?

Pot Luck 6 (see Quiz 12, page 132)

1 Yellowstone National Park. **2** International Monetary Fund. **3** Volcanic gases.
4 Lentils. **5** Sheffield. **6** Kate Bush. **7** Cashew nut. **8** Hattie Jacques. **9** A
will. **10** Thanksgiving. **11** Black. **12** The Wailers. **13** International Velvet.
14 National Exhibition Centre. **15** Boy George. **16** 21. **17** Versailles.
18 Iraq. **19** Scotland. **20** Belshazzar. **21** White rum. **22** Thunder &
lightning. **23** Mick Hucknall. **24** The Andes. **25** The Derby. **26** An unborn
baby. **27** Prunella Scales. **28** The peacock. **29** The Baltic. **30** Frogmore.

Quiz 12 Pot Luck 6

Answers - see Quiz 11, page 131

LEVEL 2

1 In which US National Park is the Old Faithful geyser?
2 What do the initials IMF stand for?
3 What is emitted from a fumarole?
4 What is the main ingredient in dhal, the Indian dish?
5 In which city is Bramall Lane?
6 Which female had a UK top-three LP in 1982 called The Dreaming?
7 Mozambique is the world's largest producer of which nut?
8 How is Josephina Jacques known in Carry On films?
9 To what would a codicil be added?
10 Which American annual celebration was first marked during 1789?
11 The first Girl Guides had to wear what colour stockings?
12 Which band claimed fifty per cent of Bob Marley's estate?
13 Which film was the follow-up to National Velvet?
14 What does NEC stand for around Birmingham?
15 Who left Bow Wow Wow to form Culture Club?
16 What is the maximum score in blackjack?
17 Which building in France has a famous Hall of Mirrors?
18 What is the modern name of the country where the Hanging Gardens of Babylon were?
19 Which country did Arsenal keeper Bob Wilson play for?
20 In The Bible, which character saw the first writing on the wall?
21 A Daiquiri is made from fruit juice and which alcoholic drink?
22 Astraphobia is the fear of which meteorological event?
23 Which male pop superstar once played with the Frantic Elevators?
24 Machu Picchu is in which mountain range?
25 What is the English equivalent of the Melbourne Cup?
26 What is surrounded by amniotic fluid?
27 Who links Fawlty Towers and After Henry?
28 Which bird is India's national symbol?
29 Which sea is the least salty in the world?
30 Where was The Duke of Windsor buried in 1972?

Answers

TV: Adverts (see Quiz 11, page 131)
1 Ariel. 2 Barclaycard. 3 Lesley Garrett. 4 Paula Hamilton. 5 Mrs Merton.
6 Asda. 7 Lily Savage. 8 Daz. 9 Joan Collins. 10 Cranberry. 11 Oxo.
12 Sainsbury's. 13 BT. 14 Arthur. 15 Arthur Fowler. 16 Karl Howman.
17 Mortimer. 18 Nescafe. 19 Jennifer Aniston. 20 Bring Me Sunshine.
21 Fairy. 22 Flora. 23 Paul Gascoigne. 24 Frozen peas. 25 Pizza Hut.
26 Shredded Wheat. 27 Yellow Pages. 28 The lamb. 29 Furniture.
30 Kwik Save.

Quiz 13 Pop Music: The 60s

LEVEL 2

Answers - see Quiz 14, page 134

1 Which No 1 hit for the Archies was in the charts for twenty six weeks?

2 Which Park was a hit for the Small Faces in 1967?

3 Who was singing about Sheila in 1962 and Dizzy in 1969?

4 Which 60s hit for Kitty Lester was an 80s hit for Alison Moyet?

5 When did the Shirelles want to know Will You Still Love Me...?

6 Which crime busting organisation gave the Shadows a 1961 hit?

7 What was Petula Clark's first No 1 UK hit in 1961?

8 Which three numbers gave Len Barry his No 3 hit in 1965?

9 Who had consecutive hits with Daydream and Summer In The City?

10 What was over for the Seekers in their 1965 UK No 1 hit?

11 Which 1965 Shirley Ellis hit was a 1982 hit for the Belle Stars?

12 What were Emile Ford and the Checkmates Counting in 1960?

13 What was the Searchers first No 1 ?

14 What was on the other side of Shirley Bassey's Reach for the Stars?

15 Whose first Top Ten hit was 5-4-3-2-1 in 1964?

16 Which country was in the title of a '63 hit by Matt Monro?

17 Who recorded the original of the song used in Four Weddings and a Funeral?

18 What Girl was Neil Sedaka singing about in 1961?

19 The song Starry Eyed was a No 1 on 1st January 1960 for which Michael?

20 Which words of exclamation were a 1960 No 4 hit for Peter Sellers?

21 Which Opportunity Knocks star had a hit with Those Were The Days?

22 What did The Move say they could hear grow in a 1967 hit title?

23 Which 60s hit for Kenny Lynch was a No 1 for Robson and Jerome in 1995?

24 Who were Glad All Over in their No 1 hit from 1963?

25 What was 'skipped' in the lyrics of Whiter Shade Of Pale?

26 What type of Feelings did Tom Jones have in his 1967 hit?

27 Which Group had consecutive No1s with Keep On Running and Somebody Help Me?

28 To which religious building were the Dixie Cups going in 1964?

29 Which weather sounding group had hits with Robot and Globetrotter?

30 Which 1960s star appeared with Zoe Wanamaker in Love Hurts?

Answers

Pot Luck 7 (see Quiz 14, page 134)

1 1950s. 2 The Undertones. 3 The Hobbit. 4 Jeanette MacDonald.
5 Excalibur. 6 Woody Allen. 7 Colchester. 8 Uncle Mac. 9 You walk.
10 McAliskey. 11 Roy Wood. 12 Brookside. 13 Arthur Lucan. 14 Eric
Idle. 15 Hairy. 16 Ernie Els. 17 George III. 18 A dog. 19 Chariots of Fire.
20 Red Square, Moscow. 21 Private Fraser. 22 Ultravox. 23 Sheep & goats.
24 Mumps. 25 Shirley Williams. 26 A bolt or quarrel. 27 Amsterdam. 28
Shirley Temple. 29 Pig. 30 George VI.

Quiz 14 Pot Luck 7

Answers - see Quiz 13, page 133

Answers - see Quiz 13, page 133

LEVEL 2

1 In which decade did Lester Piggott first win the Derby?
2 Who had hits with My Perfect Cousin and Jimmy Jimmy?
3 Which folklore fantasy tale is subtitled There and Back Again?
4 Who was Nelson Eddy's singing partner in many musical films?
5 Which famous sword is sometimes called Caliburn?
6 Which famous film director has a son called Satchel?
7 Which is further north, Chelmsford or Colchester?
8 Children's broadcaster Derek McCulloch was known on the radio as whom?
9 What is your mode of transport if you go by Walker's Bus?
10 What is former MP Bernadette Devlin's married name?
11 Which Wizzard star formed ELO in 1971?
12 In which TV soap was Trevor Jordache buried under the patio?
13 Who played Old Mother Riley in films and on stage?
14 Which member of the Monty Python team was born on the same day as John Major?
15 What does the word piliferous mean?
16 Who won the Toyota world matchplay championship at his first attempt in 1994?
17 Which King George bought Buckingham Palace?
18 What kind of animal is a Schnauzer?
19 Which Oscar winning film gave Vangelis a No 12 hit in 1981?
20 In which famous Square is St Basil's cathedral?
21 In the series Dad's Army which soldier's daytime job was an undertaker?
22 Who had hits with All Stood Still and Visions in Blue?
23 Which animals are attacked by a disease called Scrapie?
24 Which childhood disease affects the parotid salivary gland?
25 Which female MP was one of the founder members of the SDP?
26 What can be fired by a crossbow?
27 In which city was Anne Frank when she wrote her diary?
28 Which actress played lead in the films Dimples and Curly Top?
29 Lard is mainly produced from which animal?
30 Which king was the last Emperor of India?

Answers - see Quiz 13, page 133

Answers

Pop Music: 60s (see Quiz 13, page 133)
1 Sugar Sugar. 2 Itchycoo Park. 3 Tommy Roe. 4 Love Letters. 5 Tomorrow. 6 FBI. 7 Sailor. 8 1-2-3. 9 Lovin' Spoonful. 10 The Carnival Is Over. 11 The Clapping Song. 12 Teardrops. 13 Sweets For My Sweet. 14 Climb Ev'ry Mountain. 15 Manfred Mann. 16 Russia. 17 Troggs. 18 Calendar Girl. 19 Holliday. 20 Goodness Gracious Me. 21 Mary Hopkin. 22 The Grass. 23 Up On The Roof. 24 Dave Clark Five. 25 The Light Fandango. 26 Funny Familiar Forgotten. 27 Spencer Davis. 28 Chapel of Love. 29 Tornadoes. 30 Adam Faith.

Quiz 15 Sport: Football UK

LEVEL 2

1   Who succeeded Ossie Ardiles as Spurs manager?
2   Which football team was involved in an aircrash in March 1998?
3   Which English international played for three Italian clubs before moving to Arsenal?
4   Who was fined £20,000 for making a video on how to foul players?
5   Whose 1996 penalty miss prompted Des Lynam to say "You can come out from behind your sofas now."?
6   Who was PFA Young Player of the year in '95 and '96?
7   Who left Tottenham immediately before George Graham took over?
8   Which football manager is singer Louise's father in law?
9   Which club side was Alan Ball playing for during the 1966 World Cup?
10 What is Glenn Hoddle in the cockney rhyming slang dictionary?
11 Which was the first Lancashire side Kenny Dalglish managed?
12 How is Mrs Paul Peschilsolido better known?
13 Which striker has been player of the year at Everton and at Spurs?
14 Who was Man Utd manager immediately prior to Alex Ferguson?
15 Ian McShane's father was on the books of which football club?
16 Who was the first UK manager to walk out on a contract and work abroad?
17 Who has managed Internazionale of Milan and Blackburn Rovers?
18 Which 80s FA Cup winners came nearest the start of the alphabet?
19 Who was Gullit's first signing when he took over at Newcastle?
20 How does the resolving of the 1999 FA CUP Final differ from those 127 years before?
21 Who did Bruce Rioch replace at Norwich for the start of the 1998-99 season?
22 Who was made Northern Ireland manager in February 1998?
23 Which England player was seen on the town wearing a sarong prior to France 98?
24 Who should Scotland have been playing when they arrived for a World Cup qualifier with no opposition?
25 Which ex international managed Burnley in the 1997-98 season?
26 Who did Jack Charlton play all his League football with?
27 George Graham was accused of taking a 'bung' in the transfer of which player?
28 Who sponsored the Scottish Premier Division in the 1995-96 season?
29 What did Man Utd have advertised on their shirts in the 1998 Charity Shield game?
30 Which Yorkshire side does actor Sean Bean support?

Pot Luck 8 (see Quiz 16, page 136)

1 Docklands. 2 Casanova. 3 David Bowie. 4 Everglades. 5 A waterhole. 6 21. 7 Asia Minor. 8 Will Carling. 9 Loose rocks. 10 Cardiff. 11 Dysentery. 12 Trilby. 13 Corinth Canal. 14 London. 15 Elizabeth Bennet. 16 Football match. 17 Bhopal. 18 Hudson Bay. 19 155. 20 Stevie Wonder. 21 Italy. 22 Agnes Baden-Powell. 23 1990. 24 Band Aid. 25 Dodecanese. 26 Clay. 27 Vogue. 28 September 15th. 29 1972. 30 The Queen was pregnant.

Quiz 16 Pot Luck 8

LEVEL 2

1 Canary Wharf is in which London development?
2 Who wrote twelve volumes on Casanova?
3 Which superstar was a former member of the group the King Bees?
4 Which Florida national park has a highway called Alligator Alley?
5 What do Australians mean when they talk about a billabong?
6 How old was Billy The Kid when he died?
7 What was the former name of Turkey?
8 Julia Smith became the wife of which famous sportsman?
9 What on a mountainside is scree?
10 Which city is James Callaghan the Baron of?
11 What killed Sir Francis Drake?
12 What type of hat took its name from a novel by George DuMaurier?
13 The Aegean Sea is linked to the Ionian Sea by which canal?
14 Florence Nightingale was given the Freedom of which city in 1908?
15 Who is the heroine in Jane Austen's Pride and Prejudice?
16 What game started the 1969 war between El Salvador and Honduras?
17 In the 80s two thousand people were killed by a gas leak in which Indian town?
18 Which Bay is the largest in the world?
19 What is the highest break in snooker with the advantage of a free black ball?
20 Which blind music star ran for Mayor of Detroit in 1989?
21 In which country was Ted Dexter born?
22 Who was responsible for setting up the Girl Guides movement?
23 In what year was Nelson Mandela released from prison?
24 Which charity was in business from 1984-89 and raised £90 million?
25 Rhodes is the largest of which group of islands?
26 What is a sumo wrestling ring made from?
27 The film Dick Tracy was promoted by which Madonna single?
28 The Battle of Britain is remembered on which date?
29 Which year did John Lennon perform his final live concert?
30 The 1959 Royal Variety Performance was cancelled for what reason?

Answers

Sport: Football UK (see Quiz 15, page 135)
1 Gerry Francis. 2 Leeds Utd. 3 David Platt. 4 Vinnie Jones. 5 Gareth Southgate. 6 Robbie Fowler. 7 Christian Gross. 8 Harry Redknapp. 9 Blackpool. 10 Doddle. 11 Blackburn Rovers. 12 Karren Brady. 13 Gary Lineker. 14 Ron Atkinson. 15 Manchester United. 16 Graeme Souness. 17 Roy Hodgson. 18 Coventry. 19 Rui Costa. 20 No replay. 21 Mike Walker. 22 Lawrie McMenemy. 23 David Beckham. 24 Estonia. 25 Chris Waddle. 26 Leeds Utd. 27 John Jensen. 28 Bell's. 29 SHARP. 30 Sheffield United.

Quiz 17 Movies: Animation

LEVEL 2

Answers - see Quiz 18, page 138

1 Which Ponchielli piece features in Fantasia?
2 Which US born Australian was the voice of John Smith in Pocahontas?
3 I
4 What was the sequel to Aladdin called?
5 What colour are Mickey Mouse's gloves?
6 Perdita and Pongo are what type of animals?
7 How many Oscars in total, was Disney given for Snow White and the Seven Dwarfs?
8 Which 1991 animated film was later a musical in London and the US?
9 Who is the best known rabbit in Bambi?
10 Which king is 'the King of the Swingers' in Jungle Book?
11 Which of the Gabor sisters was a voice in The Aristocats?
12 Who created Tom and Jerry at MGM in the 40s?
13 What did Dumbo do immediately before his ears grew so big?
14 Which film of a fairy tale features the song Bibbidy Bobbidy Boo?
15 Which part did Kathleen Turner voice in Who Framed Roger Rabbit??
16 Which Disney film was the first with a synchronised soundtrack?
17 Colours of the Wind was a hit song from which movie?
18 Which film with an animated sequence featured Angela Lansbury using her magic powers against the Nazis?
19 Who sings 'he's a tramp' in Lady and the Tramp?
20 Where did Kim Basinger star as a sexy animated doodle, Holly, brought over to the real world?
21 Who sang in Aladdin after making her name in Miss Saigon?
22 Which 1990 film was about pizza loving, sewer dwelling reptiles?
23 Which was the first film to feature, appropriately enough, computer-animated sequences?
24 What type of orphaned creature featured in The Land Before Time?
25 Which was the first animated film in the 90s which Tim Rice won an Oscar for?
26 Which dancer commissioned Hanna and Barbera to do an animation sequence in Anchors Aweigh in 1945?
27 Which Tchaikovsky ballet piece features in Fantasia?
28 In which film does Shere Khan appear?
29 Which characters made their debut in Puss Gets the Boot in 1940?
30 Which animals feature in Oliver and Company?

Quiz 18 Pot Luck 9

Answers - see Quiz 17, page 137

LEVEL 2

1   Cars with the international vehicle registration C come from where?
2   The Paul Getty Museum is in which American state?
3   What is the American equivalent of an English bilberry?
4   What is added to Galliano to make a Harvey Wallbanger?
5   Which country is nearest to where the Titanic was found?
6   An average man has twenty square feet of what about his person?
7   In which country were the last summer Olympics of the 20th century in Europe?
8   In which decade was Cassius Clay - later Muhammad Ali - born?
9   From which tree family is the basket making osier a member?
10 Which sport other than rugby is played for the Currie Cup?
11 In which country is the Great Sandy Desert?
12 Who had Sticky Moments On Tour?
13 The Cheviot hills run along the boundary between which countries?
14 Which seeds are in the sweet, Halva?
15 What note does an orchestra tune to?
16 In which county is Damon Hill's mansion called Hydon End?
17 Which Shakespeare play was banned during George III's time of madness?
18 Before being used as a name for US soldiers, what did 'GI' stand for?
19 Who played Pauli in the TV series Liverpool One?
20 Which gas is produced by adding water to calcium carbide?
21 Which berries are used in a Cumberland sauce?
22 What is a wadi?
23 In which country is the Potomac River?
24 Which element has the highest melting point?
25 Which University did Jeffrey Archer attend?
26 Which part of a tree gives Angostura Bitters its taste?
27 What is the metric word for a million?
28 What is the southern American stew of rice and okra called?
29 Which famous pop guitarist performed with the Notting Hillbillies?
30 Whose catchphrase was "Hello my darlings"?

Movies: Animation (see Quiz 17, page 137)
1 Dance of the Hours. 2 Mel Gibson. 3 The Lion King. 4 The Return of Jafar.
5 White. 6 Dalmatians. 7 Eight. 8 Beauty and the Beast. 9 Thumper. 10
Louie. 11 Eva. 12 Hanna & Barbera. 13 He sneezed. 14 Cinderella. 15
Jessica Rabbit. 16 Steamboat Willie. 17 Pocahontas. 18 Bedknobs &
Broomsticks. 19 Peggy Lee. 20 Cool World. 21 Lea Salonga. 22 Teenage
Mutant Ninja Turtles. 23 Tron. 24 Dinosaur. 25 Aladdin. 26 Gene Kelly.
27 Nutcracker Suite. 28 Jungle Book. 29 Tom & Jerry. 30 Cats and dogs.

Answers

Quiz 19 Leisure: Books 1

LEVEL 2

Answers - see Quiz 20, page 140

1 Where according to The Bible is the site of the final battle between nations which will end the world?

2 In which Dickens novel did Uriah Heep appear?

3 Old Possum's Book of Practical Cats is composed of what?

4 To £5,000 how much do you receive for winning the Booker Prize?

5 In which book did John Braine introduce Joe Lampton?

6 What type of book is the OED?

7 What is the subject of Desmond Morris's The Naked Ape?

8 What type of books did Patricia Highsmith write?

9 Which detective first appeared in A Study in Scarlet in 1887?

10 In which Holy Book other than The Bible is there the Garden of Eden?

11 Which Gothic horror story has the alternative title The Modern Prometheus?

12 For what types of book is Samuel Pepys famous for?

13 Who wrote The Female Eunuch in 1970?

14 In which county were Jane Austen and Charles Dickens born?

15 Which former politician narrated the diaries of his dog Buster?

16 In Charlie and the Chocolate Factory, what is Charlie's surname?

17 Which ex jockey wrote a book of short stories called Field of Thirteen?

18 Whose horror stories include Carrie and The Shining?

19 According to the 1998 Guiness Book of Records, who is the most mentioned man on the Internet?

20 Who wrote Das Kapital?

21 How many lines are there in a limerick?

22 Which writer and politician bought poet Rupert Brooke's house?

23 Which fictional barrister was created by John Mortimer?

24 Whose first novel, A Woman of Substance became a best seller?

25 Which nonagenarian has written nearly 700 romantic novels?

26 The Day of the Jackal is about an assassination plot on whom?

27 For which Salman Rushdie book did the Ayatollah impose a fatwa?

28 Who wrote It's All Over Now after her brief marriage to Bill Wyman?

29 To five years, how old was Mary Wesley when her first bestseller was published?

30 Award winning novelist Ben Okri hails from which country?

Pot Luck 10 (see Quiz 20, page 140)
1 Cross Fell, Cumbria. 2 McLaren. 3 27. 4 Henry Cooper. 5 Their Mum. 6 Hyde Park. 7 Frank Bruno. 8 Phone cards. 9 Steve Davis. 10 Graeme Hick. 11 Sullivan. 12 Tottenham Hotspur. 13 20th. 14 Nevada. 15 Five. 16 Pavlova. 17 Volga. 18 Asparagus. 19 Clint Eastwood. 20 Mack Sennett. 21 Michael Henchard. 22 The alphabet. 23 Queen Mother's 90th birthday. 24 Montreux. 25 Rhodes. 26 Pickwick Papers. 27 Ferrari. 28 Lily. 29 Tea. 30 1960s.

Answers

Quiz 20 Pot Luck 10

1 What is the highest point of the Pennines?
2 What F1 team was James Hunt in when he won the World Championship?
3 How many years was Nelson Mandela held in prison?
4 Which British boxer was the first to win three Lonsdale belts outright?
5 Who, according to a NOP survey in 1998, do young men call most on their mobile phones?
6 In which London park is Rotten Row?
7 Who said, "Scared of Tyson? I'm more scared of your hair-do"?
8 What will a green phone kiosk only take for payment?
9 Which snooker star was nicknamed 'Interesting' by Spitting Image?
10 In 1988 who scored 405 not out at Taunton?
11 Who died first Gilbert or Sullivan?
12 Which was the first London football club to win a European title?
13 In which century did Joan of Arc become a saint?
14 Which American state is called the 'Gambling State'?
15 Did John Glenn's first spaceflight last five, ten or 24 hours?
16 Which dessert is named after a famous ballerina?
17 Which river flows from northern Moscow to the Caspian Sea?
18 A Bruxelloise sauce is flavoured with which vegetable?
19 Who was the leading actor in Play Misty for Me with Jessica Walker?
20 Who created the Keystone Cops?
21 Who was the Mayor of Casterbridge in the Thomas Hardy novel?
22 What does an alphabetarian study?
23 What occasioned the replacement of the Royal Variety Performance in 1990 with a concert?
24 In which Swiss resort are the Golden Rose TV accolades awarded?
25 Which island is the largest of the Dodecanese group?
26 In which Papers would you find Count Smorltork?
27 Which F1 team scored a 1-2 at Monza during the 1998 Italian GP?
28 To which flower family does garlic belong?
29 Which drink can be green, black and oolong?
30 In which decade was the first American Superbowl?

Answers

Leisure: Books 1 (see Quiz 19, page 139)
1 Armageddon. 2 David Copperfield. 3 Poems. 4 £20,000. 5 Room at the Top. 6 Dictionary. 7 Man. 8 Crime fiction. 9 Sherlock Holmes. 10 Al Koran. 11 Frankenstein. 12 Diary. 13 Germaine Greer. 14 Hampshire. 15 Roy Hattersley. 16 Buckett. 17 Dick Francis. 18 Stephen King. 19 Bill Clinton. 20 Karl Marx. 21 Five. 22 Jeffrey Archer. 23 Rumpole. 24 Barbara Taylor Bradford. 25 Barbara Cartland. 26 Charles de Gaulle. 27 The Satanic Verses. 28 Mandy Smith. 29 70. 30 Nigeria.

Quiz 21 Food & Drink 2

Answers - see Quiz 22, page 142

LEVEL 2

1   What colour is the flesh of a cantaloupe melon?
2   Simnel cake was traditionally eaten on which Sunday?
3   What is the fishy ingredient in Scotch woodcock?
4   What is a champignon?
5   Which spirit is Russia famous for producing?
6   Which drink did Paul Hogan advertise?
7   What is added to pasta to make it green?
8   Which drink is grown in the Douro basin and exported from Oporto?
9   Which cooking pot boils food at a higher temperature than boiling point?
10 What is another name for dietary fibre?
11 Which sauce/salad shares its name with Latin big band music?
12 Where did satsumas originate?
13 What are cornichons?
14 Puerto Rico and Jamaica are the main producers of which spirit?
15 What colour is cayenne pepper?
16 What type of pastry is used to make a steak and kidney pudding?
17 Which drink is served in a schooner?
18 What is a Laxton's Superb?
19 Which seafood, usually fried in breadcrumbs, is the Italian name for shrimps?
20 Tofu and TVP come from which bean?
21 Tartrazine colours food which colour?
22 What is added to whisky to make a whisky mac?
23 Where would you buy a pint of Shires?
24 What colour is Double Gloucester cheese?
25 Which Mexican drink is distilled from the agave plant?
26 Which black, gourmet fungus is a native of France's Perigord region?
27 Which expensive vinegar is aged in wooden barrels?
28 Which grain is whisky made from?
29 What is red wine made with that white wine is not?
30 Vermouth is wine flavoured with what?

TV: Children's TV (see Quiz 22, page 142)
1 Sesame Street. 2 Keith Chegwin. 3 Play School. 4 Jamie Theakston.
5 Lulu. 6 Doctor. 7 Live & Kicking. 8 Johnny Ball (Zoe). 9 Grange Hill.
10 Janet Street-Porter. 11 Dr Who. 12 The Top Ten of Everything. 13 Blue & white stripes. 14 Basil Brush. 15 Richard Briers. 16 Flag. 17 Home Hill.
18 Ed Stewart. 19 Fred Flintstone. 20 Neil Buchanan. 21 Tony Hart.
22 Fred Dineage. 23 Playdays. 24 He-Man. 25 Blue. 26 Poddington Peas.
27 Greendale. 28 Snake. 29 Rainbow. 30 David Jason.

Answers

Quiz 22 TV: Children's TV

LEVEL 2

Answers - see Quiz 21, page 141

1 On which show did The Muppets first regularly appear?
2 Which star of Swop Shop and Saturday Superstore went to the same university as Bill Clinton?
3 In which show was Humpty a regular feature?
4 Who presented Live and Kicking with Zoe Ball?
5 What was the name of elephant who disgraced herself on Blue Peter?
6 What is the profession of Newsround's David Bull?
7 Rugrats appears within which other programme?
8 Which former Play School presenter has a famous DJ daughter?
9 Tucker's Luck was a spin off from which drama series?
10 Who was executive director of 'yoof TV's' Def II?
11 Which sci fi series hit the screens at teatime the day after Kennedy was assassinated?
12 Which best selling book by Russell Ash was turned into a TV show?
13 What colour was Andy Pandy's suit?
14 Which puppet fox had the catchphrase "Boom boom"?
15 Which Good Life star narrated Roobarb and Custard?
16 Other than a TV show what is a Blue Peter?
17 Where do The Teletubbies live?
18 Which ex Crackerjack presenter now has a daily show on Radio 2?
19 Whose catchphrase is "Yabba dabba doo!"?
20 Which Neil has presented Art Attack?
21 Which TV artist designed the Blue Peter logo?
22 Who has presented How and How 2?
23 Which show has a Poppy Stop?
24 Which hero did Prince Adam turn into with the aid of power from Greyskull castle?
25 What colour are Smurfs?
26 In which show would you see Zip-Pea?
27 Where is the Rev Timms' parish in Postman Pat?
28 What sort of creature is Sooty's friend Ramsbottom?
29 Rod, Jane and Freddy was a spin off from which children's series?
30 Who was the voice of Dangermouse?

Answers

Leisure: Food & Drink 2 (see Quiz 21, page 141)
1 Orange. 2 Mothering Sunday. 3 Anchovies. 4 Mushroom. 5 Vodka.
6 Foster's lager. 7 Spinach. 8 Port. 9 Pressure cooker. 10 Roughage.
11 Salsa. 12 Japan. 13 Gherkins (pickled cucumbers). 14 Rum. 15 Red.
16 Suet pastry. 17 Sherry. 18 Apple. 19 Scampi. 20 Soya. 21 Yellow.
22 Ginger wine. 23 Ambridge. 24 Orange-red. 25 Tequila. 26 Truffle.
27 Balsamic. 28 Malted barley. 29 Skins of the grape. 30 Bitter herbs.

Quiz 23 Pot Luck 11

LEVEL 2

Answers - see Quiz 24, page 144

1 Who supposedly brought about the downfall of Barings Bank?
2 Which country was the first to legalise abortion?
3 Which Eurovision winning group formed the Polar Music Company?
4 In 1954, which Chris won the first BBC Sports Personality of the Year?
5 Mount Elbert is the highest peak in which American mountain range?
6 Adam and Eve were the main characters in which work by John Milton?
7 In 1992, London and which other English city were home to over a million people?
8 Whose murder conviction was overturned after 45 years in 1998?
9 Which famous riding school is in Austria?
10 What colour traditionally is an Indian wedding sari?
11 Which county first won the Benson and Hedges Cricket Cup twice?
12 Which Copenhagen statue is a memorial to Hans Christian Andersen?
13 Which Derbyshire town is famous for the church with a crooked spire?
14 The Parthenon in Athens was built as a temple to whom?
15 Martin Fry and Mark White were members of which 1980s band?
16 Which glands produce white blood cells?
17 What sort of creature is a guillemot?
18 What was the first film Bogart and Bacall starred in together?
19 Which Norfolk model advertises L'Oreal Elvive hair products?
20 Which girl's name gave the Damned their only top ten hit?
21 Which chess piece can only move diagonally?
22 Which gentle water creature gives its name to a Florida river?
23 William 'Fatty' Foulkes played which sport?
24 Which oil company was founded by John D Rockefeller?
25 At which Southwark inn did Chaucer's Canterbury Pilgrims meet?
26 Joseph Marie Jacquard is most remembered for which invention?
27 Before Winston Churchill went bald, what colour was his hair?
28 The word micro is what fraction in the metric system?
29 Which county included W. G. Grace as a team member?
30 Which musical instrument was first developed by Bartolomeo Cristofori?

Answers

Past Law & Order (see Quiz 24, page 144)
1 Haiti. 2 Bluebeard. 3 20th (1941). 4 Ruth Ellis. 5 Dr Crippen. 6 Philip Lawrence. 7 Official Secrets Act. 8 Lester Piggott. 9 Slavery. 10 Director of Public Prosecutions. 11 Cape Town. 12 St Valentine's Day. 13 Nick Leeson. 14 Michael Howard. 15 Iceland. 16 Back To Basics. 17 Treason. 18 Colditz. 19 Ethiopia didn't have electricity. 20 Cromwell Street. 21 Richard I. 22 Jack Straw. 23 Louise Woodward. 24 Road rage attack. 25 Robert Maxwell. 26 Peter Sutcliffe. 27 The Butcher of Lyon. 28 The Ritz. 29 Saudi Arabia. 30 The Clintons.

Quiz 24 Past Law & Order

LEVEL 2

Answers - see Quiz 23, page 143

1 Which country had the private security force the Tontons Macoutes?
2 What was the nickname of mass murderer Gilles de Rais who killed six of his seven wives?
3 In which century was the last execution at the Tower of London?
4 Which woman was hanged in 1955 for murdering David Blakely?
5 Cora was the wife of which doctor who murdered her?
6 In the 90s which London head teacher was killed outside his school?
7 Which Act bans the disclosure of confidential items from government sources by its employees?
8 Which world famous jockey was jailed in 1987 for tax evasion?
9 What did abolitionism seek to abolish?
10 What is the DPP, a post created in 1985?
11 Robben Island was a prison near which city?
12 Which Day saw seven of Bugs Moran's gang murdered by members of Al Capone's, disguised as policemen?
13 Whose crime was recounted in the film Rogue Trader?
14 Which ex Home Secretary spent a night behind bars in October '98?
15 The Althing is the parliament of which country?
16 Which phrase used by John Major in 1993 was used as a slogan to return to traditional British values?
17 In 1965 capital punishment was abolished except for which crime?
18 How was the prison camp Oflag IVC near Leipzig better known?
19 In what way was Ethiopian Emperor Menelik III thwarted in bringing the electric chair to his country?
20 What was the Gloucester street where Rose & Frederick West lived?
21 Robin Hood is said to have lived in Sherwood Forest during the reign of which king?
22 Which Home Secretary took his son to the police after allegations of drug selling?
23 Which British nanny's US trial was televised after a baby died in her care?
24 Why was the death of Stephen Cameron in 1996 a tragic first?
25 Who fell from the Lady Ghislaine leaving debts behind him?
26 What is the real name of the criminal dubbed The Yorkshire Ripper?
27 What was the nickname of Nazi war criminal Klaus Barbie?
28 Jonathan Aitken's court case centred on a stay in which Paris hotel?
29 Where had Deborah Parry been imprisoned before her return in '98?
30 In the US whose involvement in the Whitewater affair had lengthy repercussions?

Pot Luck 11 (see Quiz 23, page 143)
1 Nick Leeson. 2 Iceland. 3 Abba. 4 Chris Chataway. 5 The Rockies. 6 Paradise Lost. 7 Birmingham. 8 Derek Bentley. 9 The Spanish Riding School. 10 Scarlet. 11 Leicestershire. 12 The Little Mermaid. 13 Chesterfield. 14 Athena. 15 ABC. 16 Lymph glands. 17 Bird. 18 To Have and Have Not. 19 Kate Moss. 20 Eloise. 21 The Bishop. 22 The Manatee. 23 Football. 24 Standard Oil. 25 The Tabard Inn. 26 The Jacquard loom. 27 Red. 28 A millionth. 29 Gloucestershire. 30 The piano.

Answers

Quiz 25 Pot Luck 12

LEVEL 2

Answers - see Quiz 26, page 146

1 What nationality was the spy Mata Hari?
2 The Dickens' work Edwin Drood is different for what reason?
3 Which Australian soap star had the biggest selling UK single in 1988?
4 What were the Boston Tea Party protesters against?
5 What is a Wessex Saddleback?
6 Which former Olympian advertised Ribena?
7 Lyncanthropy involves men changing into what?
8 Which city's American football team is known as the Vikings?
9 Queen Wilhelmina who died in 1962 was Queen of which country?
10 The pop band America were formed in which country?
11 In curling how many shots at the target is each player allowed?
12 What was Janet Street-Porter's beastly last name before marriage?
13 Which Band Aid No 1 hit was written by Midge Ure and Bob Geldof?
14 What was the capital of West Germany?
15 Which American symbol was famously painted by Jasper Johns?
16 In fencing how many hits must a male fencer score for a win?
17 In gin rummy how many cards are dealt per player?
18 What nationality was the inventor of the Geiger counter?
19 Before it moved to Wales on which London hill was the Royal Mint?
20 In which century was the first circumnavigation of the earth?
21 Which is further south, Cardiff or Oxford?
22 Which river rises in the Black Forest?
23 Which road vehicle takes its name from the Hindu God Jagganath?
24 In which South American country is the condor sacred?
25 The first modern Olympics were held in which city?
26 Which East Anglian Cathedral spire is second highest in the country?
27 What have you on your mouth if you suffer from herpes labialis?
28 Prince Edward resigned from which part of the military in 1987?
29 Mike Burden is the sidekick to which TV detective?
30 What was Fred Wedlock according to the title of his one off hit?

Answers

Communications (see Quiz 26, page 146)
1 Stansted. 2 Leeds. 3 Philips. 4 Decibel. 5 British Airways. 6 Telephone
handset. 7 Trans Siberian. 8 Paris. 9 999 service. 10 Nothing. 11 £500.
12 Acoustics. 13 The Speaking Clock. 14 Swiftair. 15 Video Cassette
Recorder. 16 USA. 17 FBI's. 18 Derbyshire. 19 A12. 20 ADA.
21 Dundee. 22 Grand Canal. 23 Alaska. 24 A. 25 M62. 26 Some
insects. 27 8. 28 Moscow. 29 Madam Mayor. 30 Channel Tunnel.

Quiz 26 Communications

LEVEL 2

1   What is Britain's third largest airport?
2   Which northern city has the dialling code 0113?
3   Which company launched the CD-i in 1992?
4   dB is the symbol for what?
5   Which major company owns the budget airline Go?
6   An acoustic coupler allows computer data to be transmitted through what?
7   Which railway links European Russia with the Pacific?
8   Which city linked up with London by phone in 1891?
9   Which vital communications linked began in July 1937?
10 How much is the maximum charge for postage in Andorra?
11 What is the maximum compensation offered by Royal Mail on their Registered service?
12 What is the science of sound and its transmission called?
13 What is another name for Timeline?
14 What is the Royal Mail's express airmail service called?
15 What is a VCR?
16 Which country has the most telephone subscribers?
17 On whose website did Leslie Ibsen Rogge appear, leading to his arrest?
18 In which county is East Midlands airport?
19 Which A road links London with East Anglia?
20 Which computer language was named after Ada Augusta Byron?
21 Which is the nearest city to the Tay road bridge?
22 Which waterway does Venice's Rialto bridge span?
23 Which state is the northern terminus of the Pan American highway?
24 In France all motorways begin with which letter?
25 Which motorway links Hull and Leeds?
26 Which living creatures can you send through the post?
27 How many bits are there in a byte?
28 In which city is the TASS news agency based?
29 How would you verbally address a Mayor who is a woman?
30 Which tunnel goes from Cheriton to Sargette?

Answers

Pot Luck 12 (see Quiz 25, page 145)
1 Dutch. 2 It is not finished. 3 Kylie Minogue. 4 Tea taxes. 5 Pig.
6 Sharron Davies. 7 Wolves. 8 Minnesota. 9 Holland. 10 England. 11 2.
12 Bull. 13 Do They Know its Christmas. 14 Bonn. 15 The stars & stripes.
16 Five. 17 10. 18 German. 19 Tower Hill. 20 16th. 21 Cardiff.
22 Danube. 23 Juggernaut. 24 Peru. 25 Athens. 26 Norwich. 27 Cold
Sores. 28 The Marines. 29 Reg Wexford. 30 The Oldest Swinger in Town.

Quiz 27 Pot Luck 13

Answers - see Quiz 28, page 148

1   Who had a No 1 UK hit with The Reflex?
2   In English what is the only anagram of the word ENGLISH?
3   Which rules are American football played to?
4   In which South African city was the 1995 Rugby Union World Cup Final?
5   Which musical was based on the play Pygmalion?
6   If you suffer from bulimia, what do you have a compulsive urge to do?
7   Who is Boo-Boo's best friend?
8   Which triangular shaped Indian pastry contains meat or vegetables?
9   Which part of Spain is named after its many castles?
10 The range of the pH scale is zero to what?
11 Which everyday objects can be decorated with the King's Pattern?
12 Stage performer Boy Bruce the Mighty Atom became known as who?
13 Which Russian word means "speaking aloud"?
14 Which Top Ten "ride" was taken by the group Roxette?
15 What is the name of the world's largest Gulf?
16 Which actor played Selwyn Froggatt on TV?
17 Ouzo is what flavour?
18 What does a trishaw driver do with his legs?
19 Which hospital did TV Doctor Kildare work at?
20 Which is the slowest swimming stroke?
21 What is the best selling single of all time?
22 What does E stand for in "E-numbers"?
23 In Peter Pan which part of Peter was kept in a drawer?
24 What word links an ice cream holder and a brass instrument?
25 The thistle is the heraldic emblem of which country?
26 What is the middle name of Princess Margaret?
27 What is the epicarp of an orange?
28 Which character was played by Ken Kercheval in Dallas?
29 Which three Time Travel films were directed by Robert Zemeckis?
30 Which European country has the only active volcanoes in Europe?

Answers

Pop Music: The 70s (see Quiz 28, page 148)
1 Love Me For A Reason. 2 Pigeon. 3 Cher . 4 Eddie Holman. 5 Dawn.
6 The Pina Colada Song. 7 Heart. 8 Squeeze. 9 January. 10 The Kinks.
11 10538. 12 Matthews Southern Comfort. 13 Girls. 14 On My Radio. 15
The Floral Dance. 16 Minnie Riperton. 17 Sweet Sensation. 18 Paul Simon.
19 Nathan Jones. 20 B A Robertson. 21 Rainbow. 22 New York. 23
Samantha. 24 Summer Nights. 25 The Commodores. 26 Rivers of Babylon.
27 Midnight. 28 In The Summertime. 29 Donna Summer. 30 Eye Level.

Quiz 28 Pop Music: The 70s LEVEL 2

Answers - see Quiz 27, page 147

1 Which 70s hit by the Osmonds gave Boyzone a hit in '94?
2 Which Lieutenant's only UK No 1 hit was Mouldy Old Dough ?
3 Who sang that she was 'born in the wagon of a travelling show'?
4 (Hey There) Lonely Girl was the only UK hit for which vocalist?
5 Tony Orlando sang in which group that had a girl's name?
6 Rupert Holmes' 1980 No 23 hit Escape is also known as what?
7 Which part of the body was mentioned in the title of a Blondie hit?
8 Who were Up The Junction in 1979?
9 Which month links Pilot and part of a song title for Barbara Dickson?
10 Whose hits from 1970 include Victoria and Apeman?
11 What was the number of ELO's Overture in their first hit?
12 The No 1 UK hit Woodstock was a one hit wonder for which group?
13 What Talk gave Dave Edmunds his 1979 No 4 UK hit?
14 What in 1979 was the only Top Ten hit by the group Selector?
15 What links Terry Wogan and the Brighouse and Rastrick Brass Band?
16 Loving You was a high pitched No 2 UK hit for which female singer?
17 Which group had a No 1 UK hit with Sad Sweet Dreamer?
18 Who wanted to be taken to the Mardi Gras?
19 Which 1971 Supremes hit was later a hit for Bananarama?
20 Who had hits with Bang Bang and Knocked It Off in 1979?
21 The 1979 No 6 hit Since You've Been Gone was a hit for who?
22 Which US city was named twice in a Gerard Kenny hit from 1978?
23 Who did Cliff Richard say Hello to when he said Goodbye to Sam?
24 In which song do the chorus beg, "Tell me more, tell me more!"?
25 Which group had hits in the 70s with Easy, Still and Sail On?
26 What was on the other side of Boney M's Brown Girl In The Ring?
27 What time was Gladys Knight's train leaving for Georgia?
28 Which Mungo Jerry hit was used in an anti drink-drive campaign?
29 Which disco style singer had the word Love in the title of four of her first five Top Ten hits?
30 Which No1 from 1972 was the theme for the Van Der Valk series?

Pot Luck 13 (see Quiz 27 page 147)
1 Duran Duran. 2 Shingle. 3 The Harvard rules. 4 Johannesburg. 5 My Fair Lady. 6 Eat. 7 Yogi Bear. 8 Samosa. 9 Castile. 10 Fourteen. 11 Cutlery. 12 Bruce Forsyth. 13 Glasnost. 14 Joyride. 15 Gulf of Mexico. 16 Bill Maynard. 17 Aniseed. 18 Pedal. 19 Blair Hospital. 20 Breast stroke. 21 Candle In The Wind (1997). 22 European. 23 His shadow. 24 Cornet. 25 Scotland. 26 Rose. 27 The peel. 28 Cliff Barnes. 29 Back to the Future. 30 Italy.

Answers

Quiz 29 Pot Luck 14

Answers - see Quiz 30, page 150

LEVEL 2

1 If a bridge player has a Yarborough, what is the top scoring card?
2 In the film Batman Forever, which actor played Batman?
3 In the Grand National, how many times did Red Rum run?
4 Which was the first railway terminus in London?
5 Which term is used when a mortgage is more than the value of a house?
6 Whose hits include Slave to Love and This is Tomorrow?
7 What is a Clouded Yellow?
8 How was Agatha Miller better known?
9 El Paso is in which American state?
10 Which road leads from Westminster to Blackfriars along the north bank of the Thames?
11 The first player to score 100 Premier League goals played for which club?
12 In which board game is FIDE the governing body?
13 Which colour links an imperial butterfly and a medal?
14 In which year did TV soap EastEnders first appear?
15 What is the Mirror of Diana, located in Northern Italy?
16 Beta Vulgaris is the Latin name for which crop?
17 Which film featured the Joe Cocker hit Up Where We Belong?
18 Who wrote the opera from which Here Comes the Bride is taken?
19 Lime Street Station is in which English city?
20 Cars with the international vehicle registration IS come from where?
21 Which magazine, established in 1922, claims to be the most widely read in the world?
22 What happened to Ken Barlow's second wife in Coronation Street?
23 What type of fruit is a Laxton Superb?
24 Which airport is near to the English city of Carlisle?
25 A sericulturist breeds which creatures?
26 Who played the young Emma Harte in A Woman of Substance?
27 What term describes the fineness of yarns?
28 Where do mice live who are proverbially poor?
29 Joseph Grimaldi achieved everlasting fame as what?
30 Who made history in 1982 by going to an Anglican service in Canterbury Cathedral?

Answers

World Football (see Quiz 30, page 150)
1 Japan. 2 Lazio. 3 Ruud Gullit. 4 Gary Lineker. 5 Australia. 6 Croatia.
7 Barcelona. 8 Prague. 9 Tenerife. 10 Mario Zagallo. 11 Benfica.
12 Germany. 13 Davor Suker. 14 Argentina. 15 Roger Milla. 16 Uraguay.
17 Gerard Houllier. 18 Edson Arrentes do Nascimento. 19 Italy. 20 Brazil.
21 Emmanuel Petit. 22 Ronaldo's. 23 Raddy Antic. 24 Dennis Bergkamp.
25 Matthias Sammer. 26 St Denis. 27 Dunga. 28 Stanley Matthews.
29 FC Copenhagen. 30 Alexi Lalas.

LEVEL 2

1   In which country is the club Grampus Eight?
2   Which Italian team did Gazza play for?
3   Who was Dutch captain when they won the European Championship in 1988?
4   Who was leading scorer in the 1986 World Cup finals?
5   Which international side did Venables manage after England?
6   Who won the third place final in the 1998 World Cup?
7   Which side did Cruyff move to from Ajax in 1973?
8   Dukla and Sparta are from which European city?
9   Where did Emerson go when he left Middlesborough?
10 Which Brazilian football coach was sacked after France '98?
11 Which Portuguese side did Graeme Souness manage?
12 Which country ran a full page 'thank you' ad in The Times after Euro 96?
13 Who won the Golden Boot in the 1998 world cup?
14 Cesar Menotti managed which victorious World Cup side?
15 Who is the oldest player ever to score in the world cup finals?
16 Penarol is a club side in which country?
17 Which Frenchman moved to Liverpool when Ronnie Moran retired?
18 What is Pele's full name?
19 Who, with England and Holland, was eliminated from France 98 on penalties?
20 In which country is the world's largest football stadium?
21 Who scored the last goal in France 98?
22 Whose much seen girlfriend in France 98 was Suzana Werner?
23 Which Yugoslavian international midfielder played for Luton Town?
24 Which overseas star won most Premiership player of the month awards in 1997-98?
25 Which German won European Player of the Year in 1996?
26 In which stadium was the opening match of France 98?
27 Who captained Brazil in the 98 World Cup Finals?
28 Who was the first European Footballer of the Year?
29 Which club did Brian Laudrup transfer to in November 1998?
30 Which US star of the 94 World Cup became the first American player to take part in Italy's Serie A?

Pot Luck 14 (see Quiz 29, page 149)
1 Nine. 2 Val Kilmer. 3 Five. 4 Euston Station. 5 Negative equity.
6 Bryan Ferry's. 7 A Butterfly. 8 Agatha Christie. 9 Texas. 10 The
Embankment. 11 Blackburn (Alan Shearer). 12 Chess. 13 Purple. 14 1985.
15 A lake. 16 Sugar beet. 17 An Officer and a Gentleman. 18 Wagner.
19 Liverpool. 20 Iceland. 21 Reader's Digest. 22 She committed suicide.
23 An apple. 24 Crosby. 25 Silkworms. 26 Jenny Seagrove. 27 Denier.
28 Church. 29 A clown. 30 The Pope.

Quiz 31 Pot Luck 15

Answers - see Quiz 32, page 152

LEVEL 2

1   In which UK city was the de Lorean sports car factory set up in '78?
2   The TV show It'll Be Alright on the Night is presented by whom?
3   Which group had a No 1 UK hit in 1992 with Ebenezer Goode?
4   In which sport were Jack Broughton and James Figg champions?
5   Which Aldous Huxley novel is set in the seventh century AF?
6   Which instrument was Jose Feliciano famous for playing?
7   Which Queen was played in films by Jean Simmons and Bette Davis?
8   Which actor links Chancer, Chariots of Fire and The Whistle Blower?
9   Which musical instruments represent Peter in Peter and the Wolf?
10 Which WPC was shot and murdered at the Libyan Embassy?
11 A glaive was what kind of weapon?
12 In which century was the first Indianapolis 500 first held?
13 In which country do soldiers wear skirts called fustanella?
14 What can be done if an object is scissile?
15 Which film studios were founded by Harry, Sam, Albert and Jack?
16 Which word can describe a listening device, an illness and an insect?
17 Which famous actress starred in Courage of Lassie and Lassie Come Home?
18 Who was older when they died, Benny Hill or Richard Burton?
19 Who did Mark Hughes join when he left Man Utd for a second time?
20 What type of fruit is a jargonelle?
21 Which part of the head is studied by a phrenologist?
22 Whose ancestral home is Woburn Abbey?
23 Who wrote the poem Four Quartets?
24 Which children's game is played on the fingers with looped string?
25 Jane Harris and Nel Mangel appeared in which soap?
26 Brassica Rapa is the Latin name for which vegetable?
27 Which band's hits include Infinite Dreams and Holy Smoke?
28 Which Generation Game assistant was born on the same day as Julian Lloyd Webber?
29 Excess bile pigment in the bloodstream causes which illness?
30 Who was Dennis Bergkamp named after?

Blockbusters (see Quiz 32, page 152)
1 Five. 2 Chocolate. 3 The Robe 4 Francis Ford Coppola. 5 Normandy.
6 M*A*S*H. 7 Hearst. 8 Crocodile Dundee. 9 Gary Oldman. 10 Midnight
Cowboy. 11 Dan Aykroyd. 12 The English Patient. 13 Vito Corleone.
14 Pierce Brosnan. 15 Ron Kovic. 16 Gone With the Wind. 17 Wall Street.
18 Braveheart. 19 Dune. 20 John Huston. 21 Terminator II. 22 Austrian.
23 All About Eve. 24 1930s. 25 Goldblum. 26 Jim Carrey. 27 Carrie Fisher.
28 Celine Dion. 29 Judi Dench. 30 Cop.

Quiz 32 Blockbusters

Answers - see Quiz 31, page 131

LEVEL 2

1   How many crew members were there in the Nostromo in Alien?
2   What type of sauce was used in the shower scene in Psycho?
3   Which 1953 film was the first made in Cinemascope?
4   Who directed The Godfather and all its sequels?
5   Saving Private Ryan dealt with events in which part of France?
6   Which antiwar comedy did Robert Altman direct?
7   Which newspaper magnate was said to be the model for Orson Welles' Citizen Kane?
8   Which 80s film was the most profitable in Australian history?
9   Who played The Count in Bram Stoker's Dracula?
10 What was John Schlesinger's first US film, made in 1969 with Dustin Hoffman and Jon Voight?
11 Who starred in, and co wrote Ghostbusters?
12 Which film starred Juliette Binoche and Kristin Scott Thomas?
13 What was the name of Marlon Brando's character in The Godfather?
14 Which James Bond actor starred in Dante's Peak?
15 What was the name of Tom Cruise's character in Born on the Fourth of July?
16 In which classic did Olivia de Havilland play Melanie Wilkes?
17 In which film did Michael Douglas say "Greed is good"?
18 What was Mel Gibson's first film as actor, director and producer?
19 Which David Lynch space epic was based on the work of Frank Herbert?
20 Who was directing The African Queen when his daughter Anjelica was born?
21 Which sequel had the subtitle Judgement Day?
22 What is Schindler's nationality in Schindler's List?
23 What was the last film before Titanic to win 14 Oscar nominations?
24 In which decade was Gone With the Wind made?
25 Which Jeff was the mathematician in Jurassic Park?
26 Who became a human cartoon in The Mask?
27 Who played Princess Leia in the Star Wars Trilogy?
28 Who sang the theme song for Titanic?
29 Who was M in Tomorrow Never Dies?
30 What was Michael Douglas' profession in Basic Instinct?

Pot Luck 15 (see Quiz 31, page 151)

Answers
1 Belfast. 2 Denis Norden. 3 The Shamen. 4 Boxing. 5 Brave New World.
6 Guitar. 7 Elizabeth I. 8 Nigel Havers. 9 Violins. 10 Yvonne Fletcher.
11 A sword. 12 20th. 13 Greece. 14 It can be cut. 15 Warner Brothers.
16 A bug. 17 Elizabeth Taylor. 18 Richard Burton. 19 Chelsea. 20 A pear.
21 The skull. 22 Dukes of Bedford. 23 T.S. Eliot. 24 Cat's Cradle.
25 Neighbours. 26 Turnip. 27 Iron Maiden. 28 Anthea Redfern.
29 Jaundice. 30 Denis Law.

Quiz 33 TV: Cops & Robbers

LEVEL 2

Answers - see Quiz 34, page 154

1 Which TV cop was christened Ilynea Lydia Mironoff?
2 In the title of the program, what shows Life on the Streets?
3 Which show features DCI Michael Jardine?
4 What was Paul Nicholls' first major series after leaving EastEnders?
5 Who was Don Johnson's character in Miami Vice?
6 What was the name of law enforcer Michael Knight's computer buddy?
7 Which show consists of films of dangerous driving shot by traffic police?
8 Which series featured the Wentworth Detention Centre?
9 Who played the TV Avengers role played by Uma Thurman on the big screen?
10 Which member of the Ruth Rendell Mysteries cast also scripted some of the shows?
11 In which series did the character Charlie Barlow first find fame?
12 Which Blue Peter presenter played Dangerfield's son in the police surgeon series?
13 In which 90s series did Neil Pearson star as Det Sup Tony Clark?
14 In which police station was Frank Farillo the chief?
15 What was Fitz's full name in Cracker?
16 Peter Falk played which offbeat TV cop?
17 Which real crime series was based on the German File XY Unsolved?
18 In which series did Rowan Atkinson appear as a police officer?
19 Who was the British half of Dempsey and Makepeace?
20 Which long-running show increased the length of episodes in 1998 to one hour in a bid to improve ratings?
21 Stacey Keach played which detective from Mickey Spillane's novels?
22 The Body in the Library was the first in an 80s series about which sleuth?
23 Which series began with an Armchair Theatre production Regan?
24 Loretta Swit from M*A*S*H was replaced by Sharon Gless in which US series?
25 Who played barrister Kavanagh in the TV series?
26 Which detective was based at Denton police station?
27 How long did the Morse episodes usually last?
28 In which series did Samantha Janus star as Isobel de Pauli?
29 In which series did Charlie Hungerford appear?
30 Which series was based on the Constable novels by Nicholas Rea?

Answers

Pot Luck 16 (see Quiz 34, page 154)
1 Hamlet. 2 Liverpool. 3 Take That. 4 Surrey. 5 Elizabeth I.
6 Argentinean. 7 Tutti Frutti. 8 A boat. 9 Rockall. 10 Portillo. 11 Fox.
12 Rudyard Kipling. 13 Van Gogh. 14 Trams. 15 George I. 16 Johnny
Dankworth. 17 Chaka Khan. 18 Martyn Lewis. 19 Stirling Moss. 20 Michel
Platini. 21 Scurvy. 22 Household linen. 23 Glucose. 24 Sheridan.
25 Cinzano. 26 Best Supporting Actress. 27 July, August. 28 Fairy tales.
29 Epiglottis. 30 Much.

Quiz 34 Pot Luck 16

Answers - see Quiz 33, page 153

LEVEL 2

1 In which Shakespeare play does a ghost walk on the battlements?
2 Which city did comedian Tommy Handley come from?
3 Which group had No 1 hits with Babe and Pray in 1993?
4 Charterhouse Public School is found in which county?
5 Miranda Richardson played who in the second Blackadder series?
6 What nationality is Javier Frana, the tennis player?
7 Which 1987 TV series featured the ageing rock band The Majestics?
8 What is a gallivat?
9 Which British island is 230 miles west of the Hebrides in the Atlantic?
10 Which Michael lost his Enfield seat in the 1997 general election?
11 A skulk is the collective name for a group of which animal?
12 Who wrote How the Leopard Got His Spots?
13 Who painted the picture called Irises?
14 On which forms of transport would you find knifeboards?
15 Handel's Water Music was composed for which English King?
16 Who is Cleo Laine's bandleader husband?
17 Who had UK hits with Ain't Nobody and I'm Every Woman?
18 Which BBC newsreader advertised Cow & Gate baby food as a child?
19 Which racing driver appeared in the film Casino Royale?
20 From 1983-85 which Frenchman was European Footballer of the Year?
21 What disease are you suffering if you are scorbutic?
22 If you bought something in a white sale, what would you be buying?
23 What is the other name for grape-sugar?
24 Who wrote the play The School for Scandal?
25 Which drink was advertised by Joan Collins and Leonard Rossiter?
26 The film The Piano received Oscars for Best Actress and Best what?
27 In a single calendar year which two consecutive months total most days?
28 What did Charles Perrault collect?
29 Which flap of cartilage prevents food from entering your windpipe?
30 Which member of Robin Hood's gang was the son of a miller?

Answers

TV: Cops & Robbers (see Quiz 33, page 153)
1 Helen Mirren. 2 Homicide. 3 Taggart. 4 City Central. 5 Sonny Crockett.
6 KITT. 7 Police, Camera, Action!. 8 Prisoner Cell Block H. 9 Diana Rigg.
10 George Baker. 11 Z Cars. 12 Tim Vincent. 13 Between the Lines.
14 Hill St. 15 Eddie Fitzgerald. 16 Columbo. 17 Crimewatch UK. 18 The
Thin Blue Line. 19 Makepeace. 20 The Bill. 21 Mike Hammer. 22 Miss
Marple. 23 The Sweeney. 24 Cagney & Lacey. 25 John Thaw. 26 Jack
Frost. 27 Two hours. 28 Liverpool One. 29 Bergerac. 30 Heartbeat.

Quiz 35 Euro Tour

Answers - see Quiz 36, page 156

LEVEL 2

1   What are the three Baltic states?
2   In which country does the Douro reach the Atlantic?
3   What is the capital of Catalonia?
4   What is Northern Ireland's chief non edible agricultural product?
5   What do the Germans call Bavaria?
6   Which European capital stands on the river Liffey?
7   What is the Eiffel Tower made from?
8   How is the Danish region of Jylland known in English?
9   In which forest does the Danube rise?
10 Which was the first country to legalise voluntary euthanasia?
11 What covers most of Finland?
12 In which country is the world's highest dam?
13 What is the capital of the Ukraine?
14 What is a remarkable feature of the caves at Lascaux in SW France?
15 What is Europe's highest capital city?
16 Where is France's Tomb of the Unknown Soldier?
17 Which area of the Rhone delta is famous for its nature reserve?
18 In which country would you find Kerkyra?
19 What are the two official European languages of Luxembourg?
20 The Magyars are the largest ethnic group of which country?
21 Where is Castilian an official language?
22 Abruzzi is a mountainous region of which country?
23 Which is the largest of the Balearic Islands?
24 On which island was the Mafia founded?
25 What is the UK's chief Atlantic port?
26 Tallinn is the capital of which Baltic state?
27 What is the main religion of Albania?
28 In which country would you meet Walloons?
29 What is the official residence of the French President?
30 Where in Britain is Europe's second tallest building?

Pot Luck 17 (see Quiz 36, page 156)

Answers

Pot Luck 17 (see Quiz 36, page 156)
1 Matt Frewer. 2 Culture Club. 3 Keith. 4 High Chapparal. 5 Midsummer Day. 6 Ronnie Biggs. 7 Elvis Presley. 8 Mary Quant. 9 Ice skating. 10 Henry Crabbe. 11 Hedges and shrubs. 12 Michael Caine. 13 Saint Swithin. 14 C & F. 15 A vaulting horse. 16 Cricket. 17 A fox. 18 A tub of lard. 19 Isle of Man. 20 Correct English. 21 1,440. 22 Dr Hook. 23 A duck. 24 Hurdles. 25 Idaho. 26 The Winchester. 27 Brunel. 28 Griffith. 29 Spiders. 30 Paul Young.

Quiz 36 Pot Luck 17

LEVEL 2

Answers - see Quiz 35, page 155

1   Which actor played the TV android Max Headroom?
2   Whose hits include Victims and Church of the Poison Mind?
3   What is Rupert Murdoch's first name?
4   Which ranch was owned by John Cannon?
5   In a calendar year what is the second quarter day in England?
6   Which robber on the run was in the film The Great Rock and Roll Swindle?
7   Who was older when they died John Lennon or Elvis Presley?
8   Which fashion designer opened a shop in 1957 called Bazaar?
9   In which sport would you find a movement called a Salchow?
10 What is the name of the detective in Pie In The Sky?
11 What material does a topiarist work with?
12 Which actor was Rita's tutor in the film Educating Rita?
13 Which Saint has 15th July as his Feast Day?
14 Which two musical notes do not have flats on black keys?
15 In The Wooden Horse what was used to disguise the digging of an escape tunnel?
16 Sabina Park is most famous for which sport?
17 Which animal can be described as vulpine?
18 In Have I Got News for You what stood in for Roy Hattersley ?
19 Where are Union Mills and Onchan Head in the British Isles?
20 Author H.W. Fowler produced a book in 1926 as a guide to what?
21 How many minutes are there in a day?
22 Who had a hit on the telephone in 1972 with Sylvia's Mother?
23 What was Howard in the film Howard - A New Kind of Hero?
24 What can be 84cm, 91cm or 106cm in height in sport ?
25 The towns of Anaconda and Moscow are in which US State?
26 In the TV series Minder which club was owned by Dave?
27 The university sited in Uxbridge is named after which engineer?
28 Which Melanie has been the partner of Antonio Banderas?
29 Which creatures mainly belong to the arachnidae family?
30 Who had hits with Senza Una Donna and Come Back and Stay?

Answers

Euro Tour (see Quiz 35, page 155)
1 Estonia, Latvia and Lithuania. 2 Portugal. 3 Barcelona. 4 Flax. 5 Bayern.
6 Dublin. 7 Iron. 8 Jutland. 9 Black Forest. 10 Netherlands. 11 Trees.
12 Switzerland. 13 Kiev. 14 Cave paintings. 15 Madrid. 16 Under L'Arc
de Triomphe. 17 Camargue. 18 Green. 19 French & German. 20 Hungary.
21 Spain. 22 Italy. 23 Majorca. 24 Sicily. 25 Liverpool. 26 Estonia. 27
Muslim. 28 Belgium. 29 Elysee Palace. 30 Canary Wharf.

Quiz 37 Hobbies & Leisure 1

Answers - see Quiz 38, page 158

1 The Sealed Knot Society re-enacts what?
2 Which racecourse has a famous Royal Enclosure?
3 What is the Quorn in Leicestershire?
4 What colour are hotels in Monopoly?
5 Where is the National Motor Museum?
6 What is the maximum number of pieces on a chessboard at any one time?
7 What was the yachting trophy the America's Cup named after?
8 In which month do the French celebrate Bastille Day?
9 If you played outdoor hockey in the US what would it be called?
10 In which musical is the song Summertime?
11 Where in London did Laura Ashley open her first shop?
12 What is the world's biggest selling copyrighted game?
13 Which organisation is the largest private landowner in Britain?
14 How high is a netball post?
15 If you have a credit card what is an APR?
16 Where did karaoke singing originate?
17 Who opened a bistro called Le Petit Blanc in 1984?
18 Who replaced Melvyn Bragg on Radio 4's Start the Week?
19 Where was the first Virgin record shop?
20 During which months was the museum to Diana, Princess of Wales open at Althorp in 1998?
21 What might a numismatist collect along with coins?
22 Which day at Royal Ascot is Ladies' Day?
23 Who founded a theme park called Dollywood?
24 Bronco busting and steer wrestling take place at what type of event?
25 Which form of tennis is played on a smaller court usually by children?
26 In which US state did skateboarding begin as an alternative to surfing?
27 How many pins must be knocked down in skittles?
28 Which game is played at Hurlingham?
29 In slalom skiing what must you turn between?
30 What would be your hobby if you used slip?

Pot Luck 18 (see Quiz 38, page 158)
1 A bear. **2** Graham Hill. **3** The Booker Prize. **4** Reet Petite. **5** A fish.
6 Kelsey Grammer. **7** Spring. **8** Roots Hall. **9** Both beheaded.
10 Rattlesnakes. **11** Larry Grayson. **12** The Comet. **13** Saxophone. **14** Iron Maiden. **15** Eliza Doolittle. **16** Land. **17** A farrow. **18** Abel Magwitch.
19 Michael Crichton. **20** 32. **21** Regent's Park. **22** Turn at different speeds.
23 Gross Domestic Product. **24** Africa. **25** Friday. **26** Manitoba. **27** A bat.
28 Stevie Wonder. **29** Antwerp. **30** Lady Day.

Quiz 38 Pot Luck 18

LEVEL 2

1 Which animal can be described as ursine?
2 Who was older when they died Graham Hill or James Hunt?
3 Which prize for fiction was instigated in 1969?
4 Which Jackie Wilson hit was No 1 nearly thirty years after it was made?
5 A tarpon is a type of what?
6 Who played Frasier Crane in Frasier and Cheers?
7 If something is vernal, what is it connected with?
8 Where do Southend United football club play their home games?
9 How did both James I's mother and son die?
10 The sidewinder belongs to which group of snakes?
11 Who in 1987 presented the TV show Sweethearts?
12 Which was the first commercial jet aircraft in the world?
13 Jazz musician John Coltrane played which instrument?
14 Who had UK hits with Run to the Hills and The Evil That Men Do?
15 Which part was played by Audrey Hepburn in the film My Fair Lady?
16 Wapentakes, hundreds and hides were all areas of what?
17 What is the collective name for a litter of piglets?
18 Who gave Pip his wealth in Great Expectations?
19 Who wrote the novel Jurassic Park?
20 How many squares have pieces on them at the start of a chess game?
21 In which London park are The Holme, The Broad Walk and Winfield House?
22 What does the differential on a car allow the driving wheels to do?
23 The abbreviation GDP stands for what?
24 The Gulf of Sidra is located off the coast of which continent?
25 Which day of the week is named after the Norse Goddess Freya?
26 Winnipeg is the capital of which Canadian province?
27 What type of creature is a flying fox?
28 Whose hits include I Wish, Lately and Do I Do?
29 Where in Belgium were the 1920 Olympics held?
30 In a calendar year what is the first quarter day in England?

Answers **Hobbies & Leisure 1** (see Quiz 37, page 157)
1 Battles of the English Civil War. 2 Ascot. 3 Hunt. 4 Red. 5 Beaulieu.
6 32. 7 Schooner America. 8 July. 9 Field hockey. 10 Porgy & Bess.
11 Kensington. 12 Monopoly. 13 National Trust. 14 10 feet (3.05m).
15 Annual Percentage Rate. 16 Japan. 17 Raymond Blanc. 18 Jeremy
Paxman. 19 Oxford Street. 20 July and August. 21 Medals. 22 Second day.
23 Dolly Parton. 24 Rodeo. 25 Short tennis. 26 California. 27 Nine.
28 Polo. 29 Flags. 30 Pottery.

Quiz 39 People & Places

Answers - see Quiz 40, page 160

LEVEL 2

1. Which US President's father was a former Ambassador in the UK?
2. Edith Cresson was which country's PM from 1991-1992?
3. The Downing Street Declaration in 1993 involved the Prime Ministers of which two countries?
4. Which family died at Ekaterinburg in 1918?
5. Which school provided the UK with 19 Prime Ministers before 2000?
6. In which war did British soldiers first wear balaclava helmets?
7. Which mountaineer was the first person since Scott to reach the South Pole overland, in 1958?
8. The 'Bomb Plot' of 1944 failed to assassinate whom?
9. What was the minimum age for joining the UK Home Guard in WWII?
10. Which former US President was a distant relative of Princess Diana?
11. Who was the first woman President of Ireland?
12. In which US state did Martin Luther King lead the 1955 bus boycott?
13. Who lost power in Germany in 1998 after 16 years?
14. Who became Secretary General of the UN in 1997?
15. Who was Bonnie Prince Charlie disguised as when he escaped to France with Flora MacDonald?
16. Who defected to the USSR with Guy Burgess in 1951?
17. Carlos Menem became President of which country in 1989?
18. Who was the first Governor General of India, until 1948?
19. What was the alliance between the Germans and the Italians in World War II called?
20. Where in the East End of London did Jack the Ripper operate?
21. As a double agent, Mata Hari was executed by whom?
22. Mrs Meir was the first woman PM in which country?
23. Who was the USA's first Roman Catholic President?
24. Aung San Suu Kyi is an opposition leader in which country?
25. Which Panamanian leader was nicknamed Pineapple Face?
26. Which Pass did Hannibal use to cross the Alps?
27. Who became President of Ireland in 1997?
28. In which Vietnamese village were 109 civilians massacred by US troops in 1968?
29. Who was the first woman US Secretary of State?
30. Where did Tung Chee-Hwa become chief executive in July 1997?

Pot Luck 19 (see Quiz 40, page 160)
1 One square mile. **2** Slaves. **3** Stocks & share prices. **4** Fleet Air Arm.
5 Father of the House. **6** 70. **7** Park Lane. **8** Moses. **9** Cunard. **10** Corgi.
11 Kent and Sussex. **12** Red. **13** RAF. **14** Director of Public Prosecutions.
15 48. **16** Ageism. **17** Antarctica. **18** Railway carriage. **19** High blood pressure. **20** Wheel clamp. **21** Vice Squad. **22** When ill. **23** The soul. **24** Smith Square. **25** A cough. **26** Westminster Cathedral. **27** Orange. **28** Siouxsie and the Banshees. **29** Single parent families. **30** A Stateless Person.

Quiz 40 Pot Luck 19

Answers - see Quiz 39, page 159

LEVEL 2

1 What is the area of the City of London?

2 What is the last word of Rule Britannia?

3 What does the Footsie show?

4 Which branch of the Royal Navy is concerned with aviation?

5 What name is given to the MP who has served in the House of Commons the longest?

6 A driving licence is issued until the driver reaches what age?

7 In which Lane is London's Dorchester Hotel?

8 In The Old Testament Aaron was the elder brother of which prophet?

9 Which shipping company operated the Queen Mary and the Queen Elizabeth?

10 Which dog's name comes from the Welsh for dwarf dog?

11 In which two English counties are the Cinque Ports?

12 What colour coats do Chelsea Pensioners wear in the summer?

13 Cranwell trains cadets for which of the armed forces?

14 Who is the DPP?

15 How many kilometres per hour is 30 miles an hour?

16 What is discrimination against the elderly called?

17 In 1991 a 50 year mining ban was agreed for which area of the world?

18 In what type of vehicle was the 1918 World War armistice signed?

19 What is another name for hypertension?

20 What is another name for a Denver boot?

21 Which police department deals with illegal gambling and pornography?

22 When might an employee receive SSP?

23 In religious terms what does absolution purify?

24 In which London square is the HQ of the Tory party?

25 Which condition will an antitussive help alleviate?

26 What is the principal Roman Catholic church in England?

27 What colour is a disabled driver's badge?

28 Who had hits with Dear Prudence and Hong Kong Gardens?

29 Which families does Gingerbread help?

30 In law, what is a citizen of no particular nation called?

People & Places (see Quiz 39, page 159)
1 Kennedy. 2 France. 3 UK & Ireland. 4 The Romanovs. 5 Eton.
6 Crimean War. 7 Edmund Hillary. 8 Hitler. 9 17. 10 Ronald Reagan.
11 Mary Robinson. 12 Alabama. 13 Helmut Kohl. 14 Kofi Annan.
15 Flora's maid. 16 Donald Maclean. 17 Argentina. 18 Lord Mountbatten.
19 Axis. 20 Whitechapel. 21 The French. 22 Israel. 23 John F Kennedy.
24 Myanmar. 25 Noriega. 26 Little St Bernard. 27 Mary McAleese.
28 My Lai. 29 Madeleine Albright. 30 Hong Kong.

Quiz 41 Pop Music: The 80s

LEVEL 2

Answers - see Quiz 42, page 162

1 Which hit was No 2 for Rick Astley and No 4 for Nat King Cole in '87?
2 What was the first Top Ten hit for Tanita Tikaram?
3 What were 'shattered' in the 1987 No 5 hit for Johnny Hates Jazz?
4 Who joined Kenny Rogers on We've Got Tonight?
5 Which Jimmy Nail hit was a cover of a Rose Royce hit?
6 New Edition got to No 1 in '83 with which Girl?
7 Who were spun around by their No 1 You Spin Me Round (like a record)?
8 Which group had top ten hits with Breakout and Surrender?
9 Whose first UK No 1 hit West End Girls?
10 What was KC and the Sunshine Band's only UK No 1 in the 80s?
11 Which twins had hits with Love On Your Side and Doctor Doctor?
12 Which town got The Specials to No 1 in 1981?
13 What followed Ooh La La La in the 1982 hit for Kool and the Gang?
14 The name of which Asian country gave Kim Wilde an 80s hit?
15 What followed the title of Soul II Soul's first UK No 1 Back To Life?
16 Where did Lipps Inc. take us to in their No 2 from 1980?
17 Which antipodean title was a No 1 for Men at Work in 1983?
18 The song Intuition was the only UK Top Ten single for which duo?
19 Mental As Anything had a No 3 with Live It Up from which film?
20 Who joined Julio Inglesias on his No 5 success My Love ?
21 Which animal was sleeping on the No 1 hit by Tight Fit?
22 Which '87 Billy Idol hit was a cover of an earlier Tommy James hit?
23 What was Simply Red's first Top Ten UK hit?
24 Which Del Shannon hit became an 80s hit for Icehouse?
25 Which Dutch female group had hits with History and Body and Soul?
26 What in 1986 was Spandau Ballet's last UK Top Ten hit?
27 Who joined Fun Boy Three on It Ain't What You Do in 1982?
28 Which day links a No 2 by the Bangles with a No 3 by New Order?
29 Who gave Karel Fialka his only Top Ten success in 1987?
30 Whose first Top Ten hit was Harvest For The World in 1988?

Pot Luck 20 (see Quiz 42, page 162)
1 Whiskey. 2 Hull. 3 The Pope. 4 Tuberculosis. 5 On the bridge.
6 Alexander Pope. 7 The Man From UNCLE. 8 Fennel. 9 Deep Purple.
10 Monkey bread. 11 A prison. 12 Kate Moss. 13 Carmichael. 14 Harold
Wilson. 15 Lassie. 16 French. 17 Trees. 18 The Sex Pistols. 19 Gardner.
20 In water. 21 A dog. 22 Harry. 23 Denmark and Norway. 24 Grace
Kelly. 25 Animals. 26 Edinburgh. 27 Ecuador. 28 George Gershwin.
29 Conciliation. 30 Que Sera Sera.

Answers

Quiz 42 Pot Luck 20

LEVEL 2

Answers - see Quiz 41, page 161

1 Which drink did American Indians call Firewater in the Wild West?
2 In which city are the Ferens Art Gallery and Town Docks Museum?
3 Who sends encyclical letters?
4 The White Death was a name for which former common disease?
5 According to the song, where does everyone dance in Avignon?
6 Who wrote, "To err is human, to forgive, divine"?
7 In which TV series were the agents given orders by Mr Waverly?
8 Which leaves taste of aniseed?
9 Which group had a top ten hit with Black Knight?
10 What is the fruit of a baobab tree called?
11 What was a bridewell?
12 Which model's childhood nickname was 'Mosschops'?
13 Which actor Ian played the leading role in the film Private's Progress?
14 "A week is a long time in politics," was said by which politician?
15 Which animal movie star was nicknamed Greer Garson in furs?
16 What is the official language of the Ivory Coast?
17 What are pruned in coppicing?
18 Which group featured in The Great Rock 'n Roll Swindle?
19 Which Ava was one of Frank Sinatra's wives?
20 If a plant is a hydrophyte where does it live?
21 A papillon is a type of what?
22 What was Bing Crosby's first name?
23 Which two countries are separated by the Skagerrak?
24 Which royal film star appeared in Dial M for Murder?
25 What does the Blue Cross Charity, founded in 1897, provide aid to?
26 In which Scottish city are Salisbury Crags?
27 Which South American country has the sucre as the unit of currency?
28 Who composed the music for the musical Strike Up The Band?
29 What does the C stand for in ACAS?
30 Which song was sung in three different films by Doris Day?

Answers

Pop Music: The 80s (see Quiz 41, page 161)
1 When I Fall In Love. 2 Good Tradition. 3 Dreams. 4 Sheena Easton.
5 Love Don't Live Here Anymore. 6 Candy Girl. 7 Dead Or Alive. 8 Swing
Out Sister. 9 Pet Shop Boys. 10 Give It Up. 11 Thompson Twins. 12 Ghost
Town. 13 Let's Go Dancin'. 14 Cambodia. 15 However Do You Want Me.
16 Funky Town. 17 Down Under. 18 Linx. 19 Crocodile Dundee.
20 Stevie Wonder. 21 Lion. 22 Mony Mony. 23 Holding Back the Years.
24 Hey Little Girl. 25 Mai Tai. 26 Through the Barricades. 27 Bananarama.
28 Monday. 29 Matthew. 30 Christians.

Quiz 43 Sport: Horse Racing

Answers - see Quiz 44, page 164

1   Which American was UK champion jockey in 1984, 1985 and 1987?
2   In which month does the Cheltenham Festival take place?
3   Which two races make up the autumn double?
4   How long is the Derby?
5   How many times did Willie Carson win the Derby?
6   Which Cabinet Minister has been the Glasgow Herald's racing tipster?
7   Who had nine Derby wins and was champion jockey 11 times?
8   Which British racehorse owner sold Vernons Pools in 1988?
9   Who was Champion Jockey a record 26 times between 1925 and 1953?
10 Which John and Peter were joint Champion Jockeys in 1982?
11 Which Classic was the first to be run on a Sunday in England?
12 In 1995 which horse won the Derby, the King George VI and the Prix de l'Arc de Triomphe?
13 Alex Greaves was the first female jockey in which race?
14 Where is Valentine's Brook?
15 At which racecourse is the Steward's Cup competed for annually?
16 Who was riding Devon Loch when it so nearly won the National?
17 What is Frankie Dettori's real first name?
18 Which Monkee was an apprentice jockey?
19 Which horse won the Cheltenham Gold Cup in 1964, '65 and '66?
20 Who was the UK's first overseas champion jockey after Steve Cauthen?
21 Where is Tattenham Corner?
22 What is the highest jump in the Grand National?
23 Where did Walter Swinburn sustain severe injuries in February 1997?
24 Who won the Grand National in 1993?
25 Which auctioneers were founded in London in 1766 but now have annual sales in Newmarket?
26 Which racecourse is near Bognor Regis?
27 What was unusual about the status of Mr Frisk's winning rider in the 1990 National?
28 How old are horses who run in nursery stakes?
29 In which month is Royal Ascot?
30 Whose total of 1,374 winners was a world record after the 1990-91 season?

Answers

TV: Sitcoms (see Quiz 44, page 164)
1 Dermot. 2 Gareth Blackstock. 3 Only Fools and Horses. 4 Drop The Dead Donkey. 5 Richard Wilson. 6 Jean Alexander. 7 Seinfeld. 8 Phoebe. 9 Till Death Us Do Part. 10 Fawlty Towers. 11 Porridge. 12 Annie. 13 Cockerel. 14 Thelma. 15 Napoleon. 16 Bubble. 17 After Henry. 18 Are You Being Served?. 19 Gary Sparrow. 20 As Time Goes By. 21 Barker. 22 Arnold Rimmer. 23 They were witches. 24 Baldrick. 25 Allo Allo. 26 Green. 27 Christopher Biggins. 28 Geraldine Grainger. 29 Bottom. 30 Gordon.

Quiz 44 TV: Sitcoms

Answers - see Quiz 43, page 163

LEVEL 2

1   What was the name of Harry Enfield's character in Men Behaving Badly?
2   What was the name of the Chef in Chef!?
3   What was the most successful sitcom of the 80s?
4   Which series took place at the Globelink News Office?
5   Which sit com star worked in a hospital laboratory before becoming an actor?
6   Which former soap star plays Auntie Wainwright in Last of the Summer Wine?
7   Which US sitcom, which had 180 episodes, finished in May 1998?
8   Who was the 40s publican's daughter in Goodnight Sweetheart?
9   All in the Family was a US spin off from which UK sitcom?
10 Where would you find guests Major Gowen, Miss Tibbs and Miss Gatsby?
11 Going Straight was the sequel to what?
12 What was the name of Jim Hacker's wife in Yes Minister?
13 In The Good Life, who or what was Lenin?
14 In The Likely Lads, who did Bob marry?
15 In Dad's Army what did the air raid warden always call Mainwaring?
16 Who was Edina's PA in Absolutely Fabulous?
17 Which series with Prunella Scales as Sarah France had three years on radio before transferring to TV?
18 Grace and Favour was a sequel to which sitcom?
19 What is the name of the time traveller in Goodnight Sweetheart?
20 Which show's theme song begins, "You must remember this..."?
21 Which Ronnie's famous roles have included Arkwright and Fletcher?
22 Which obnoxious character did Chris Barrie play in Red Dwarf?
23 What was strange about Samantha Stephens and her mother Endora?
24 Who was Blackadder's servant?
25 Which sitcom was a send up of Secret Army?
26 What was Dorien's surname in Birds of a Feather?
27 Who was the effeminate Lukewarm in Porridge?
28 What was the Vicar of Dibley's name?
29 In which series did Richie and Eddie first appear?
30 What was Brittas's first name in The Brittas Empire?

Sport: Horse Racing (see Quiz 43, page 163)
1 Steve Cauthen. 2 March. 3 Cesarewitch and the Cambridgeshire. 4 A mile and a half. 5 Four. 6 Robin Cook. 7 Lester Piggott. 8 Robert Sangster. 9 Gordon Richards. 10 Scudamore & Francome. 11 1,000 Guineas. 12 Lammtarra. 13 The Derby. 14 Aintree. 15 Goodwood. 16 Dick Francis. 17 Lanfranco. 18 Davy Jones. 19 Arkle. 20 Frankie Dettori. 21 Epsom. 22 The Chair. 23 Hong Kong. 24 No one, it was abandoned. 25 Tattersall's. 26 Fontwell Park. 27 Amateur. 28 Two. 29 June. 30 Peter Scudamore.

Answers

Quiz 45 Pot Luck 21

Answers - see Quiz 46, page 166

LEVEL 2

1   If you nictitate at someone, what do you do?
2   Who offered Demi Moore a million dollars in Indecent Proposal?
3   Monument Valley is in which American state?
4   Which island off the north Devon coast is named after the Norse for puffin?
5   Who had a Top Ten hit in the 80s with Sledgehammer?
6   On 14th April 1912, what occurred off Newfoundland?
7   Who was Des Lynam's co-presenter on the first series of How Do They Do That?
8   Which instrument was played by David in The Bible?
9   Who is taller Madonna or Dawn French?
10 Which organisation was founded in 1953 by Reverend Chad Varah?
11 In corned beef what are the corns?
12 Which people used knotted cords called quipu for calculation?
13 Which character was played by Maggie Smith in Sister Act?
14 Who wrote the novel Journey to the Centre of the Earth?
15 At which school was Thomas Arnold a famous headmaster?
16 What was a Mae West to an airman?
17 How many squadrons make up a wing in the Royal Air Force?
18 Who followed U Thant as Secretary General of the United Nations?
19 Which high street chain was founded in 1961 by Selim Zilkha?
20 What does the book Glass's Guide contain?
21 Who had a big hit with Sowing the Seeds of Love?
22 Actor Bruce Willis played which character in Moonlighting?
23 What is an aspen?
24 The Battle of Pinkie of 1547 was fought in which country?
25 What nationality was Amy Johnson?
26 Which animal has the longest pregnancy?
27 Anything above scale 12 on the Beaufort Scale would describe what?
28 Which group were made up of Cass, Michelle, John and Denny?
29 Cars with the international vehicle registration PA come from where?
30 Who did Shylock want to take his pound of flesh from?

Musical Movies (see Quiz 46, page 166)

Answers

1 Abba: The Movie. 2 Ursula Andress. 3 Cyd Charisse. 4 Maurice Chevalier. 5 The Philadelphia Story. 6 Martin Scorsese. 7 The Blackboard Jungle. 8 Whitney Houston. 9 Richard E Grant. 10 Master of ceremonies. 11 Antonio Banderas. 12 The Nightmate Before Christmas. 13 Rex Harrison. 14 Paris. 15 Marlon Brando. 16 Yul Brynner. 17 Baron Georg Von Trapp. 18 Freddie Eynsford-Hill. 19 Saturday Night Fever. 20 Autry. 21 1950s. 22 Albert Finney. 23 South Pacific. 24 Chim Chim Cheree. 25 Help! 26 Fiddler on the Roof. 27 Jonathan Pryce. 28 Sammy Davis Jr. 29 Cabaret. 30 Monroe.

Quiz 46 Musical Movies

Answers - see Quiz 45, page 145

LEVEL 2

1   What was the name of the smash movie about 70s superband Abba?
2   Which Bond girl starred with Elvis Presley in Fun in Acapulco?
3   Who danced with Gene Kelly in the Broadway Ballet section Of Singin' In the Rain?
4   Who sang Thank Heaven for Little Girls in Gigi?
5   High Society was a musical version of which classic?
6   Which controversial figure directed the musical New York, New York?
7   In which film did Bill Haley sing Rock Around the Clock?
8   Who sang most of the soundtrack of The Bodyguard?
9   Who had a managerial role in Spiceworld?
10 Joel Grey won an Oscar for which role in the 70s classic Cabaret?
11 Who played Che in the film version of Evita?
12 Which Tim Burton film featured a hostile takeover of present delivery at Christmas?
13 Who played the Doctor in the musical film version of Doctor Doolittle?
14 Where is Gigi set?
15 Which tough guy actor played Sky Masterson in Guys and Dolls?
16 Which star of The King and I was born in Russia?
17 Who does Julie Andrews marry in The Sound of Music?
18 Which character sings On the Street Where You Live in My Fair Lady?
19 Which 70s film became a stage musical in London in 1998?
20 Which Gene was the singing cowboy?
21 In which decade does the action of Grease take place?
22 Which English actor played the millionaire benefactor in Annie?
23 In which musical does Nurse Nellie Forbush appear?
24 Which of the many songs in Mary Poppins won the Oscar?
25 What was The Beatles' second film?
26 Which musical is the tale of a Jewish milkman in pre revolutionary Russia?
27 Who played Eva's husband in Evita?
28 Who led 'The Rhythm of Life' sequence in Sweet Charity?
29 Which 70s musical film was set in pre war Berlin?
30 Which Marylin sung Diamonds are a Girl's Best Friend?

Answers

Pot Luck 21 (see Quiz 45, page 165)
1 Wink. 2 Robert Redford. 3 Arizona. 4 Lundy. 5 Peter Gabriel. 6 The Titanic sank. 7 Jennie Hull. 8 Harp. 9 Madonna. 10 Samaritans. 11 Salt. 12 The Incas. 13 Mother Superior. 14 Jules Verne. 15 Rugby School. 16 Lifejacket. 17 Three. 18 Kurt Waldheim. 19 Mothercare. 20 Vehicle prices. 21 Tears for Fears. 22 David Addison. 23 A tree. 24 Scotland. 25 British. 26 Elephant. 27 Hurricane. 28 The Mamas and Papas. 29 Panama. 30 Antonio.

1 What is a pickled gherkin made from?
2 Which cricketer is a team captain on TV's They Think It's All Over?
3 Who had hits with Ben and Take That Look Off Your Face?
4 Pooh Bah appears in which Gilbert and Sullivan operetta?
5 Which Classic race is run over the longest distance?
6 Who was the brother of Flopsy, Mopsy and Cottontail?
7 What form did the head of the Sphinx take?
8 Which voice in singing is pitched between a tenor and a soprano?
9 Which birds collect in a covey?
10 Who wrote The Phoenix and the Carpet?
11 Titian is what colour?
12 What part did Madonna play in the film Shanghai Surprise?
13 Which former England manager was born on the same day as Yoko Ono?
14 Which almost eradicated disease was called Phthisis?
15 The Moonstone by Wilkie Collins is about a jewel from which country?
16 In which country is Lake Bala the largest natural lake?
17 In which town were the Marsh Farm riots in July 1995?
18 The US state of Maryland was named after the wife of which King?
19 Who had hits with Be Bop A Lula and Pistol Packin' Mama?
20 Which tennis star was sued by Judy Nelson for palimony?
21 Who played Mark Antony opposite Liz Taylor in the film Cleopatra?
22 Who was Gloria Hunniford named after?
23 Which football manager once played in a band called Revelation Time?
24 What is the first name of P.D. James' detective Dalgleish?
25 Which part did Dustin Hoffman play in the film Hook?
26 What was the title of the 1994 East 17 Christmas No 1 UK hit?
27 Who was British PM directly before Edward Heath?
28 Which Open win was Nick Faldo's first?
29 What can be solo boxing, a lush mineral or a round timber?
30 Which part did Gene Hackman play in the Superman films?

Answers

Living World (see Quiz 48, page 168)
1 Tidal wave. 2 On the skin. 3 CJD. 4 Worm. 5 Haematology.
6 Hermaphrodite. 7 Falcon. 8 Ear. 9 Marine snail. 10 Knee. 11 Pigeons.
12 Anaemia. 13 Orange. 14 Fungus. 15 Skin. 16 Abdomen.
17 Shoulder blade. 18 Fish. 19 Short sighted. 20 12. 21 Lungs.
22 Acne. 23 The kiss of life. 24 Tuberculosis. 25 Base of the brain.
26 Achilles tendon. 27 Liver. 28 Green. 29 Kidney. 30 Herring.

Quiz 48 Living World

Answers - see Quiz 47, page 147

LEVEL 2

1 Tsunami is another name for what type of wave?
2 Where would a melanoma appear?
3 Which disease in humans has been linked to the cattle disease BSE?
4 What sort of creature is a fluke?
5 Which branch of medicine is concerned with disorders of the blood?
6 What name is given to an organism which is both male and female?
7 What sort of bird is a Merlin?
8 Which part of the body might suffer from labyrinthitis?
9 What sort of creature is an abalone?
10 Where is a bird's patella?
11 Which racing creatures live in lofts?
12 What condition is caused by a shortage of haemoglobin?
13 What colour are the spots on a plaice?
14 What is a puffball?
15 Which part of the body does scabies affect?
16 Which digestive organ lies below the thorax in invertebrates?
17 Where is a human's scapula?
18 What do most sharks live on?
19 If a person has myopia what problem does he or she have?
20 How many pairs of ribs does a human have?
21 Pulmonary refers to which part of the body?
22 Which skin disorder is caused by inflammation of the sebaceous glands?
23 What is the popular name for mouth to mouth recussitation?
24 A BCG is a vaccination against which disease?
25 Where is the pituitary gland?
26 Which tendon pins the calf muscle to the heel bone?
27 Hepatic refers to which organ of the body?
28 What colour head does a male mallard usually have?
29 The adrenal gland is above which organ?
30 The pilchard is a member of which fish family?

Pot Luck 22 (see Quiz 47, page 147)

Answers

1 A cucumber. 2 David Gower. 3 Marti Webb. 4 The Mikado. 5 St Leger.
6 Peter(Rabbit). 7 A Human. 8 An Alto. 9 Partridges. 10 E. Nesbit.
11 Red. 12 A missionary. 13 Bobby Robson. 14 Tuberculosis. 15 India.
16 Wales. 17 Luton. 18 Charles I. 19 Gene Vincent. 20 Martina
Navratilova. 21 Richard Burton. 22 Gloria Swanson. 23 Ruud Gullit.
24 Adam. 25 Captain Hook. 26 Stay Another Day. 27 Harold Wilson.
28 British. 29 Spar. 30 Lex Luthor.

LEVEL 2

1   Which Diane has been Sean Connery's partner?
2   The city of Philadelphia was founded by which religious group?
3   Where would you normally play shovel-board?
4   Which is further north Blackburn or Blackpool?
5   Whose hits include Gangsters and Too Much Too Young?
6   Which motor racing team is named after the sacred flower in India?
7   Donald McGill was particularly associated with what seaside art form?
8   Who wrote Willie Wonka and the Chocolate Factory?
9   Who narrates Treasure Island other than Jim Hawkins?
10 What is the New Zealand National Day called?
11 Paul Merson made his league debut with which club?
12 Which ship sent the first S.O.S?
13 What did the craft in the film Fantastic Voyage enter into?
14 In the Bond movie Goldeneye which Dame played M?
15 Which flower is on the badge of the Boy Scouts?
16 Which former Lebanese hostage wrote a book with Jill Morrell?
17 Maddy Magellan is the partner of which fictional detective?
18 Which Marlon Brando film is based on Conrad's Heart of Darkness?
19 In which group of islands is Panay?
20 HMS Ark Royal featured in which TV series?
21 The Sierra Nevada mountains are in which American state?
22 Who played Edward in TV's Edward and Mrs Simpson?
23 STASHING is an anagram of which famous battle?
24 Which pop star Linda took the lead in the film of Pirates of Penzance?
25 Whose hits include Kayleigh and Lavender?
26 Was the Sopwith Camel designed by Sopwith or Camel?
27 Which county did Godfrey Evans play cricket for?
28 Who wrote The Singing Detective?
29 Which word links a pastime, a small horse and a small falcon?
30 Which daily food includes the protein casein?

Famous Celebs (see Quiz 50, page 170)
1 Mohammed Al-Fayed. 2 Longleat. 3 Sarah. 4 Pamela Anderson. 5 Alan Clark. 6 Antonia de Sancha. 7 Edwina Currie. 8 Countess Spencer. 9 Holloway Prison. 10 Credit card fraud. 11 Texas. 12 Michael Heseltine. 13 Everton. 14 Jemima Khan. 15 Max Clifford. 16 Loos. 17 Sir Cameron Mackintosh. 18 Julia Carling. 19 David Bailey. 20 Elizabeth Hurley . 21 Diana, Princess of Wales. 22 Lord Snowdon. 23 Spencer. 24 Peter Stringfellow. 25 French. 26 Vivienne Westwood. 27 Chef. 28 Prince Andrew. 29 Tesco. 30 Rod Stewart.

Quiz 50 Famous Celebs

LEVEL 2

Answers - see Quiz 49, page 169

1 Who owns The Ritz in Paris?
2 Which stately home and safari park belongs to the Marquis of Bath?
3 What were two out of Andrew Lloyd-Webber's three wives called?
4 Who has Tommy Lee's name tattooed on her wedding finger?
5 Which Tory MP philanderer said "Only domestic servants apologise" after his Diaries were published?
6 The story of whose affair with David Mellor broke in 1992?
7 Which outspoken ex MP shares her birthday with Margaret Thatcher?
8 What was the previous title of Raine, Comtesse de Chambrun?
9 Where did Geri Halliwell have a meeting behind closed doors to launch 1998 Breast Cancer Awareness Week?
10 For what offence was Stephen Fry jailed, aged 17?
11 Jerry Hall is from which US state?
12 Whose heart attack in Venice prevented him from pursuing the Tory leadership?
13 Theatre impresario Bill Kenwright is a director of which soccer club?
14 Which late billionaire's daughter has a son called Sulaiman?
15 Which PR man acted for Mandy Allwood and Bienvenida Buck?
16 Lady Lucinda Lambton is an expert on which convenient necessity?
17 Which knighted impresario had a record six West End musicals running in 1996?
18 Which estranged wife made a spoof film clip of Diana watching open heart surgery?
19 Which photographer discovered Jean Shrimpton in the Sixties?
20 Who became the face of Estee Lauder in the mid 90s?
21 Who was Mrs Frances Shand Kydd's youngest daughter?
22 How was Anthony Armstrong-Jones known after his royal marriage?
23 Which future Earl did model Victoria Lockwood marry in 1990?
24 Which Sheffield born nightclub owner's most famous club is named after him?
25 What is the nationality of designer Catherine Walker?
26 Which outrageous designer was once the partner of Sex Pistols' manager Malcolm McLaren?
27 In which profession did Marco Pierre White find fame?
28 Whose name was linked with researcher Henrietta Peace's in '97?
29 Dame Shirley Porter is heiress to which supermarket chain?
30 Model Rachel Hunter married which rock star in 1990?

Answers

Pot Luck 23 (see Quiz 49, page 169)

1 Cilento. 2 The Quakers. 3 On a ship's deck. 4 Blackpool. 5 The Specials.
6 Lotus. 7 Postcards. 8 Roald Dahl. 9 Dr Livesey. 10 Waitangi Day.
11 Arsenal. 12 Titanic. 13 A Man's body. 14 Judi Dench. 15 Fleur de Lis.
16 John McCarthy. 17 Jonathan Creek. 18 Apocalypse Now. 19
Philippines. 20 Sailing. 21 California. 22 Edward Fox. 23 Hastings.
24 Ronstadt. 25 Marillion. 26 Sopwith. 27 Kent. 28 Dennis Potter.
29 A hobby. 30 Milk.

Quiz 51 Pot Luck 24

Answers - see Quiz 52, page 172

LEVEL 2

1 Which England player was likened to Mary Poppins by a director of his own club?
2 What would you do with a saxhorn?
3 Who was singer Lorna Luft's famous actress mother?
4 Who had hits with Living on the Ceiling and Blind Vision?
5 Who built the second block of nine cells at Wormwood Scrubs?
6 In Moonlighting which actress played Maddie Hayes?
7 Which is the largest and oldest Australian city?
8 Which sport says "Go out there and win one for the Gipper"?
9 How is the wife of a Knight addressed?
10 Light, Home and Third used to be what?
11 What name is given to a person who eats no food of animal origin?
12 Who wrote the song Moon River?
13 Who led the Scottish troops at Bannockburn?
14 Which Palace is the official home of the French president?
15 What is a water moccasin?
16 In which group of islands are St Martin's, St Mary's and Tresco?
17 Which people made an idol in the form of a Golden Calf in The Bible?
18 Which actor starred in the film North By Northwest?
19 Which city is called the City of Brotherly Love?
20 In which sport were John Louis and Barry Briggs associated?
21 Whose biography was called Neither Shaken Nor Stirred?
22 Which famous Falls are on the Zambezi river?
23 What kind of flower can be a goldilocks?
24 Which state was TV's Knots Landing set in?
25 If you are member of the Q Guild, what is your profession?
26 Which creature's name can go in front of crab, plant, wasp and monkey?
27 How many cards are in a tarot pack?
28 In Trading Places who traded places with Dan Aykroyd?
29 Diluted acetic acid is the correct name for which foodstuff?
30 Whose hits include The Bitch is Back and Kiss the Bride?

Leisure 2 (see Quiz 52, page 172)
1 Role Playing. 2 Boules. 3 May. 4 Scotland. 5 22. 6 Sumo wrestling.
7 Lawn tennis. 8 Their hands. 9 Yin and Yang. 10 York. 11 Weightlifting.
12 Bonsai. 13 Plastic shuttlecocks. 14 Scotland. 15 Windsurfing. 16 Lego.
17 Horse racing, cards. 18 Michael Caine. 19 Phillip Schofield. 20 Three
hours. 21 Fibreglass. 22 One. 23 AA. 24 China. 25 MCC. 26 Hamley's
Regent Street, London. 27 In its ear. 28 Ever After. 29 Swimming. 30 Four.

Answers

Quiz 52 Leisure 2

Answers - see Quiz 51, page 151

LEVEL 2

1   What imaginative type of Game is known by the initials RPG?
2   Which French game's name is the French word for balls?
3   In which month is Spring Bank Holiday?
4   In World Cup Monopoly which team was the equivalent of Old Kent Road?
5   How many balls are needed to play a game of snooker?
6   What is the national sport of Japan?
7   What is lawn tennis called when played on shale or clay?
8   In volleyball what do players hit the ball with?
9   What is the Chinese for 'dark' and 'light' believed to maintain equilibrium?
10 Where is the Jorvik Viking Museum?
11 In which sport would you snatch and jerk?
12 The name of which type of tree cultivation comes from the Japanese for 'bowl cultivation'?
13 Which major change was introduced in badminton in 1949?
14 In which country is the oldest angling club in the world?
15 What is another name for boardsailing?
16 Which toy was invented by Danes Ole and Godtfred Christiansen?
17 If you were at or playing Newmarket which leisure pursuits would you be following?
18 Which cockney actor was a part owner of Langan's Brasserie?
19 Who played Dr Doolittle when it first appeared on the London stage?
20 Approximately how long does the journey from London to Paris take via Eurostar?
21 What are canoes made from?
22 If you received cotton, how many wedding anniversaries would you be celebrating?
23 Which UK motoring association describes itself as the fourth emergency service?
24 Which is the largest country where membership of the Scouts is not allowed?
25 Which club founded in 1787 voted to allow women members in 1998?
26 Where is the world's oldest toyshop?
27 Where does a Steiff teddy bear have its tag of authenticity?
28 What was the 1998 movie based on Cinderella, and starring Drew Barrymore called?
29 If you joined the Wasps in Wigan what sport would you compete in?
30 How many tournaments make up the Grand Slam in golf?

Answers

Pot Luck 24 (see Quiz 51, page 171)
1 Alan Shearer. 2 Play it. 3 Judy Garland. 4 Blancmange. 5 The convicts.
6 Cybill Shepherd. 7 Sydney. 8 American Football. 9 Lady. 10 Radio
channels. 11 A vegan. 12 Henry Mancini. 13 Robert the Bruce.
14 Elysee. 15 Snake. 16 Scilly Isles. 17 The Israelites. 18 Cary Grant.
19 Philadelphia. 20 Speedway. 21 Sean Connery. 22 Victoria Falls.
23 A buttercup. 24 California. 25 A Butcher. 26 Spider. 27 78.
28 Eddie Murphy. 29 Vinegar. 30 Elton John.

Quiz 53 Pot Luck 25

Answers - see Quiz 54, page 174

1 Dame Anna Neagle played which part in the 1950 film Odette?
2 Dove Cottage was home of which poet?
3 Which Pole was first reached in 1909?
4 Which Day replaced Empire Day in 1958?
5 Alfred the Great ruled which Kingdom?
6 Estoril is a resort north east of which major city?
7 The Duke of Windsor was Governor of which island group in 1939?
8 Who was the founder lead singer with Led Zeppelin in 1968?
9 Freddie Powell found fame as which crazy comic?
10 Which British surgeon was a pioneer in improving surgery hygiene?
11 Who was the female lead in Singing in the Rain?
12 Which common garden flower has the name Dianthus barbatus?
13 Where were the Spode pottery works established in the 1760s?
14 Cars with the international vehicle registration BG come from where?
15 Which Club included Mr Winkle and Mr Tupman as members?
16 Never Say Die was the first Derby winner for which famous jockey?
17 Which steam locomotive record is held by The Mallard?
18 Which castle is the largest in Britain?
19 Edwin Hubble was concerned with which branch of science?
20 Which part did Albert Finney play in the 1974 film Murder on the Orient Express?
21 Sir Alfred Munnings is famous for painting which animals?
22 Comic character Dan Dare was known as the pilot of what?
23 Colonel Thomas Blood tried to steal what in 1671?
24 Which country is the major exporter of teak in the world?
25 What sort of creature was a brawn?
26 If you suffered a myocardial infraction, what would have happened?
27 Who partnered Annie Lennox in the Eurythmics?
28 The Peace River is in which country?
29 In 1957, in which US state were there race riots at Little Rock?
30 Which racing driver once played in a band called Sex Hitler and the Hormones?

Answers

Pop Music: The 90s (see Quiz 54, page 174)
1 I Believe. 2 Clannad. 3 Sting & Bryan Adams. 4 Saturday. 5 Gabrielle.
6 Boombastic. 7 Colchester. 8 Dunblane. 9 Without You. 10 Would I Lie To
You. 11 Gina G. 12 The Bodyguard. 13 Shanice. 14 Fairground. 15 Boyz
II Men. 16 Looking Up. 17 I Wonder Why. 18 Spice Girls. 19 Cecilia.
20 Peter Andre. 21 Too Young to Die. 22 Ebeneezer Goode. 23 The
Simpsons. 24 Kylie Minogue. 25 Think Twice. 26 Shiny Happy People.
27 Doop. 28 Beverley Craven. 29 The Real Thing. 30 Lady Marmalade.

Quiz 54 Pop Music: The 90s

LEVEL 2

Answers - see Quiz 53, page 173

1 What was the other side of Robson and Jerome's Up On The Roof?
2 Which Irish band did a TV concert as a tribute to Brian Keenan in '91?
3 Which two singers joined Rod Stewart on the 1994 hit All For Love?
4 What night links Whigfield, Alexander O'Neal and Omar?
5 Who featured on East 17's No. 2 If You Ever in 1996?
6 Which 1995 hit gave Shaggy his second No 1?
7 Blur were formed in which East Anglian town?
8 Knockin' On Heaven's Door was covered following which tragedy?
9 Which song title links No 1s for Mariah Carey and Nilsson?
10 Which title links the Eurythmics to a 1992 No 1 for Charles and Eddy?
11 Which female sang the British Eurovision entry the year before Katrina and the Waves?
12 Which film featured the song that was Whitney Houston's fourth UK No 1?
13 I Love Your Smile was a hit in '92 for which US female artist?
14 What was Simply Red's first UK No 1 in 1995?
15 Who partnered Mariah Carey on One Sweet Day?
16 What was EastEnders' Michelle Gayle's first hit?
17 What was Curtis Stigers' first UK Top Ten success?
18 Which group held the Christmas single and album top spots in 1996?
19 Which female name was a No. 4 hit for Suggs in 1996?
20 Whose first two UK No 1s were Flava and I Feel You?
21 What was Jamiroquai's first UK Top Ten hit?
22 Which song title gave The Shamen their only No 1 in 1992?
23 Who were No.1 in 1991 with Do the Bartman?
24 Better the Devil You Know was a hit for Sonia and which soap star?
25 What was the first UK No 1 for Celine Dion?
26 What kind of people did R.E.M. take to No 6 in 1991?
27 What was the one hit wonder of the Dutch duo Doop?
28 Whose highest chart position was No 3 in 1991 with Promise Me?
29 Which Tony Di Bart No 1 hit from 1994 is the name of a group?
30 Which All Saints No 1 was a cover of a 70s hit for Labelle?

Pot Luck 25 (see Quiz 53, page 173)
1 Odette. 2 William Wordsworth. 3 North. 4 Commonwealth Day.
5 Wessex. 6 Lisbon. 7 Bahamas. 8 Robert Plant. 9 Freddie Starr.
10 Joseph Lister. 11 Debbie Reynolds. 12 Sweet William. 13 Stoke.
14 Bulgaria. 15 Pickwick Club. 16 Lester Piggott. 17 Speed record.
18 Windsor. 19 Astronomy. 20 Hercule Poirot. 21 Horses. 22 The Future.
23 Crown Jewels. 24 Myanmar (Burma). 25 A wild pig. 26 A heart attack.
27 Dave Stewart. 28 Canada. 29 Arkansas. 30 Damon Hill.

Answers

Quiz 55 TV: Soaps

Answers - see Quiz 56, page 176

Answers - see Quiz 56, page 176

LEVEL 2

1   Who in EastEnders had an affair with his mother in law?
2   What was Coronation Street originally going to be called?
3   What was the name of Joan Collins' character in Dynasty?
4   The Hart family appeared in which daily soap?
5   Which ex husband of Joan Collins appeared on EastEnders?
6   Who played mechanic Chris in Coronation Street and left to pursue a pop career?
7   Which Corrie star produced a fitness video called Rapid Results?
8   In Coronation Street, what is Spider's real name?
9   In which soap were Shane and Angel an item?
10 How did Kathy Glover's husband die in Emmerdale?
11 In Coronation Street what was Fiona's baby called?
12 Where did Kathy Mitchell go when she left Albert Square?
13 What form of transport did Cindy use to leave for France in EastEnders?
14 Who did Dannii Minogue play in Home & Away?
15 Which Kemp joined Ross Kemp on the EastEnders cast?
16 In Corrie which of the Battersby girls is Janice's daughter?
17 Which Kim disappeared from Emmerdale and was thought to have been murdered?
18 Which soap did Silent Witness star Amanda Burton appear in?
19 Which TV company first produced Emmerdale Farm?
20 Which role did Norman Bowler play in Emmerdale?
21 Who left Albert Square for America but returned as a director of the soap?
22 Which member of Emmerdale's Dingle family went on to present You've Been Framed?
23 Who was buried under the patio in Brookside?
24 Which TV comedian's daughter is in the radio soap The Archers?
25 Whose son in Corrie was once played by his real son Linus?
26 Where did Mavis go when she left The Street?
27 Which country group is made up of members of the Emmerdale cast?
28 Damon & Debbie was a short lived spin off from which soap?
29 Which star of The Good Sex Guide shared a cell with Deirdre in Coronation Street?
30 Which soap had a bar called the Waterhole?

Answers

Pot Luck 26 (see Quiz 56, page 176)
1 Quantum Leap. 2 Lucille. 3 Fencing. 4 John Fowles. 5 John Major.
6 Sam the piano player. 7 Noel Coward. 8 Tony Blair. 9 Simple Minds.
10 Dr Who. 11 Beatrix Potter. 12 10,800. 13 Timmy. 14 Bricklaying.
15 I'm Into Something Good. 16 India. 17 Begging. 18 Agatha Christie.
19 Aberdeen. 20 Whitechapel. 21 Hitler. 22 Middlemarch. 23 Peak
District. 24 Table Tennis. 25 Dog licence. 26 Vulture. 27 Australia. 28
Beverley Craven. 29 Ben Kingsley. 30 Ray Reardon.

1   In which TV series did Scott Bakula leap in time?
2   Which Kenny Rogers' hit starts, "On a bar in Toledo..."
3   In which sport is there a piste other than skiing?
4   Who wrote The French Lieutenant's Woman?
5   Which Chancellor of the Exchequer introduced TESSA?
6   Which character was played by Dooley Wilson in Casablanca?
7   Who wrote the play Private Lives?
8   Which politician once played in a band called Ugly Rumours?
9   Whose hits include Waterfront and Alive and Kicking?
10 Voords, Krotons and Autons have all appeared on which TV series?
11 Which children's writer's real name was Mrs Heelis?
12 How many seconds are there in three hours?
13 What was the dog called in the Famous Five books?
14 If you were using Dutch or Diaper Bonds what would you be doing?
15 What was Herman's Hermits only No 1 UK hit?
16 In which country was Salman Rushdie born?
17 What are you doing if you are mendicating?
18 Who wrote the novel Murder in Mesopotamia in 1936?
19 Which team from outside Glasgow won the Scottish FA Cup three times from 1982-84?
20 In Monopoly, what is the next property after the Old Kent Road?
21 Whose mountain retreat was at Berchtesgaden?
22 Dorothea Brooke is the central character in which novel?
23 Which was the first British National Park?
24 Fred Perry was World Champion in 1929 in which sport?
25 Which licence was abolished in 1988 after 192 years?
26 The condor belongs to which family of birds?
27 In which country is Arnhem Land?
28 Whose hits include Promise Me and Woman to Woman?
29 Which actor was Gandhi in the 1982 film?
30 Who was first to win four World Snooker Championships in a row?

Answers

TV: Soaps (see Quiz 55, page 175)
1 Grant Mitchell. 2 Florizel Street. 3 Alexis Carrington. 4 Family Affairs.
5 Anthony Newley. 6 Matthew Marsden. 7 Beverley Callard. 8 Geoffrey.
9 Home and Away. 10 In a fire. 11 Morgan. 12 South Africa. 13 Eurostar.
14 Emma. 15 Martin. 16 Toyah. 17 Tate. 18 Brookside. 19 Yorkshire
TV. 20 Frank Tate. 21 Susan Tully (Michelle Fowler). 22 Mandy. 23 Trevor
Jordache. 24 Jasper Carrott. 25 William Roache's. 26 Lake District. 27 The
Woolpackers. 28 Brookside. 29 Margi Clarke. 30 Neighbours.

Quiz 57   Sport: Hot Wheels

Answers - see Quiz 58, page 178

LEVEL 2

1   What does TT stand for in the Isle of Man races?
2   Who first had a record breaking car and a boat called Bluebird?
3   Which is the nearest motor racing track to Towcester?
4   Which team did Jim Clark spend all his racing career with?
5   How many people are in the car in drag racing?
6   Which Belgian cyclist was known as 'The Cannibal'?
7   How many times did Stirling Moss win the world championship?
8   In which country was the first organised car race?
9   Which Labour Party supporter is the head of Formula 1?
10   By 1993 which French driver had won 51 Grand Prix from 199 starts?
11   Which ex world champion was killed at the San Marino Grand Prix in 1993?
12   Which motor racing Park is east of Chester?
13   What type of racing is known in the US as Demolition Derbies?
14   How frequently does the Tour de France take place?
15   Who was the first man to be world champion on two and four wheels?
16   What relation was Emerson to Christian Fittipaldi?
17   Which Japanese team won its first F1 Grand prix in 1967?
18   Who was the first man to win a Grand Prix in a car he designed?
19   Who was Williams' highest placed driver in 1995?
20   In 1994 who was the first Austrian to win the German Grand Prix since Niki Lauda?
21   Which Briton was the first world driver's champion to win Le Mans, in 1972?
22   In which country did the first mountain bike world championship take place?
23   Which Briton did Alain Prost overtake for a record number of Grand Prix wins?
24   Which was the first manufacturer to have over 100 Grand Prix wins?
25   Which famous British car won the Monte Carlo rally in 1967?
26   Who was the first Briton to wear the Tour de France yellow jersey after Tommy Simpson?
27   Who was the first British F1 Champion after James Hunt?
28   Who was the first driver to be sacked by Benetton twice?
29   Who was the first Frenchman to win the World Grand Prix title in '85?
30   Where is the home of the French Grand Prix?

Pot Luck 27 (see Quiz 58, page 178)
1 Fred Perry. 2 Wizzard. 3 Karl Marx. 4 An insect. 5 Skull. 6 Woody Guthrie. 7 Winston Graham. 8 A clock. 9 Russia. 10 Belfast. 11 Bruce Lee. 12 Joy Adamson. 13 Flies. 14 First signatory. 15 Michaelmas Day. 16 A dress. 17 Volcanic eruption. 18 Oak. 19 Goldfinger. 20 Desert-dweller. 21 Remington. 22 Augustus. 23 Rod. 24 Bob Hoskins. 25 The haggis. 26 Jim Reeves. 27 Messengers. 28 Una Stubbs. 29 Tomato. 30 Neneh Cherry.

Quiz 58 Pot Luck 27

Answers - see Quiz 57, page 177

LEVEL 2

1 Which tennis player died on the same day as Donald Pleasence?
2 Whose hits include Ball Park Incident and Rock'n Roll Winter?
3 Who produced the Communist Manifesto with Friedrich Engels?
4 What is a firebrat?
5 Where are your fontanelles?
6 Which American protest singer is linked to the 'dustbowl ballads'?
7 Who wrote the stories subsequently televised as Poldark?
8 In which time device would you find an escapement?
9 The port of Archangel is in which country?
10 The Titanic was launched in which city?
11 Film star Lee Yuen Kam achieved fame as which kung fu expert?
12 Which famous woman who worked with African wildlife was murdered in 1985?
13 Which dirty insects are members of the Diptera family?
14 John Hancock was first to do what at the American Declaration of Independence?
15 In a calendar year what is the third quarter day in England?
16 What is a dirndl?
17 What, in 1902, destroyed the Martinique village of St Pierre?
18 Cork is produced mainly from which species of tree?
19 In which Bond film does the character 'Oddjob' appear?
20 What does the word 'Bedouin' mean?
21 Which family made typewriters and invented the breech-loading rifle?
22 Who was the first Roman Emperor?
23 Which word can be a unit of measure, a stick or a fishing implement?
24 Which actor played a black prostitute's minder in the film Mona Lisa?
25 What did Robert Burns call "great chieftain o' the puddin' race"?
26 Welcome To My World was the first Top Ten hit for whom?
27 Is St Gabriel the patron saint of messengers, millers or musicians?
28 Which actress played the daughter of Alf Garnett?
29 A love apple is an archaic term for what?
30 Whose hits include Manchild and Buffalo Stance?

Answers

Sport: Hot Wheels (see Quiz 57, page 177)
1 Tourist Trophy. 2 Malcolm Campbell. 3 Silverstone. 4 Lotus. 5 One.
6 Eddie Merckx. 7 Never. 8 France. 9 Bernie Ecclestone. 10 Alain Prost.
11 Ayrton Senna. 12 Oulton Park. 13 Stock car racing. 14 Annually.
15 John Surtees. 16 Uncle. 17 Honda. 18 Jack Brabham. 19 Damon Hill.
20 Gerhard Berger. 21 Graham Hill. 22 France. 23 Jackie Stewart.
24 Ferrari. 25 Mini. 26 Chris Boardman. 27 Nigel Mansell. 28 Johnny
Herbert. 29 Alain Prost. 30 Magny Cours.

1 Which actor/director started the trend for spaghetti westerns?
2 What was the nationality of Meryl Streep's character in A Cry in the Dark?
3 Who was shunned by Hollywood in the 40s when she left her husband for Roberto Rossellini?
4 Which poet's name was the middle name of James Dean?
5 Who was Hollywood's first black superstar?
6 Which famous dancer played a straight role in On the Beach?
7 Which Burt appeared in Bean-The Ultimate Disaster Movie?
8 On the set of which film did the Richard Burton/Elizabeth Taylor affair begin?
9 Who, famous as a gangster roles, was a founder of the Screen Actors Guild?
10 Who received her first Oscar nomination for Silkwood?
11 Whose roles vary from Cruella de Vil on film to Norma Desmond on stage?
12 How old was Macaulay Culkin when he was first married?
13 Which married superstars starred in The Big Sleep in 1946?
14 Which comedian co founded United Artists in 1919?
15 Dietrich appeared in the German The Blue Angel, who appeared in the US version?
16 Which actor's last film was The Misfits in 1960?
17 Who was voted No 1 pin up by US soldiers in WWII?
18 How many parts did Alec Guinness play in Kind Hearts and Coronets?
19 What is the profession of Nicole Kidman's father?
20 In which country did Charlie Chaplin spend the final years of his life?
21 Who was Truman in The Truman Show?
22 Which superstar did Tony Curtis parody in Some Like It Hot?
23 Who played the title role in the 1990 Cyrano de Bergerac?
24 Who is the physician in the 90s remake of Doctor Doolittle?
25 How many Road films did Crosby, Hop and Lamour make?
26 Who was the psychotic cabbie in Scorsese's Taxi Driver?
27 Who announced her retirement when she married Ted Turner in '91?
28 Who was Jodie Foster's character in The Silence of the Lambs?
29 Who directed The Horse Whisperer?
30 Who played Margo Channing in All About Eve?

Answers

Pot Luck 28 (see Quiz 60, page 180)
1 Three. 2 A Helicopter. 3 Maria Callas. 4 M People. 5 Labrador.
6 Gabrielle. 7 The Old Curiosity Shop. 8 Greece. 9 On the seabed. 10 Kent.
11 Shoes. 12 Melvyn Hayes. 13 Sistine. 14 Sonny Bono. 15 Bismarck.
16 Le Mans. 17 Sap. 18 Peru. 19 The World War. 20 Pregnant. 21 Jackie
Rae. 22 Aphrodite. 23 Bits and pieces. 24 Guildford. 25 Isle of Wight.
26 The Lion King. 27 Nkima. 28 Whitesnake. 29 Commissioner Dreyfus.
30 A supermarket.

1   How many times did Joe Frasier fight Muhammad Ali?
2   What was designed and made in a viable form by Sikorsky in 1941?
3   Which opera singer died on the same day as Marc Bolan?
4   Who had hits with One Night in Heaven and Moving On Up?
5   Which 'dog like' peninsula formed Canada's tenth province in 1949?
6   What was Coco Chanel's Christian name?
7   Quilp appears in a book about what kind of Shop?
8   In which European country are the Pindus Mountains?
9   If a creature is demersal, where does it live?
10 In which county was the first Youth Custody Centre set up in 1908?
11 Espadrilles are a type of what?
12 Who played the part of 'Gloria' in It Ain't Half Hot, Mum?
13 Michaelangelo painted the ceiling of which famous Chapel?
14 Which rock musician died on the same day as cricketer David Bairstow?
15 Who was called the 'Iron Chancellor'?
16 Where is motor racing's Grand Prix d'Endurance staged?
17 If a creature is succivorous what does it feed on?
18 The source of the Amazon is in which South American country?
19 Al Capone said he was accused of every death except the casualty list of what?
20 If something or someone is gravid what does it mean?
21 Who was the first presenter of the TV series The Golden Shot?
22 In Greek mythology, who was the mother of Eros?
23 What does 'Chop Suey' literally mean?
24 In which city is the University of Surrey?
25 Carisbrooke Castle is on which Isle?
26 In which Disney film is a young lion called Simba?
27 What was the name of Tarzan's monkey friend in the Tarzan stories?
28 Which heavy band's hits include Here I Go Again and Is This Love?
29 Which part was played by Herbert Lom in the Pink Panther films?
30 The 1984 TV series Tripper's Day was set in what type of shop?

Answers

Movie Superstars (see Quiz 59, page 179)
1 Clint Eastwood. 2 Australian. 3 Ingrid Bergman. 4 Byron. 5 Sidney
Poitier. 6 Fred Astaire. 7 Reynolds. 8 Cleopatra. 9 James Cagney. 10 Cher.
11 Glenn Close. 12 17. 13 Lauren Bacall and Humphrey Bogart. 14 Charlie
Chaplin. 15 Dietrich. 16 Clark Gable. 17 Betty Grable. 18 Eight.
19 Psychologist. 20 Switzerland. 21 Jim Carrey. 22 Cary Grant.
23 Gerard Depardieu. 24 Eddie Murphy. 25 Seven. 26 Robert de Niro.
27 Jane Fonda. 28 Clarice Starling. 29 Robert Redford. 30 Bette Davis.

Quiz 61 · On the Map

Answers - see Quiz 62, page 182

1   Which South American city has a famous Copacabana beach?
2   The Bass Strait divides which two islands?
3   Which Middle East capital is known locally as El Qahira?
4   Where is the official country home of US Presidents?
5   Whose Vineyard is an island off Cape Cod?
6   Where was Checkpoint Charlie?
7   Which US state has a 'pan handle' separating the Atlantic from the Gulf of Mexico?
8   In which two countries is the Dead Sea?
9   The site of ancient Babylon is now in which country?
10   On which river is the Aswan Dam?
11   Which continent produces almost 50% of the world's cars?
12   The Fens were formerly a bay of which Sea?
13   What is Japan's highest peak?
14   To which country do the Galapagos Islands belong?
15   Aconcagua is an extinct volcano in which mountain range?
16   Where in California is the lowest point of the western hemisphere?
17   In which London Square is the US Embassy?
18   Ellis Island is in which harbour?
19   Which city is known to Afrikaaners as Kaapstad?
20   On which Sea is the Gaza Strip?
21   What are the three divisions of Glamorgan?
22   Which river cuts through the Grand Canyon?
23   In which Ethiopian city is the HQ of the Organisation of African Unity?
24   Which continents are separated by the Dardanelles?
25   Which US state capital means 'sheltered bay' in Hawaiian?
26   Hampstead is part of which London borough?
27   Which country owns the southernmost part of South America?
28   Where is the seat of the UN International Court of Justice?
29   The Golan Heights are on the border of which two countries?
30   Which is the saltiest of the main oceans?

Answers

Pot Luck 29 (see Quiz 62, page 182)
1   West Side Story. **2**   Tom and Jerry. **3**   Love. **4**   John Hunt. **5**   Solomon.
6   The Real Thing. **7**   Rugby League. **8**   Potato famine. **9**   Language sounds.
10   Joe Louis. **11**   Tom Cruise. **12**   Robert Mugabe. **13**   Calcium. **14**   40.
15   Honeysuckle. **16**   Basil Brush. **17**   Mike McGear. **18**   Nine. **19**   Rock
Hudson. **20**   Fred Astaire. **21**   Trampolining. **22**   Niagara Falls.
23   Bournemouth. **24**   Pele. **25**   Mariah Carey. **26**   A Nelson. **27**   Britain.
28   Freddie Laker. **29**   Holland. **30**   15th.

Quiz 62 Pot Luck 29

Answers - see Quiz 61, page 181

LEVEL 2

1 The song America comes from which musical?

2 Which cartoon duo starred in the Oscar winning film Quiet Please?

3 Kate Bush had an album called The Hounds Of ...what?

4 In 1953 who was leader of the British expedition which conquered Everest?

5 In The Bible who did the Queen of Sheba visit according to Kings I?

6 Who had a UK Top Ten hit with Can You Feel the Force?

7 Which sport was founded in Britain on 28th August 1895?

8 Black Forty Seven in Ireland in the 19th century related to what?

9 What is phonetics the study of?

10 Who was World Heavyweight boxing champion in WWII?

11 Which actor links Risky Business, Cocktail and Top Gun?

12 Who was the first president of Zimbabwe?

13 Which element is found in shells, bones and teeth?

14 How old are you if you are a quadragenarian?

15 Which flower is also called the Woodbine?

16 Which children's TV puppet was operated by Ivan Owen?

17 Paul McCartney's brother Mike is known as whom?

18 What is the most times a day of the week can occur in two months?

19 Who was older when they died Humphrey Bogart or Rock Hudson?

20 Who starred opposite Judy Garland in the film Easter Parade?

21 In which sport are there moves called Triffus, Rudolf and Miller?

22 The Horseshoe and American combine to form which famous falls?

23 Which is further west, Bognor or Bournemouth?

24 Which Brazilian footballer appeared in a film called Hotshot?

25 Who has had hits with Hero and Anytime You Need A Friend?

26 What name is given to a score of 111 in cricket?

27 In Orwell's 1984 what is called Airstrip One?

28 Whose cheap transatlantic air service in 1977 was called 'Skytrain'?

29 Which team did Argentina beat in the 1978 Football World Cup Final?

30 In which century was the Battle of Agincourt?

Answers

On the Map (see Quiz 61, page 181)
1 Rio de Janeiro. 2 Australia & Tasmania. 3 Cairo. 4 Camp David.
5 Martha's Vineyard. 6 Between East and West Berlin. 7 Florida. 8 Israel &
Jordan. 9 Iraq. 10 Nile. 11 Europe. 12 North Sea. 13 Mount Fujiyama.
14 Ecuador. 15 Andes. 16 Death Valley. 17 Grosvenor. 18 New York.
19 Cape Town. 20 Mediterranean. 21 Mid, South, West. 22 Colorado.
23 Addis Ababa. 24 Europe & Asia. 25 Honolulu. 26 Camden. 27 Chile.
28 The Hague. 29 Israel & Syria. 30 Atlantic.

Quiz 63 Nature: Plant World

LEVEL 2

Answers - see Quiz 64, page 184

1   Which cereal can survive in the widest range of climatic conditions?
2   The hellebore is known as what type of rose?
3   What colour are edelweiss flowers?
4   Which plant is St Patrick said to have used to illustrate the Holy Trinity?
5   Succulents live in areas lacking in what?
6   How many points does a sycamore leaf have?
7   What is the ornamental shaping of trees and shrubs called?
8   What is an alternative name for the narcotic and analgesic aconite?
9   What colour are laburnum flowers?
10   What is another name for a yam?
11   What shape are flowers which include the name campanula?
12   What is a frond on a plant?
13   Which climbing plant is also called hedera helix?
14   Agronomy is the study of what?
15   What is a Sturmer?
16   Which fruit is called 'earth berry' in German from where the plant grows?
17   What is another name for belladonna?
18   What is the effect on the nervous system of taking hemlock?
19   Are the male, female or either hop plants used to make beer?
20   What is the most common plant grown in Assam in India?
21   Aspen is what type of tree?
22   Which ingredient in tonic water is found in cinchona bark?
23   The ground powder form turmeric dyes food which colour?
24   The pineapple plant is native to which continent?
25   What is the purpose of a plant's petals?
26   Which type of pesticide is used to kill weeds?
27   What colour are the leaves of a poinsettia?
28   What name is given to the wild yellow iris?
29   Which plant is famous for having a 'clock'?
30   What colour are borage flowers?

Answers

Pot Luck 30 (see Quiz 64, page 184)
1 Nancy Reagan. 2 Kool & The Gang. 3 The sun (Bright area). 4 Australia.
5 Sierra Leone. 6 Devon. 7 Sherry. 8 Lotus. 9 Statue of Zeus. 10 15th.
11 Cacao. 12 G B Shaw. 13 An elephant. 14 Firm when bitten. 15 Oliver
Cromwell. 16 Emporio Label. 17 Bob Geldof. 18 A weaver. 19 The lion.
20 Tom Kite. 21 London. 22 Thanksgiving Day. 23 Jemma Redgrave.
24 Van Gogh. 25 A cob. 26 I'm Still Waiting. 27 Offspring. 28 Genesis.
29 Richard O'Brien. 30 A juke box.

Quiz 64   Pot Luck 30

LEVEL 2

Answers - see Quiz 63, page 183

1   Which former First Lady was nicknamed 'The Smiling Mamba'?
2   Who had hits with Joanna and Celebration?
3   Where would you see a facula?
4   DJ Alan Freeman was born in which country?
5   Which country has a unit of currency called the Leone?
6   The seaside town of Westward Ho is in which county?
7   Oloroso is a type of which drink?
8   Which car manufacturer designed the winning bike for Chris Boardman?
9   Which Wonder of the World statue was at Olympia?
10 In which century did William Caxton establish the first English printing press?
11 Cocoa is prepared from the seeds of which tree?
12 Who wrote Androcles and the Lion?
13 What is driven by a mahout?
14 What does the cooking expression al dente mean?
15 Which Oliver was Lord Protector of Britain?
16 Which label is distinguished as fashion designed by Armani?
17 Which celeb's childhood nickname was Liver Lips?
18 Who would use a jacquard?
19 In The Wizard of Oz, which animal was seeking courage?
20 Who captained the US Ryder Cup team in 1997?
21 In which city is the HQ of Amnesty International?
22 Pumpkin Pie is the traditional dessert on which special American day?
23 Who played Eleanor Bramwell in the TV series of the same name?
24 Who painted The Starry Night?
25 Which word can be a swan, a horse, a bread roll and a basket?
26 What was Diana Ross's first solo Number 1 in the UK?
27 What are progeny?
28 Who had hits with I Can't Dance and Invisible Touch?
29 Who preceded Ed Tudor-Pole as host of the Crystal Maze?
30 If you heard a John Gabel Entertainer, what would be playing?

Nature: Plant World (see Quiz 63, page 183)

Answers

1 Barley. 2 Christmas rose. 3 White. 4 Shamrock. 5 Water. 6 Five.
7 Topiary. 8 Monkshood. 9 Yellow. 10 Sweet potato. 11 Bell shaped.
12 Leaf. 13 Ivy. 14 Crops and soils. 15 Apple. 16 Strawberry.
17 Deadly nightshade. 18 Paralysis. 19 Female. 20 Tea. 21 Poplar.
22 Quinine. 23 Yellow. 24 South America. 25 Attract pollinators.
26 Herbicide. 27 Red. 28 Flag. 29 Dandelion. 30 Blue.

Quiz 65 Past Times: The 70s

Answers - see Quiz 66, page 186

LEVEL 2

1. Germany's Red Army Faction was popularly called what after its two founders?
2. The Equal Opportunities Commission was set up to implement which act?
3. Who became US Vice President after Spiro Agnew resigned?
4. Where did the Gang of Four seize power in 1976?
5. Which natural disaster did Guatemala city suffer in 1976?
6. In the Vietnam War who or what was Agent Orange?
7. Who was Nixon's White House Chief of Staff at the height of the Watergate scandal?
8. On which Pennsylvania Island was there a nuclear leak in 1979?
9. In 1978 Mujaheddin resistance began in which country?
10. Who made a precocious speech aged 16 at the 1977 Tory Party conference?
11. Who opened her first Body Shop in 1976?
12. Where was Obote replaced by Amin in 1971?
13. The Pahlavi Dynasty was overthrown by the Islamic revolution in which country?
14. Which Argentine leader died in 1974 and was succeeded by his third wife?
15. Which woman MP did Jack Straw replace as MP for Blackburn?
16. How were Patrick Armstrong, Gerard Conlon, Paul Hill and Carole Richardson known collectively?
17. Which dictator was deposed in Cambodia in 1979?
18. Which 'King' died in 1977 aged 42?
19. What was Harare called until the end of the 1970s?
20. What was inside US incendiary bombs during the Vietnam War?
21. Which title did Quintin Hogg take when made Lord Chancellor in '70?
22. SALT negotiations took place between which two countries?
23. Which future Labour leader became Trade & Industry Secretary in '78?
24. Mario Soares was exiled from which country in 1970?
25. In which country was a monarchy restored in 1975?
26. The Sandinistas overthrew which government in 1979?
27. Who succeeded Heath as Tory leader?
28. Sapporo was the centre of the 1972 winter Olympics in which country?
29. Which country did the USSR invade in 1979?
30. In which department was Thatcher a Minister before leading the Party?

Answers

TV: TV Times 1 (see Quiz 66, page 186)
1 The Teletones. 2 Nephew. 3 Warrior. 4 Miss America. 5 New Faces.
6 Helicopters. 7 Liverpool. 8 Eddie Izzard. 9 Elton John. 10 Ulrika
Jonsson. 11 Assumpta. 12 Carla Lane. 13 Shoplifting. 14 David Coleman.
15 Pink. 16 Trevor McDonald. 17 Bingo. 18 Jennifer Patterson. 19 Tony
Slattery. 20 Torvill & Dean. 21 Delia Smith. 22 Televangelism. 23 Anthony
Andrews. 24 Sian Lloyd. 25 Sam Malone. 26 The Bee Gees. 27 Wimbledon.
28 Ricki Lake. 29 John Virgo. 30 On a bed.

Quiz 66 TV: TV Times 1

LEVEL 2

1   What is the name of the singing group in The Hello Girls?

2   What relation is ER's George Clooney to US singer Rosemary?

3   Which Gladiator was jailed in 1998 for corruption?

4   Superwoman Lynda Carter held which beauty queen title?

5   On which TV show was Jim Davidson 'discovered'?

6   Outside TV what type of transport business does Noel Edmonds run?

7   Where was This Morning first broadcast from?

8   Which They Think It's All Over panellist wears most make up?

9   The TV profile Tantrums and Tiaras was about which pop superstar?

10   Which TV presenter's relationship with Stan Collymore ended violently in Paris during the 1998 World Cup?

11   Who was the first landlady of Fitzgerald's in Ballykissangel?

12   Which TV playwright founded Animal Line with Linda McCartney?

13   What was Richard Madeley arrested for in 1990?

14   Which veteran sports commentator won the Manchester Mile in 1949?

15   What colour does TV critic Nina Myskow usually wear?

16   Which News At Ten presenter had the first British TV interview with Nelson Mandela after his release?

17   Which game was Bob's Full House based on?

18   Which TV cook wears a diamond studded crash helmet?

19   Who presented the C5 medical quiz show Tibs and Fibs?

20   Who were the first couple to be BBC Sports Personality of the Year?

21   Which cook founded Sainsbury's The Magazine with her husband?

22   In the US Jim Bakker and Jimmy Swaggart are famous for what type of show?

23   Which star of Brideshead Revisited shares a birthday with sports commentator Brendan Foster?

24   Which weather girl went to the same university as Glenys Kinnock?

25   Which character did Ted Danson play in Cheers?

26   Which pop group walked out on Clive Anderson on his All Talk show?

27   Which London soccer side does June Whitfield support?

28   Which talk show hostess appeared in the film Hairspray with Divine?

29   Who is the resident snooker player on Big Break?

30   Where did Paula Yates conduct her Big Breakfast interviews?

Answers

Past Times: The 70s (see Quiz 65, page 185)

1 Baader-Meinhof Gang. 2 Sex Discrimination Act. 3 Gerald Ford. 4 China. 5 Earthquake. 6 Weedkiller. 7 Alexander Haig. 8 Three Mile Island. 9 Afghanistan. 10 William Hague. 11 Anita Roddick. 12 Uganda. 13 Iran. 14 Peron. 15 Barbara Castle. 16 The Guildford Four. 17 Pol Pot. 18 Elvis Presley. 19 Salisbury. 20 Napalm. 21 Lord Hailsham. 22 USA & USSR. 23 John Smith. 24 Portugal. 25 Spain. 26 Nicaragua. 27 Thatcher. 28 Japan. 29 Afghanistan. 30 Education.

Quiz 67 Pot Luck 31

Answers - see Quiz 68, page 188

LEVEL 2

1   What was Annie Oakley's first name?
2   Which famous survey started in 1086?
3   What was Roger's wife called in the film Who Framed Roger Rabbit?
4   Ronald Reagan was in which political party?
5   Who is taller – Claire Rayner or Pauline Quirke?
6   In The Bible, what was the prophet Elijah carried up to heaven in?
7   What nationality was Casanova?
8   What was Al Jolson's most famous line?
9   If a substance is oleaginous what does it mainly contain?
10 Which General led the junta in the 1982 seizure of the Falklands?
11 Which famous Castle is on the River Dee?
12 What did the Owl and the Pussycat dine on?
13 Vera Welch sang under what name?
14 Which Christopher was a policeman before he became a champion skater?
15 Which outlandish musician's real name was Simon Ritchie?
16 Which handicapped physicist has appeared in adverts for 'BT'?
17 Who is buried at the Arc de Triomphe?
18 During exercise which acid builds up in the muscles?
19 Who is spiritual leader to the Ismaili sect of Muslims?
20 Which singer had a backing group called the Checkmates?
21 What is added to egg yolks and vanilla to make advocaat?
22 Who played 'Blanco' in the TV series Porridge?
23 What nationality was Rachmaninov the composer?
24 What is xerography?
25 Which 1956 hit links The Platters with a 1987 Freddie Mercury hit?
26 Which Dutch town is particularly famous for its blue pottery?
27 Where would you find an apse?
28 What was abolished on 18th December 1969 in Britain?
29 Which tycoon started the newspaper called Today?
30 Who was the first golfer to lose play-offs in all four majors?

Pop Music: Albums (see Quiz 68, page 188)
1 Chris Rea. 2 Chicago XIII. 3 Eternal. 4 George Michael. 5 News of the World. 6 The Revolution. 7 Pet Shop Boys. 8 Frank Sinatra. 9 Wet Wet Wet. 10 Sting. 11 No Parlez. 12 River Deep - Mountain High. 13 Wannabe. 14 Definitely/Maybe. 15 Pulp. 16 Just Good Friends. 17 Emmerdance. 18 Blue. 19 Physical. 20 Slippery When Wet. 21 The Rolling Stones. 22 Sex. 23 Nigel Kennedy. 24 Gasoline Alley. 25 Goat. 26 The Wall. 27 Enya. 28 Waterloo. 29 Ten. 30 Diva.

Quiz 68 Pop Music: Albums

Answers - see Quiz 67, page 187

LEVEL 2

1   Who released the album Auberge?
2   What was the thirteenth album released by Chicago?
3   Which group's debut album, Always & Forever, shadowed their name?
4   Whose debut solo album was called Faith?
5   Which Queen album shares its name with a newspaper?
6   On the 80s album Purple Rain who backed Prince?
7   Which duo released albums called Introspective and Very?
8   Which US superstar has had over 70 chart albums in his career?
9   High On the Happy Side was a No 1 album for which band in '92?
10 Who guested with Dire Straits on the Money For Nothing track?
11 Which phrase with a French flavour was the title of Paul Young's debut album?
12 What was the title of Ike and Tina Turner's only album?
13 What is the first track on Spice?
14 A picture of Burt Bacharach appeared on the cover of which best selling 90s album?
15 Whose debut album was called Different Class?
16 Which Paul Nicholas album was named after a sitcom in which he starred?
17 What was the title of the album by the Woolpackers?
18 On the Beautiful South's 1996 album what is the Colour?
19 Which Olivia Newton-John '81 album could describe some exercise?
20 Which Bon Jovi album was best kept dry?
21 What was the title of the first album released by The Rolling Stones?
22 What were Madonna's book and 1992 album called?
23 Which musician took Vivaldi's The Four Seasons into the charts?
24 Rod Stewart's first album was called after which alley?
25 What animal is on the cover of the Beach Boy's album Pet Sounds?
26 Which construction has given its name to a Pink Floyd album?
27 Which Irish singer got to No 1 with Shepherd Moons?
28 Which battle was the title of the first Abba album?
29 How many Good Reasons had Jason Donovan on his first No 1?
30 Which Annie Lennox album topped the charts in 1993?

Pot Luck 31 (see Quiz 67, page 187)
Pot Luck 31 1 Phoebe. 2 Domesday Book. 3 Jessica. 4 Republican Party. 5 Claire
Rayner. 6 A fiery chariot. 7 Italian. 8 You ain't heard nothing yet. 9 Oil.
10 Galtieri. 11 Balmoral. 12 Mince and slices of quince. 13 Vera Lynn .
14 Dean. 15 Sid Vicious. 16 Stephen Hawking. 17 The Unknown Soldier.
18 Lactic Acid. 19 The Aga Khan. 20 Emile Ford. 21 Brandy. 22 David
Jason. 23 Russian. 24 Photocopying. 25 The Great Pretender. 26 Delft. 27
A church. 28 Death Penalty. 29 Eddie Shah. 30 Greg Norman.

Quiz 69 Pot Luck 32

Answers - see Quiz 70, page 190

LEVEL 2

1 Who formed the famous dance troupe the Bluebell Girls?
2 Whose CDs include Seven Year Itch and Stickin' to my Guns?
3 What would you do with a futon?
4 Which play is performed every ten years at Oberammagau?
5 Which wood was mainly used by Thomas Chippendale?
6 In which London area is The Royal Hospital?
7 Which Lynne is Duggie Brown's sister?
8 Bruce Willis destroyed a plane with his cigarette lighter in which film?
9 What does a blue flag at a beach mean?
10 Which carbohydrate causes jam to gel?
11 If a dog is suffering from 'hard pad' what form of disease has it got?
12 What is a hawser?
13 What was Roy Schneider's profession in the film Jaws?
14 Theophobia is a fear of what?
15 In which French town was Joan of Arc burnt at the stake?
16 What was the name of cowboy Tom Mix's horse ?
17 The quail is the smallest member of which bird species?
18 What is the singular of axes in mathematics?
19 Which actress's real name was Maria Magdalena von Losch?
20 Which port is the most easterly in Britain?
21 What is the common weather in a pluvial region?
22 Which Polynesian word means prohibited or forbidden?
23 What colour is the egg of a kingfisher?
24 The Dodecanese Islands are in which sea?
25 What nationality was Secretary General of the UN Boutros Boutros Ghali?
26 What part was played by Irene Handl in For the Love of Ada?
27 Whose hits include Sunny Afternoon and Tired of Waiting For You?
28 What is on top of the Mona Lisa's left hand?
29 What do Americans call Perspex?
30 In fishing what is another name for a pike-perch?

Leisure 3 (see Quiz 70, page 190)

Answers

1 Deep sea diving. 2 Stamps. 3 Green. 4 Circular. 5 Yoga. 6 Cribbage.
7 Admiral's Cup. 8 Lacrosse. 9 Gare Du Nord. 10 RSPB. 11 Pottery.
12 Star Wars. 13 13 tricks by one team. 14 Harrods. 15 Synchronised
swimming. 16 Cadbury, Fry, Rowntree. 17 The Netherlands. 18 Tennis.
19 Pizza Express. 20 Golf Club. 21 Women's Institute. 22 World Wildlife
Fund. 23 Whipsnade. 24 Tintin. 25 Dark green. 26 Hammer.
27 Wrestling. 28 Isle of Wight. 29 York. 30 Leicester.

Quiz 70 Leisure 3

1 After what sort of activity might you suffer from the bends?
2 What would you buy from Stanley Gibbons?
3 What colour are houses in Monopoly?
4 What shape is a sumo wrestling ring?
5 Which Hindu system of philosophy is used as a means of exercise and meditation in the west?
6 In which game do you score 'one for his knob'?
7 The Fastnet race is part of the contest for which Cup?
8 Which game's name comes from a piece of its equipment looking like a bishop's crosier?
9 At which station do you arrive in Paris if you have travelled from the UK by Eurostar?
10 The YOC is the junior branch of which organisation?
11 If you were a collector of Clarice Cliff what would you collect?
12 A Monopoly game based on which Sci-fi film was released in 1997?
13 What is a grand slam in Bridge?
14 House of Fraser owns which major London store?
15 What sort of swimming takes place with musical accompaniment?
16 Which three Quaker families made most of Britain's chocolate?
17 In which country is De Efteling Theme Park?
18 Which sport is played at London's Queen's Club?
19 Which pizza restaurant was the first of a chain founded in London?
20 What sort of club is the Royal and Ancient?
21 Which organisation's anthem is Jerusalem?
22 What was the Worldwide Fund for Nature formerly called?
23 Which open air zoo is near Dunstable in Bedfordshire?
24 Which boy reporter was created by Belgian artist Herge?
25 What colour carrier bag do you get when you shop at Laura Ashley?
26 In athletics, what is attached to a chain and a handle and thrown?
27 Which sport has Greco-Roman and Freestyle, as two distinct styles?
28 The annual Round the Isle race goes round which Isle?
29 Where is the National Railway Museum?
30 Where were Walker's Crisps first made?

Answers

Pot Luck 32 (see Quiz 69, page 189)

1 Margaret Kelly. 2 Etta James. 3 Sleep on it. 4 The Passion Play. 5 Mahogany. 6 Chelsea. 7 Lynne Perrie. 8 Die Hard 2. 9 Clean & pollution free. 10 Pectin. 11 Distemper. 12 A rope. 13 Police Chief. 14 God. 15 Rouen. 16 Tony. 17 Partridge. 18 Axis. 19 Marlene Dietrich. 20 Lowestoft. 21 Rain. 22 Taboo. 23 White. 24 Aegean Sea. 25 Egyptian. 26 Ada. 27 The Kinks. 28 Her right hand. 29 Plexiglass. 30 Zander.

Quiz 71 Pot Luck 33

Answers - see Quiz 72, page 192

LEVEL 2

1 What describes descending a sheer face by sliding down a rope?
2 Donna Reed replaced Barbara Bel Geddes in which TV series?
3 Who is Princess Alexandra's son?
4 Which animal is feared by a hippophobe?
5 Whose hits include Wide Boy and Wouldn't It Be Good?
6 The novel Shirley was written by which of the Bronte sisters?
7 In which London building does the Lutine Bell hang?
8 Which is further south, Folkestone or Southampton?
9 Which American sportsman was said to be earning more than the US president in 1925?
10 Which famous bear came from Peru?
11 What did the S stand for in Charlie Chaplin's middle name?
12 Who was Shirley Maclaine named after?
13 What is a passepied?
14 Which species can be Fairy, Black-footed and Crested?
15 Which game uses flattened iron rings thrown at a hob?
16 What was the title of Captain Sensible's No 1 UK hit in 1982?
17 Which European Commissioner once played in a band called The Rebels?
18 Which country won the 1992 World Cup cricket final?
19 What is tansy?
20 Which island is in the Bay of Naples?
21 Whose hits include Something About You and Lessons In Love?
22 Cyril Mead became known as which comic?
23 In the order of accession to the British throne who is the first female?
24 In which London Square is the American Embassy?
25 What is a taipan?
26 Is Coventry north or south of Leicester?
27 Which English King was the last to die in battle?
28 Who was older when they died Peter Sellers or Tony Hancock?
29 What is the smallest administrative unit in the Church of England?
30 In Pride and Prejudice who does Elizabeth Bennet finally marry?

Answers

Record Breakers (see Quiz 72, page 192)
1 Donald Budge. 2 Kapil Dev. 3 Stefan Edberg. 4 Chris Evert. 5 Nick Faldo. 6 Sally Gunnell. 7 Billie Jean King. 8 Skiing. 9 Gabriela Sabatini. 10 Brian Lara. 11 Seven. 12 Ian Woosnam. 13 Steve Ovett's. 14 Karen Pickering. 15 Steve Davis. 16 Frankie Fredericks. 17 Sandy Lyle. 18 Sugar Ray Leonard. 19 Monica Seles. 20 James Wattana. 21 Freestyle & butterfly. 22 Ian Rush. 23 Mike Powell. 24 Seve Ballesteros. 25 Johnny Haynes. 26 Ed Moses. 27 Geoff Capes. 28 McColgan. 29 Ipswich. 30 Graham Hill.

Quiz 72 Record Breakers

Answers - see Quiz 71, page 191

1 Which American was the first to win the Men's Singles Grand Slam?

2 Who in 1979 became the youngest player to complete the double of 1,000 runs and 100 wickets?

3 Which Swede, in 1987 was the first man for 40 years to win a match at Wimbledon without losing a game?

4 Who was the first woman tennis player to win $1 million?

5 Who was the first Briton after 1950 to win the British Open golf three years in succession?

6 Who was the first woman athlete to win the athletics Grand Slam?

7 Which woman won 20 Wimbledon titles between 1961 and 1979?

8 Franz Klammer was a record breaker in which sport?

9 Which woman became the youngest Wimbledon semi finalist for 99 years in 1986?

10 Who broke the world record for an individual innings of 501 in 1994?

11 How many world records did Mark Spitz break when he won his seven gold medals?

12 Who, in 1987, was the first British golfer to win the World Match-Play Championship?

13 Whose 1500m world record did Steve Cram break in 1985?

14 Who was the first British woman swimmer to win a world title?

15 Who made the first televised 147 break in snooker in 1982?

16 Which Namibian was the first to break the indoor 20 second barrier?

17 Who was the first British winner of the US Masters in 1988?

18 In 1988 who became the first boxer to win world titles at five official weights?

19 Who in 1991 was the youngest woman ever to have the No 1 tennis ranking?

20 Who was the first Thai snooker player to win a major tournament?

21 In 1972 Mark Spitz broke Olympic records doing which two strokes?

22 Who holds the record for most goals scored in FA Cup Finals?

23 Who broke Bob Beaman's long jump record set at the 1968 Olympics?

24 Who was the then youngest ever winner of the US Masters in 1980?

25 Who was the first British soccer player to earn £100 per week?

26 Which US hurdler was undefeated in 122 races?

27 Which British shot putter was world No 1 in 1975?

28 Which Liz won the fastest ever debut marathon when she won in New York in 1991?

29 Which Town did Man Utd beat by a record nine goals in 1995?

30 Who in 1968 became the oldest Briton to win a Grand Prix?

Pot Luck 33 (see Quiz 71, page 191)

Answers

1 Abseiling. 2 Dallas. 3 James Ogilvy. 4 Horses. 5 Nik Kershaw.
6 Charlotte. 7 Lloyds of London. 8 Southampton. 9 Babe Ruth.
10 Paddington. 11 Spencer. 12 Shirley Temple. 13 A dance. 14 Penguins.
15 Quoits. 16 Happy Talk. 17 Neil Kinnock. 18 Pakistan. 19 A herb.
20 Capri. 21 Level 42. 22 Syd Little. 23 Princess Beatrice. 24 Grosvenor
Square. 25 A snake. 26 South. 27 Richard III. 28 Peter Sellers. 29 A
Parish. 30 Mr Darcy.

Quiz 73 Pot Luck 34

Answers - see Quiz 74, page 194

LEVEL 2

1   Where is fibrin found in your body?

2   Which two countries are on the Iberian peninsula?

3   Which group had hits including Homely Girl and Kingston Town?

4   The word 'ketchup' comes which language?

5   Who played the priest in the TV series The Paradise Club?

6   Which species of bird does the wapacat belong to?

7   Which Marx brother died on the same day as Joyce Grenfell?

8   Woburn Abbey is the home of which family?

9   What is a durian?

10 Which film starred John Cleese as an under pressure headmaster?

11 The composer Bela Bartok came from which country?

12 What can be an animal enclosure or a unit of weight?

13 What does the abbreviation BHP stand for?

14 Which poetic names lend themselves to an expression for a devoted, elderly couple?

15 How does a judge hear a case when it is heard In Camera?

16 From 1968 to 1970 which actor was Mr Universe?

17 What does the word 'biscuit' literally mean?

18 The Lent Lily is sometimes used as another name for which flower?

19 What is a Tree Ear?

20 What was Little Lord Fauntleroy's name?

21 Toad of Toad Hall was a dramatised version of which Kenneth Grahame tale?

22 Which sport is Clare Francis famous for?

23 In the film Look Who's Talking whose voice was the baby's thoughts?

24 Which tree usually provides the wood for the Highland Games caber?

25 Whose hits include Wishing Well and All Right Now?

26 What colour is the tongue of a giraffe?

27 Which actor played the title role in Judge Dredd?

28 Californian, Yellow Horned and Opium are all types of which flower?

29 Where is the Sea of Vapours?

30 What is the wading bird the bittern's cry called?

The Oscars (see Quiz 74, page 194)
1 Cher. 2 Casablanca. 3 The Deer Hunter. 4 Christy Brown. 5 Henry Fonda. 6 As Good As It Gets. 7 Philadelphia. 8 Marlee Matlin. 9 James Cameron. 10 Philadelphia, Forrest Gump. 11 Gary Cooper. 12 Butler. 13 1930s. 14 Woody Allen. 15 The Godfather. 16 Dustin Hoffman. 17 Frank Sinatra. 18 Schindler's List. 19 She never spoke. 20 Walter & John Huston. 21 Meryl Streep. 22 Bette Davis. 23 Jessica Tandy. 24 Eight (all of them). 25 Kathy Bates. 26 Oscar. 27 Vivien Leigh. 28 Anthony Minghella. 29 Tatum O'Neal. 30 Helena Bonham-Carter.

Quiz 74 The Oscars

Answers - see Quiz 73, page 193

1   Which singing Oscar winner said, "women get all excited about nothing - then marry him"?

2   Which World War II film would have been called Dar el-Beida had it been titled in the local language?

3   Which Michael Cimino film about Vietnam won five Oscars in the 70s?

4   Who did Daniel-Day Lewis portray in My Left Foot?

5   Which veteran won an Oscar in 1981 two years after his daughter?

6   For which movie did Helen Hunt win in 1997?

7   For which film did Tom Hanks win playing a lawyer dying from AIDS?

8   Who overcame deafness to win for Children of a Lesser God?

9   Who won the Best Director award for Titanic?

10   For which films did Tom Hanks win in successive years?

11   Who won the Best Actor Oscar for High Noon?

12   What type of worker did John Gielgud play when he won his Oscar for Arthur?

13   In which decade did Katharine Hepburn win her first Oscar?

14   Who won three Oscars for Annie Hall?

15   For which film did Brando win his second Oscar?

16   Who won his first best actor Oscar for Kramer vs. Kramer?

17   Which singer won an Oscar for From Here to Eternity?

18   For which film did Steven Spielberg win his first award?

19   What was unusual about Holly Hunter's performance in The Piano?

20   Which father and son actor and director won for The Treasure of the Sierra Madre?

21   In the year Gandhi won almost everything who was Best Actress for Sophie's Choice?

22   Who won Oscars for Dangerous, Jezebel and All About Eve?

23   Who won as Dan Aykroyd's mother in Driving Miss Daisy?

24   How many times between 1990 and 1997 did Best Picture and Best Director Oscars go to the same film?

25   Who played the psychotic nurse in Misery and won Best Actress?

26   What did Anthony Hopkins win first, a knighthood or an Oscar?

27   Who won for her role as Blanch in A Streetcar Named Desire?

28   Who won Best Director for The English Patient?

29   Who won for her first film Paper Moon?

30   Which actress was nominated for The Wings of the Dove?

Answers

Pot Luck 34 (see Quiz 73, page 193)
1   In the blood. 2   Spain and Portugal. 3   UB40. 4   Chinese. 5   Don Henderson. 6   An owl. 7   Zeppo. 8   Dukes of Bedford. 9   A fruit. 10   Clockwise. 11   Hungary . 12   Pound. 13   Brake horse-power. 14   Darby and Joan. 15   In private. 16   Arnold Schwarzenegger. 17   'Twice-cooked'. 18   Daffodil. 19   A mushroom. 20   Cedric Errol. 21   The Wind In The Willows. 22   Sailing. 23   Bruce Willis. 24   Larch. 25   Free. 26   Blue. 27   Sylvester Stallone. 28   Poppy. 29   The Moon. 30   A Boom.

Quiz 75 Pot Luck 35

Answers - see Quiz 76, page 196

LEVEL 2

1   What are Spode, Bow and Chelsea all types of?
2   A covey is the collective name for a group of which birds?
3   Which Italian area produces Chianti?
4   Which scale measures the level of alkalinity and acidity?
5   Who did Jackie Kennedy marry in 1968?
6   Where will you return to if you throw a coin into the Trevi Fountain?
7   What in your body are affected by phlebitis?
8   In which Open did Ballesteros win his first pro tournament, in 1974?
9   Whose hits include Again and That's the Way Love Goes ?
10 Which TV character lived on Scatterbrook Farm?
11 Which High Street travel agent's devised the holiday package tour?
12 In finance what is a PEP?
13 Which store chain claims they are "never knowingly undersold"?
14 What does the Greek odeon mean?
15 If you were using a tambour, what needlecraft would you be doing?
16 What is the currency of Greece?
17 Which TV detective was played by George Peppard?
18 In which century was cockfighting banned?
19 Which supermarket chain paid for the new National Gallery wing opened in 1991?
20 Cars with the international vehicle registration ET come from where?
21 Who started the Habitat chain of shops in 1964?
22 Who is smaller Janet Street Porter or Naomi Campbell?
23 Edmonton is the capital of which Canadian province?
24 Who played Shirley Valentine in the film?
25 What is the white of an egg called as an alternative to albumen?
26 Which 007 actor was also TV's Remington Steele?
27 The Ashanti tribe live in which African country?
28 Whose hits include Finally and We Got a Love Thing?
29 What is held annually in London in Ranelagh Gardens?
30 Where was tennis star Monica Seles playing when she was stabbed?

Answers

Famous Names (see Quiz 76, page 196)
1 Gianni Versace. 2 Pierre Cardin. 3 Queen Mother. 4 Ffion. 5 Getty.
6 Madonna. 7 Elizabeth. 8 Pakistan. 9 Mao Zedong. 10 Monica Lewinsky.
11 Bryan Ferry. 12 Vivienne Westwood. 13 Pamela Anderson. 14 Emma
Forbes. 15 Both vicars. 16 Tony Blair. 17 Jack Rosenthal. 18 Brian Jones.
19 The Duchess of York. 20 Carol. 21 Football. 22 Egyptian. 23 Jane.
24 Gloria Hunniford. 25 Imelda Marcos. 26 Step daughter. 27 Michael.
28 Lord of the Dance. 29 Magic Johnson. 30 A fashion label.

195

Quiz 76 Famous Names

Answers - see Quiz 75, page 195

LEVEL 2

1 Whose funeral in Milan in 1997 was attended by Elton John and Naomi Campbell?
2 Which Frenchman was the first to launch menswear and ready to wear collections?
3 How is the former Lady Elizabeth Bowes-Lyon better known?
4 What is the first name of Mrs William Hague?
5 Which oil billionaire founded the world's highest funded art gallery?
6 Which famous American enrolled her baby daughter for Cheltenham Ladies College in September 1998?
7 What is John and Norma Major's daughter called?
8 Where did Diana make a fund raising trip to with Jemima Khan?
9 Chiang Ching was the third wife of which political leader?
10 Linda Tripp was the confidante of which famous name?
11 Which singer has a son called Otis after Otis Redding?
12 Which fashion designer launched a perfume called Boudoir?
13 According to the Guiness Book of Records who is the most mentioned woman on the Internet?
14 Who is Nanette Newman's famous TV presenter daughter?
15 What did David Frost's and Virginia Wade's father have in common?
16 Whose first names are Anthony Charles Lynton?
17 Which playwright is Maureen Lipman's husband?
18 Which Rolling Stone bought, and died at A.A. Milne's house?
19 Who was described in Blackwell's Worst Dressed list as 'the bare toed terror of London town'?
20 What is Margaret Thatcher's journalist daughter called?
21 At which sport did Pope John Paul II excel in his youth?
22 What is the nationality of ex UN secretary Boutros Boutros-Ghali?
23 Which name is shared by the Duchess of York's sister and one of Princess Diana's sisters?
24 Who married millionaire hairdresser Stephen Way in 1998?
25 Who was the wife of Ferdinand Marcos at the time of his death?
26 What relation was Cherie Blair to Pat Phoenix, who played Elsie Tanner in Coronation Street?
27 What was the first name of Marks of Marks & Spencer?
28 What links Nataraja in Hinduism and performer Michael Flatley?
29 Who was the first basketball player to declare he was HIV positive?
30 What is Red or Dead?

Pot Luck 35 (see Quiz 75, page 195)
1 Porcelain. 2 Partridges. 3 Tuscany. 4 pH scale. 5 Aristotle Onassis. 6 Rome. 7 Veins. 8 Dutch. 9 Janet Jackson. 10 Worzel Gummidge. 11 Thomas Cook. 12 Personal Equity Plan. 13 John Lewis Partnership. 14 Theatre. 15 Embroidery. 16 Drachma. 17 Banacek. 18 19th century. 19 Sainsbury's. 20 Egypt. 21 Terence Conran. 22 Naomi Campbell. 23 Alberta. 24 Pauline Collins. 25 Glair. 26 Pierce Brosnan. 27 Ghana. 28 Ce Ce Peniston. 29 Chelsea Flower Show. 30 Hamburg.

Answers

Quiz 77 TV: TV Times 2

LEVEL 2

Answers - see Quiz 78, page 198

1   Which show provided BBC sales with a third of their 1997 profits?
2   Which woman writer created the character Jane Tennison?
3   Which ex Home Secretary was born the same day as ex Goodie Bill Oddie?
4   What is Dr Ross's first name in ER?
5   In which decade was Parliament first televised?
6   Which daughter of a famous footballer presented On The Ball with Barry Venison?
7   Which rugby player joined Ulrika Jonsson as a Gladiators presenter?
8   Who played Owen Springer in Reckless?
9   Which priest replaced Father Peter in Ballykissangel?
10 Who presents the rural life show Countryfile?
11 On GMTV where did Mark Freden regularly report from?
12 Which superstar did Matthew Corbett abandon finally in 1998?
13 Which role did Denise Robertson have on This Morning?
14 Who is the male wine expert on Food and Drink?
15 Who was the blonde captain on Shooting Stars?
16 How is TV presenter Leslie Heseltine better known?
17 How many letter make up the conundrum in Countdown?
18 What is Channel 5's daily quiz for older contestants called?
19 Who contracted amoebic dysentery while making a Holiday show with her daughter?
20 Frasier was a spin off from which series?
21 Who plays Ally McBeal?
22 How many points do you get for a starter in University Challenge?
23 To whom did The Duchess of York dedicate the first of her Sky chat shows in October 1998?
24 On which show did Tommy Walsh and Charlie Dimmock find fame?
25 For which sport did Frank Bough win an Oxbridge blue?
26 Who did David Dimbleby replace on Question Time?
27 Who wrote the acclaimed series of monologues Talking Heads?
28 Who played Darcy in Pride and Prejudice?
29 Which fivesome helped launch Channel 5?
30 Jimmy Savile received an honorary doctorate from which university?

Pot Luck 36 (see Quiz 78, page 198)
1 Michael Praed. 2 Leprosy. 3 Sugar Candy. 4 Mustard. 5 Tam O'Shanter.
6 On the Moon. 7 Peach & plum. 8 Chromium. 9 The bones. 10 An oak
tree. 11 Aspirin. 12 Your Eminence. 13 1983. 14 Vicky MacDonald.
15 Blackcurrant. 16 Belisha Beacon. 17 Arizona. 18 Daphne du Maurier.
19 Leo Sayer. 20 The Netherlands. 21 1/10th. 22 Aestivation. 23 88.
24 Niamh Kavanagh. 25 A flower. 26 Oxo. 27 The brain. 28 Cannon.
29 Bathsheba. 30 J. B. Priestley.

Answers

Quiz 78 Pot Luck 36

LEVEL 2

Answers - see Quiz 77, page 197

1   Which actor played both Prince of Moldavia and Robin Hood on TV?
2   What did Robert the Bruce die of?
3   What type of kisses did Mac and Katie Kissoon sing about?
4   Dijon is famous for which condiment?
5   Which Robbie Burns hero gave his name to a flat cap?
6   Where is the Bay of Rainbows?
7   A nectarine is a cross between which two fruits?
8   What makes stainless steel stainless?
9   What is affected by osteomyelitis?
10 What is Charles II said to have hidden in after the Battle of Worcester?
11 What is the common name for the medication acetylsalicylic acid?
12 How is a Cardinal addressed?
13 When was the wearing of seat belts in the front of a car made compulsory?
14 In Coronation Street who was Alec Gilroy's grand daughter?
15 Which fruit is in creme de cassis?
16 Which beacon was named after a 1930s Minister of Transport?
17 The Painted Desert is in which American state?
18 Who wrote My Cousin Rachel and Frenchman's Creek?
19 Whose hits include Moonlighting and More Than I Can Say?
20 Queen Juliana abdicated from which country's throne in 1980?
21 What fraction is a cable of a nautical mile?
22 What is the opposite of hibernation?
23 How many keys does a normal piano have?
24 Which female Irish singer won the Eurovision Song Contest with In Your Eyes?
25 What is a corn-cockle?
26 What did Mary Holland advertise on TV for eighteen years?
27 Which part of the body uses forty per cent of the oxygen in blood?
28 Which corpulent TV detective was played by William Conrad?
29 Who was the mother of King Solomon?
30 Who wrote The Good Companions?

Answers

TV: TV Times 2 (see Quiz 77, page 197)
1 The Teletubbies. 2 Lynda La Plante. 3 Michael Howard. 4 Doug.
5 1980s. 6 Gabby Yorath. 7 Jeremy Guscott. 8 Robson Green. 9 Father
Aidan. 10 John Craven. 11 Hollywood. 12 Sooty. 13 Agony aunt. 14 Oz
Clarke. 15 Ulrika Jonsson. 16 Les Dennis. 17 Nine. 18 100 Per Cent Gold.
19 Esther Rantzen. 20 Cheers. 21 Calista Flockhart. 22 10. 23 Her late
mother. 24 Ground Force. 25 Soccer. 26 Peter Sissons. 27 Alan Bennett.
28 Colin Firth. 29 The Spice Girls. 30 Leeds.

Quiz 79 Science: Space

LEVEL 2

Answers - see Quiz 80, page 200

1 Where are the headquarters of the European Space Agency?
2 Which word describes a body in free fall in space?
3 Which planet has the satellite Europa?
4 Which space station is named after the Russian word for 'peace'?
5 Ranger and Surveyor probes preceded exploration of where?
6 What name is given to a site for watching astronomical phenomena?
7 In which decade was Sputnik 1 launched?
8 Saturn rockets were developed for which moon programme?
9 Who was Soyuz TM-12's British passenger in 1991?
10 The first non-stop transatlantic flight was between which two countries?
11 What does a space shuttle land on when it returns to Earth?
12 What is the Oort cloud made out of?
13 Which Space Agency built Ariane?
14 Which communications satellite was the first to relay live TV transmissions?
15 Which rockets shared their name with the giant children of Uranus and Gaia in Greek myth ?
16 Which part of the moon did Armstrong first walk on?
17 Which of our planets is nearest the end of the alphabet?
18 Claudie Andre-Deshays was the first woman in space from which country?
19 Whose spacecraft was Vostok 1?
20 After retiring as an astronaut John Glenn followed a career in what?
21 Which clouds are formed highest above the ground?
22 How was Michael Collins a pioneer of lunar flight?
23 What is the largest planet in the solar system?
24 Phobos is a moon of which planet?
25 What was Skylab?
26 Which pioneering spacecraft was first launched in April 1981?
27 What is Jupiter's red spot made from?
28 Which country launched the first space probe in 1959?
29 Which constellation is known as The Hunter?
30 Which is larger, Mars or Earth?

Pot Luck 37 (see Quiz 80, page 200)
1 Make-up artist. 2 George V. 3 A Will. 4 Nixon. 5 Daphne du Maurier.
6 Rioja. 7 Clot. 8 1959. 9 Tampa. 10 Steven Spielberg. 11 17th.
12 Shallot. 13 The Grampians. 14 Optician's. 15 Blind. 16 Grounds
called The Stadium Of Light. 17 St. Mark. 18 The Great Pyramids of Giza.
19 Sausage. 20 Joseph Priestley. 21 Geoffrey Boycott. 22 B2. 23 British
Prime Ministers. 24 Zacharias. 25 Eat. 26 W.H. Smiths. 27 Sinn Fein.
28 Legs. 29 Danube. 30 Yoghurt.

Answers

Quiz 80 Pot Luck 37

LEVEL 2

Answers - see Quiz 79, page 199

1 In what capacity did Boy George work for the RSC?
2 Which king unveiled the Victoria memorial?
3 What is made by a testator?
4 Who telephoned Neil Armstrong during his first moon walk?
5 Which novelist had three novels adapted by Alfred Hitchcock to films?
6 Which wine growing region is divided into Baja, Alta and Alavesa?
7 What does fibrin cause to happen to blood?
8 Did Buddy Holly die in 1956, 1959 or 1961?
9 Which Florida city was the setting for Burt Reynolds' Bandits?
10 Which director appeared in The Blues Brothers?
11 In which century was the Taj Mahal constructed?
12 A Bordelaise sauce is flavoured by which vegetable?
13 Ben Nevis is in which mountain range?
14 Where would you probably be looking at a Snellen Chart?
15 In Bingo, what are numbers ending in zero called?
16 What do Sunderland and Benfica soccer clubs share?
17 Who is the Patron Saint of Venice?
18 What are Mycerinus and Cheprun the second two greatest of?
19 What would you be eating if you ate a Spanish chorizo?
20 Which scientist first discovered the composition of air?
21 Which ex Yorkshire cricketer was born on the same day as Manfred Mann?
22 Which letter and number represent the vitamin riboflavin?
23 Derby, Pelham and Russell have all been what?
24 Who was John the Baptist's father?
25 In 1909 what were imprisoned suffragettes forced to do?
26 Euston became Britain's first railway station to have what in 1848?
27 In 1921 which political party burnt down Dublin's Custom House?
28 Which part of your body is protected by puttees?
29 Which river flows through six different European countries?
30 What is the main ingredient in an Indian raita?

Answers

Science: Space (see Quiz 79, page 199)
1 Paris. 2 Weightless. 3 Jupiter. 4 Mir. 5 The Moon. 6 Observatory.
7 50s. 8 Apollo. 9 Helen Sharman. 10 Canada & Ireland. 11 Runway.
12 Comets. 13 European. 14 Telstar. 15 Titan. 16 Sea of Tranquillity.
17 Venus. 18 France. 19 Yuri Gagarin. 20 Politics. 21 Cirrus. 22 He didn't
walk on the moon on the first lunar flight. 23 Jupiter. 24 Mars. 25 Space
station. 26 Space shuttle. 27 Gases.. 28 USSR. 29 Orion. 30 Earth.

Quiz 81 Performing Arts

Answers - see Quiz 82, page 202

LEVEL 2

1   Which opera venue is near Lewes?
2   Sir John Barbirolli was conductor of which orchestra at the time of his death?
3   If a sonata is for instruments what is a cantata written for?
4   Which London theatre was the home of Gilbert & Sullivan operas?
5   Sadler's Wells theatre is famous for which performing arts?
6   Equity in the USA deals only with performers where?
7   Wayne Sleep was principal dancer with which ballet company?
8   What do you press with the right hand on an accordion?
9   Which of the Three Tenors played the title role in the film version of Otello in 1986?
10 How many strings are there on a double bass?
11 Richard Eyre replaced Peter Hall as artistic director at which London theatre?
12 What were all Joseph Grimaldi's clowns called?
13 What shape is the sound box on a balalaika?
14 Which male voice is between bass and tenor?
15 Where is an annual Fringe Festival held?
16 In which US city was the Actors Studio founded?
17 What is the official name of London's Drury Lane theatre?
18 Miles Davis is famous for playing which musical instrument?
19 Which king did Handel write The Water Music for?
20 Whose 1986 recording of Vivaldi's The Four Seasons sold over a million copies?
21 What was Paul McCartney's first classical oratorio?
22 An anthem is usually accompanied by which musical instrument?
23 Which mime artist created the clown-harlequin Bip?
24 Who is The Violinist?
25 Which theatre near Blackfriars was London's first new theatre in 300 years when opened in 1959?
26 What was the slogan of London's Windmill Theatre?
27 Which musical instruments did Leo Fender create?
28 What was the first black-owned record company in the USA?
29 Who has written more plays, Shakespeare or Ayckbourn?
30 Alan Bleasdale hails from which city?

Pot Luck 38 (see Quiz 82, page 202)
1 Hertfordshire. 2 A miller. 3 Frank Morgan. 4 Tax Exempt Special Savings
Account. 5 Rome. 6 Canada. 7 Michael Bentine. 8 Nijinsky. 9 Grass.
10 Ten Pole Tudor. 11 Star fish. 12 Quaver. 13 Vicarage. 14 Glenn
Miller. 15 Trollope. 16 Borneo. 17 The Trunk. 18 Maggie Smith.
19 Lactose. 20 Fluke. 21 Vera Lynn. 22 Little Women. 23 Mick Jagger.
24 Dachshunds. 25 Judaea. 26 Prince Edward. 27 Maud Grimes.
28 Tavares. 29 A barrister. 30 Shell-shaped.

Answers

Quiz 82 Pot Luck 38

LEVEL 2

1　Hemel Hempstead and St Albans are in which county?
2　Who would use a quern?
3　Who played the title role in the film The Wizard of Oz?
4　What does the acronym TESSA stand for?
5　The Spanish Steps are in which European city?
6　Cars with the international vehicle registration CDN come from where?
7　Which zany comedian devised the TV show It's A Square World?
8　Which Russian sounding horse won the 2000 Guineas, St Leger and the Derby in 1970?
9　What kind of a plant is fescue?
10　Who had hits with Swords of a Thousand Men and Who Killed Bambi?
11　What type of sea creature is a brittle star?
12　Musically which note is half the value of a crotchet?
13　Murder At The... where was Miss Marple's first appearance?
14　Who was Glenn Hoddle named after?
15　Which writer Anthony created the county of Barsetshire?
16　What is the largest island in Asia?
17　Which part of an elephant has 40,000 muscles?
18　Who played the lead role in the film The Prime Of Miss Jean Brodie?
19　Which type of sugar is found in milk?
20　What word can describe a lucky chance and the hook of an anchor?
21　Which female vocalist was known as 'The Forces Sweetheart'?
22　Which novel preceded Good Wives?
23　Which pop star married Bianca de Macias in May 1971?
24　Which breed of dog were originally bred to hunt badgers?
25　Herod the Great ruled which kingdom?
26　Which Prince's childhood nickname was JAWS?
27　In Coronation Street who was Reg Holdsworth's mother-in-law?
28　Who had hits with Whodunnit and More Than A Woman?
29　What is the English equivalent of a Scottish Advocate?
30　What shape is a dish called a coquille?

Answers

Performing Arts (see Quiz 81, page 201)
1　Glyndebourne. 2　Halle. 3　Voices. 4　Savoy. 5　Opera and ballet.
6　Theatre. 7　Royal Ballet. 8　Piano-style keyboard. 9　Placido Domingo.
10　Four. 11　National. 12　Joey. 13　Triangular. 14　Baritone.
15　Edinburgh. 16　New York. 17　Theatre Royal. 18　Trumpet. 19　George I.
20　Nigel Kennedy. 21　Liverpool Oratorio. 22　Organ. 23　Marcel Marceau.
24　Vanessa Mae. 25　Mermaid. 26　We never closed. 27　Electric guitars.
28　Tamla Motown. 29　Ayckbourn. 30　Liverpool.

Quiz 83 Country & Western

LEVEL 2

Answers - see Quiz 84, page 204

1 Who had a hit in 1972 with A Thing Called Love?
2 Which hit in letters followed Stand by Your Man for Tammy Wynette?
3 Which group had a No 1 hit in 1976 with Mississippi?
4 Which famous country singer was kidnapped in 1979?
5 Whose song was a No. 1 for John Denver in 1974?
6 Which Patsy Cline hit was covered by Julio Iglesias in 1994?
7 In which year was Achey Breaky Heart a hit for Billy Ray Cyrus?
8 Who had a No 11 UK hit with Talking In Your Sleep in 1978?
9 Hiram Williams is the real name of which singer?
10 Which opera singer joined John Denver to record Perhaps Love?
11 What surname links 70s star Daniel and 50s star Pat?
12 Which Kris wrote Help Me Make It Through the Night?
13 Who had a hit in the summer of 1998 with How Do I?
14 Who wrote the autobiography Coal Miner's Daughter?
15 Who joined Kenny Rogers on the No 7 hit Islands In The Stream?
16 What is Reba McEntire's real name?
17 Which specialist type of singing links Frank Ifield and Slim Whitman?
18 Who duetted with Mark Knopfler on the album Neck and Neck?
19 In the No 1, which drums were heard by Jim Reeves?
20 Who sang All I Have To Do Is Dream with Bobbie Gentry in 1969?
21 Who had a backing band called the Waylors?
22 What is the name of the theme park owned by Dolly Parton?
23 George Jones' 1975 hit The Battle told of the split from his wife. Who was she?
24 Which Banks were a hit in 1971 for Olivia Newton-John?
25 Which song was a No 2 UK hit for Tammy Wynette and KLF in 1991?
26 Who wrote the classic song Crazy?
27 Who formed the Trio with Dolly Parton and Linda Ronstadt?
28 Who took Cotton Eye Joe to No 1 in 1994?
29 Which No 9 for Elvis was a No 10 for Carl Perkins in 1956?
30 Which 'modern girl' joined Kenny Rogers on We've Got Tonight?

Answers

Pot Luck 39 (see Quiz 84, page 204)
1 Rose. 2 Cousins. 3 Cuba. 4 Seaweed. 5 Sweet. 6 Victoria. 7 Oil tanker. 8 Theatre Royal. 9 Blood poisoning. 10 Leopards. 11 Anthony Eden. 12 Macduff. 13 Automatic pilot. 14 Suffolk. 15 Soles of your feet. 16 Bolero. 17 Racehorses. 18 Passepartout. 19 Pierre Trudeau. 20 Cary Grant. 21 1970s. 22 The Lion, The Witch and the Wardrobe. 23 Nose. 24 British Grand Prix. 25 Iraq. 26 Supergrass. 27 William Beveridge. 28 I Just Called to say I Love You. 29 A horse. 30 Thumb.

1 What was the name of Kate Winslet's character in Titanic?
2 What is the relationship between Prince Edward and Lord Lindley?
3 Which Caribbean country won the 1992 Olympic Gold Medal for baseball?
4 What is kelp?
5 Who had hits with Fox On The Run and Wig-Wam Bam?
6 What name is an African lake, a station and a former Queen?
7 What type of vessel was the Torrey Canyon?
8 What is the name of the most famous theatre in London's Drury Lane?
9 What is the more common name for toxaemia?
10 Which members of the big cat family collect in a leap?
11 Who preceded Harold Macmillan as Prime Minister?
12 In the Shakespeare play who killed Macbeth?
13 The Christian name George lends itself to which part of a plane?
14 Newmarket and Ipswich are both in which county?
15 Reflexology treats your body through what?
16 What can be a short jacket and a dance?
17 What are auctioned at Tattersalls?
18 Who was Phileas Fogg's companion in Around the World in 80 Days?
19 Which French-Canadian became Canadian Prime Minister in 1968?
20 Archibald Leach born in Bristol became which Hollywood star?
21 In which decade did John Wayne die?
22 Which novel was set in the magical kingdom of Narnia?
23 Which part of your body would interest a rhinologist?
24 In 1926 what was held for the first time at Brooklands?
25 Mesopotamia was the ancient name for which modern day country?
26 Who had hits with Alright and Going Out in '95 and '96?
27 Whose report in the 1940s was vital in setting up the welfare state?
28 Which Stevie Wonder No 1 was in the film The Woman In Red?
29 What type of animal is a Lippizaner?
30 Which digit is your pollex?

Answers

Country & Western (see Quiz 83, page 203)
1 Johnny Cash. 2 D.I.V.O.R.C.E. 3 Pussycat. 4 Tammy Wynette. 5 Annie's
Song. 6 Crazy. 7 1992. 8 Crystal Gayle. 9 Hank Williams. 10 Placido
Domingo. 11 Boone. 12 Kristofferson. 13 Leanne Rimes. 14 Loretta Lynn.
15 Dolly Parton. 16 Reba McEntire. 17 Yodelling. 18 Chet Atkins. 19
Distant Drums. 20 Glen Campbell. 21 Waylon Jennings. 22 Dollywood. 23
Tammy Wynette. 24 The Ohio. 25 Justified and Ancient. 26 Willie Nelson.
27 Emmylou Harris. 28 Rednex. 29 Blue Suede Shoes. 30 Sheena Easton.

LEVEL 2

1 Which Australian was the first to score 60 tries in international rugby?
2 Who will play the opening match at the new Millennium Stadium for the 1999 World Cup?
3 Who was the first English player to play in 50 internationals?
4 Which country in 1995 asked to increase the number of teams in the Five Nations Cup?
5 Which colours do Bath play in?
6 Which Welsh Union player was a regular captain on A Question of Sport?
7 In which part of London did the London Bronco's start out?
8 Which TV channel sponsored a Floodlit Rugby League Trophy?
9 For which side did Brian Bevan score 740 tries in 620 matches?
10 What were Bradford before they were Bulls?
11 Who retired as Scottish captain after the 1995 World Cup?
12 Who was Wigan's leading try scorer in the 1994/5 season?
13 Where would you watch Rhinos playing rugby?
14 Which Harlequins hooker was nicknamed 'Pitbull'?
15 Which international side has the shortest name?
16 Who are the two sides in the Varsity Match?
17 Which rugby team plays its home games at Welford Road?
18 Who was leading try scorer in the 1995 rugby union World Cup?
19 In 1998 what colour cards were substituted for yellow ones?
20 Who joined Leeds in 1991 after playing on the other side of the Pennines since 1984?
21 What did Bath Football Club change its name to in the mid 90s?
22 Who was the first non-white Springbok, before the end of apartheid?
23 Which rugby side added Warriors to its name?
24 In which decade was Rugby Union last played in the Olympics?
25 How old was Will Carling when he was first made England Captain?
26 Who played a record breaking 69 times at fly half for England between 1985 and 1995?
27 In 1980 who led England to their first Grand Slam in 23 years?
28 Where is the annual Varsity match played?
29 How many years had Wigan's unbeaten run in the FA Challenge Cup lasted when it ended in 1996?
30 Who did Martin Offiah play for in his first years as a League player?

Pot Luck 40 (see Quiz 86, page 206)
1 Shoulder blade. 2 Stour. 3 Sex Pistols. 4 Falmouth and Cambourne.
5 India. 6 Judo. 7 Henry I. 8 The wind. 9 Maastricht. 10 Oscar Blaketon.
11 British Honduras. 12 Don Johnson. 13 Jenkins. 14 River Soar.
15 Francis. 16 My Son, My Son. 17 Individual Savings Account. 18 Duke of Marlborough. 19 Peter. 20 A knot. 21 Zirconium. 22 London. 23 A ship.
24 Colorado. 25 Racey. 26 The Castle of Mey. 27 London's Burning.
28 The Merry Monarch. 29 Norfolk. 30 Patrick Duffy.

1   Where in your body is your scapula?
2   Canterbury stands on which river?
3   Who had hits with God Save The Queen and C'Mon Everybody?
4   Sebastian Coe became MP for which constituency in 1992?
5   Which former colony was called the jewel in Queen Victoria's crown?
6   What was the sport of Karen Briggs and Nicola Fairbrother?
7   Which Henry became King of England in 1100?
8   In the film Mary Poppins, Mary said she would stay until what changed?
9   Which Treaty on European Union was signed in December 1991?
10 Which character is played by Derek Fowlds in Heartbeat?
11 What was the former name of Belize?
12 Which actor married Melanie Griffith twice?
13 What was Ffion Hague's maiden name?
14 Which River does Leicester stand on?
15 What is decathlon champion Daley Thompson's first name?
16 Which Vera Lynn song was a No 1 UK hit in 1954?
17 In finance what is an ISA?
18 Who was given Blenheim Palace as a reward for his military service?
19 In The Bible, who denied Jesus three times before the cock crowed twice?
20 A Turk's Head is a type of what?
21 Alphabetically which chemical element is the last?
22 Which European capital was considered cleanest in a 1995 survey?
23 What is a frigatoon?
24 'The Garden of the Gods' is in which American state?
25 Who had hits with Lay Your Love On Me and Some Girls?
26 Which castle was bought by the Queen Mother in 1952?
27 Which TV series has characters called Gracie, Sicknote and George?
28 What was King Charles II's nickname?
29 Kings Lynn and Norwich are both in which county?
30 Which actor links Bobby Ewing to The Man From Atlantis?

Answers

Sport: Rugby (see Quiz 85, page 205)
1 David Campese. 2 Wales & Argentina. 3 Rory Underwood. 4 Italy.
5 Blue, black and white. 6 Gareth Edwards. 7 Fulham. 8 BBC2.
9 Warrington. 10 Northern. 11 Gavin Hastings. 12 Martin Offiah. 13
Leeds. 14 Brian Moore. 15 Fiji. 16 Oxford University and Cambridge
University. 17 Leicester. 18 Jonah Lomu. 19 White. 20 Ellery Hanley.
21 Bath Rugby Club. 22 Errol Tobias. 23 Wigan. 24 1920s. 25 22.
26 Rob Andrew. 27 Bill Beaumont. 28 Twickenham. 29 Eight. 30 Widnes.

Quiz 87 Movies: Westerns

LEVEL 2

Answers - see Quiz 88, page 208

1   What was the first film in which Clint Eastwood starred as 'The man with no name'?
2   Who played the sadistic sheriff in Eastwood's Unforgiven?
3   Which actor's films include Big Jim McLain, McLintock and McQ?
4   Which star of Maverick played Brett Maverick in the TV series?
5   Which Oscar did Kevin Costner win for Dances With Wolves?
6   What is the name of the original tale that the Magificent Seven is based on?
7   What weather feature was in the title of the song from Butch Cassidy won an Oscar?
8   Who was the star of Jeremiah Johnson?
9   Which comedy actor starred in the comedy western The Paleface?
10   Who starred with brother Charlie Sheen in Young Guns?
11   Who was the title character in the surreal western The Seven Faces of Dr. Lao?
12   Who played the woman poker player in Maverick?
13   Which actor was The Bad?
14   Which Back to the Future film returns to the Wild West?
15   In which musical western does the song Wandrin' Star appear?
16   Which Hollywood legend was the narrator in How The West Was Won?
17   Which film was originally called Per un Pugno di Dollari?
18   Which country singer was in True Grit?
19   Which son of a M*A*S*H star appeared in Young Guns II?
20   Who did John Wayne play in The Alamo?
21   Clint Eastwood became mayor of which town?
22   Which 1985 film was a revised remake of the classic Shane?
23   Where is the village where the action of The Magnificent Seven centres?
24   Where was The Good, the Bad and the Ugly made?
25   What was the name of Mel Brooks' spoof western?
26   Which English comic appeared in Desperado?
27   Which 80s teenage western starred actors known as the Brat Pack?
28   What was Tonto's horse called?
29   Who was Gene Autry's most famous horse?
30   Traditionally, what colour is the western hero's hat?

Answers

TV: TV Times 3 (see Quiz 88, page 208)
1 Andrew. 2 William G Stewart. 3 Watchdog. 4 Coronation Street. 5 Helen Baxendale. 6 Anna. 7 Holiday Heaven. 8 Blue Peter. 9 Geoff Hamilton. 10 Liverpool. 11 Mel Smith & Griff Rhys-Jones. 12 Los Angeles. 13 Sandi Toksvig. 14 BBC Breakfast News . 15 BBC2. 16 John Stapleton. 17 Murray Walker. 18 Blockbusters. 19 Spencer Tracy. 20 Shauna Lowry. 21 Kevin. 22 Gymnastics. 23 All Creatures Great and Small. 24 Hugh Scully. 25 Michael Palin. 26 Monica Lewinsky. 27 Blackburn Rovers. 28 Selfridges. 29 £5. 30 Cook.

1   Men Behaving Badly's Leslie Ash was born the same day as which Prince?
2   Who presents Channel 4's Fifteen To One?
3   Alice Beer first found fame on which show?
4   Which show was first broadcast on Friday 9th December 1960?
5   Which Cardiac Arrest star also starred in Friends?
6   What was the lawyer played by Daniela Nardini in This Life called?
7   Which series featured celebs returning to a previous vacation destination?
8   Which children's show has the theme music Barnacle Bill?
9   Whose last series was Paradise Gardens?
10 In which city did the docu soap Hotel take place?
11 Which comedy duo are famous for their head-to-head discussions?
12 In which city did lifeguard Mitch Buchanan work?
13 Who was the female team captain in the 90s Call My Bluff?
14 What did the BBC's Breakfast Time change its name to?
15 Fully Booked was first on which channel?
16 Who moved to GMTV after his The Time The Place was axed?
17 Which voice of motor racing moved to ITV to cover the sport?
18 In which show might a contestant ask "Could I have a P please, Bob?"
19 Who is Robbie Coltrane's son Spencer named after?
20 Which redhead assists Rolf Harris at the Animal Hospital?
21 What was the name of the spotty teenager played by Harry Enfield?
22 Presenter Suzanne Dando represented Great Britain at which sport?
23 Which series centred on Skeldale House?
24 Who has hosted Antiques Roadshow through most of the 90s?
25 Who tried to emulate Phileas Fogg in a 1989 documentary?
26 Who did Roseanne offer a million dollars to appear on her talk show in October 1998?
27 Which Lancashire soccer side does Jim Bowen support?
28 Which store was the subject of The Shop?
29 How much are the ingredients worth on Ready Steady Cook?
30 What did Susan Brookes do on This Morning?

Answers

Movies: Westerns (see Quiz 87, page 207)
1 A Fistful of Dollars. 2 Gene Hackman. 3 John Wayne. 4 James Garner.
5 Best Director. 6 The Seven Samurai. 7 Raindrops. 8 Robert Redford.
9 Bob Hope. 10 Emilio Estevez. 11 Tony Randall. 12 Jodie Foster. 13 Lee
van Cleef. 14 No. III . 15 Paint Your Wagon. 16 Spencer Tracy. 17 A Fistful
of Dollars. 18 Glen Campbell. 19 Kiefer Sutherland. 20 Davy Crockett.
21 Carmel. 22 Pale Rider. 23 Mexico. 24 Italy. 25 Blazing Saddles.
26 John Cleese. 27 Young Guns. 28 Scout. 29 Champion. 30 White.

Quiz 89 Pot Luck 41

Answers - see Quiz 90, page 210

LEVEL 2

1. Which Queen wrote the Casket Letters?
2. Which former Take That star had Child at No 3 in 1996?
3. What can be metric royal, metric demy and metric crown?
4. In which TV series was the character 'Boss Hogg'?
5. Which film star married Prince Aly Khan?
6. Which almond cake is traditionally made for Mothering Sunday?
7. Who had hits with We Are Glass and Cars ?
8. What would an Australian call trousers?
9. Which actress had lead roles in the films Out of Africa and Silkwood?
10. Which two European languages are spoken in Madagascar?
11. Which country has the shortest coastline in the world?
12. What were the giant insects in the science fiction film Them?
13. Which famous TV cook took his show Around Britain?
14. During which war does Norman Mailer's The Naked and the Dead take place?
15. Aylesbury and Milton Keynes are both in which county?
16. Which actress is Jack Davenport's mother?
17. Which animal was used by Jenner to develop the vaccine against smallpox?
18. What is a davenport?
19. Which singer starred alongside Kyle McLachlan in Dune?
20. Who composed the music for The Good, the Bad and the Ugly?
21. Who had hits with Blue Monday and World In Motion?
22. What kind of musical instrument was a kit?
23. Which former tennis player bought Hull FC?
24. Which John Carpenter film set in the antarctic starred Kurt Russell?
25. Name the first yacht to win the America's Cup?
26. Which singing sisters were called Patti, Laverne and Maxine?
27. In which country are the guerrilla group the Tamil Tigers?
28. What name is given to the principal female singer in an opera?
29. The dish Eggs Florentine contains which vegetable?
30. Which town was Barbara Castle's parliamentary constituency?

World Tour (see Quiz 90, page 210)
Answers
1 Atlantic. 2 Las Vegas. 3 Broadway. 4 Inuit (Eskimos). 5 Cape of Good Hope. 6 Wind. 7 Honshu. 8 Australia. 9 Washington. 10 K2. 11 Okovango. 12 Indian. 13 Hawaii. 14 China. 15 Namibia. 16 Gobi. 17 Dow Jones. 18 Eskimo. 19 Michigan. 20 Zambia and Zimbabwe. 21 Trinidad. 22 French. 23 Canaries. 24 North coast of Africa. 25 Manhattan. 26 Tip of South America. 27 Greenland. 28 Kilimanjaro. 29 Israel. 30 Pakistan & Afghanistan.

Quiz 90 World Tour

Answers - see Quiz 89, page 209

LEVEL 2

1 The Sargasso Sea is part of which ocean?
2 Which US city's name means 'The Fields'?
3 How is New York's 'Great White Way' also known?
4 Which Canadians speak Inuktitut?
5 Which Cape was originally called the Cape of Storms?
6 In America what type of natural phenomenon is a Chinook?
7 What is the principal island of Japan?
8 Where is the town of Kurri Kurri?
9 Where is the HQ of the International Monetary Fund?
10 By which abbreviation is the mountain Chogori known?
11 What is the only permanent river in the Kalahari desert?
12 Which Ocean's deepest point is the Java Trench?
13 Where would you be if someone put a lei round your neck?
14 Where is the world's longest canal?
15 Afrikaans is the official language of which country in addition to South Africa?
16 In which desert is the Bactrian camel found?
17 What is the name of the index on the New York Stock Exchange?
18 Which group of people have a name meaning 'eater of raw meat'?
19 Which is the only Great Lake wholly in the USA?
20 The Kariba Dam is on the border of which two countries?
21 Calypso is the traditional song form of which Caribbean island?
22 Which European language is spoken in Chad?
23 Las Palmas is in which island group?
24 Approximately where was Carthage to be found?
25 Wall Street and Broadway lie on which island?
26 Where is the Magellan Strait?
27 What is the largest island between the North Atlantic and the Arctic?
28 What is Africa's highest volcano?
29 Where is there a Parliament called the Knesset?
30 Which two countries does the Khyber Pass separate?

Answers

Pot Luck 41 (see Quiz 89, page 209)
1 Mary, Queen of Scots. 2 Mark Owen. 3 Sizes of paper. 4 The Dukes of Hazzard. 5 Rita Hayworth. 6 Simnel Cake. 7 Gary Numan. 8 Strides. 9 Meryl Streep. 10 French & English. 11 Monaco. 12 Ants. 13 Gary Rhodes. 14 WWII. 15 Buckinghamshire. 16 Maria Aitken. 17 Cow. 18 A sofa or desk. 19 Sting. 20 Ennio Morricone. 21 New Order. 22 A small violin. 23 David Lloyd. 24 The Thing. 25 America. 26 The Andrews Sisters. 27 Sri Lanka. 28 Prima Donna. 29 Spinach. 30 Blackburn.

Quiz 91　Pot Luck 42

Answers - see Quiz 92, page 212

LEVEL 2

1　What is saxifrage?
2　Family wise what do Henry Cooper and Carol Thatcher have in common?
3　Who hoisted himself onto Sinbad the Sailor's shoulders?
4　How much are you paid if you hold an honorary post?
5　Which actor played the leading role in the film Brothers In Law?
6　What can be a five card game, a smooth, woolly surface or a sleep?
7　Which club did Will Carling play for?
8　Which sport is Britain's Yvonne MacGregor associated with?
9　Whose music albums have included An Innocent Man?
10　'Englander' is an anagram of which country?
11　Which actress played Michael Douglas's wife in Fatal Attraction?
12　What is a melodeon?
13　Which animal family are impala, eland and dik-dik all from?
14　Who would have been granted a Ticket of Leave?
15　In TV's Upstairs Downstairs what was the name of the cook?
16　Whose hits include Dancin' On the Ceiling and Do It To Me?
17　Which stone is inscribed "Cormac McCarthy fortis me fieri fecit AD 1446"?
18　Which actor played the leading role in the TV drama Shogun?
19　What name is given to withered apples used to make rough cider?
20　Who composed the music for the musical Lady Be Good?
21　What is a grackle?
22　Which building was erected in 1851 for the Great Exhibition?
23　Which children's TV series has included Tucker Jenkins and Zammo?
24　Which Corrie character died with Gilbert and Sullivan playing in his car?
25　Which branch would you hold out to seek peace?
26　Arthur Hastings was the sidekick of which fictional sleuth?
27　Whose hits include Detroit City and Love Me Tonight?
28　The leader of an orchestra plays which instrument?
29　What was Mab's job in fairy folklore?
30　Which actress was left on a desert island in TV's Girl Friday?

Answers

Past Times: The 80s (see Quiz 92, page 212)
1　UK and Eire.　2　Chernobyl.　3　FW de Klerk.　4　Dubcek.　5　Salman Rushdie.
6　Michael Foot.　7　Mitterrand.　8　Galtieri.　9　Derek Hatton.　10　Jamaica.
11　Greenpeace.　12　Iceland.　13　Twice.　14　Shirley Williams.　15　Ken
Livingstone.　16　Monday.　17　The Labour Party.　18　Grand Hotel.
19　Slobodan Milosevic.　20　Montserrat.　21　Mubarak.　22　Irangate.　23　David
Blunkett.　24　Jimmy Carter.　25　Peter Mandelson.　26　Local authority.
27　Benazir Bhutto.　28　Zimbabwe.　29　South Africa.　30　Mikhail Gorbachev.

Quiz 92 Past Times: The 80s

Answers - see Quiz 91, page 211

1. The Hillsborough Agreement was between which two countries?
2. Where was there a major nuclear leak in the USSR in 1986?
3. Who was the last white President of South Africa, elected in 1989?
4. Which former liberal leader was made speaker of the national assembly of Czechoslovakia in 1989?
5. A fatwa calling for the death of which writer was made by Iran in '89?
6. Who succeeded Callaghan as Labour leader?
7. Who became France's first socialist president in 1981?
8. Who was Argentine President during the Falklands Conflict?
9. Which ex deputy leader of Liverpool Council was expelled form the Labour Party in 1987?
10. Michael Manley became leader of where in 1989?
11. Who owned Rainbow Warrior, sunk by the French in 1985?
12. Vigdis Finnbogadottir became head of state in which country?
13. How many times was Margaret Thatcher elected PM in the 80s?
14. Who was the only woman founder of the SDP?
15. Who was leader of the GLC from 1981-86?
16. What was the Black day of the week of the 1987 stockmarket crash?
17. Who moved from Transport House to Walworth Road in 1980?
18. In which hotel was the Brighton bomb in 1984?
19. Who became President of Serbia in 1986?
20. Most of which Caribbean island's buildings were destroyed by hurricane Hugo in 1989?
21. Who became Egyptian President after Sadat's assassination?
22. What was the name of the scandal over arms for hostages in which Oliver North was implicated?
23. Which Cabinet Minister was leader of Sheffield City Council for most of the 80s?
24. Who did Ronald Reagan defeat to become US President in 1980?
25. Which spin doctor did Neil Kinnock engage to run the 1987 election campaign?
26. In 1989 state schools were allowed to opt out of whose control?
27. Which woman became PM of Pakistan after the death of Zia in a plane crash?
28. Where did the parties of ZANU and ZAPU merge in 1987?
29. In 1986 the pass laws, concerning the carrying of identity documents, were repealed in which country?
30. Which Russian leader introduced the policy of perestroika?

Answers

Pot Luck 42 (see Quiz 91, page 211)
1 A small rock plant. 2 Twins. 3 The Old Man of the Sea. 4 Nothing. 5 Ian Carmichael. 6 A nap. 7 Harlequins. 8 Cycling. 9 Billy Joel. 10 Greenland. 11 Anne Archer. 12 A musical instrument. 13 Antelope. 14 A convict. 15 Mrs Bridges. 16 Lionel Richie. 17 The Blarney Stone. 18 Richard Chamberlain. 19 Scrumps. 20 George Gershwin. 21 A bird. 22 Crystal Palace. 23 Grange Hill. 24 Derek Wilton. 25 Olive. 26 Hercule Poirot. 27 Tom Jones. 28 Violin. 29 A midwife. 30 Joanna Lumley.

Quiz 93 Pot Luck 43

Answers - see Quiz 94, page 214

LEVEL 2

1. What type of animal is a Sooty Mangabey?
2. Which drink was advertised as 'drunk for a penny; dead drunk for tuppence'?
3. Who did William III defeat in 1690 at the Battle of the Boyne?
4. Rupert Bear is linked with which newspaper?
5. In Old English which word meant a field?
6. What were the eldest sons of French kings called from the 14th century?
7. Ely stands on which river?
8. Which 60s singer married the designer Jeff Banks?
9. In 1945, who became British Prime Minister?
10. Which plant has a flower called the 'poor man's weather-glass'?
11. Who had hits with The Streak and Misty in the 70s?
12. Who was President of the Philippines from 1965 to 1986?
13. Which Gate is a memorial for British Soldiers who fell at Ypres?
14. Who played Fred Kite in the film I'm Alright, Jack?
15. Which entertainer was married to his manager Cheryl St Clair?
16. Which complaint was the Jacuzzi originally developed to help?
17. What did Anna Karenina throw herself under in the Tolstoy novel?
18. Who wrote Dr Zhivago?
19. In which soap does the Cat & Fiddle rival The Bull?
20. Which comedian was Connie Booth married to?
21. What did people find in the book Lost Horizon?
22. Who preceded Edward VI as Monarch?
23. In the film The Tommy Steele Story who played Tommy Steele?
24. Who finished his radio show with "B.F.N. Bye for now"?
25. Who had hits with The Logical Song and Dreamer?
26. In which year was Lord Mountbatten murdered?
27. What is the start of Psalm 23?
28. Which shaggy horned wild cattle live in the Tibetan mountains?
29. What was a gulag in Russia?
30. In the 1953 film Houdini who played the title role?

Leisure: Books 2 (see Quiz 94, page 214)
Answers
1 Oxford. 2 Lake District. 3 Slavery. 4 Dictionary. 5 Jeeves. 6 The Greatest. 7 Lord Peter Wimsey. 8 Black Beauty. 9 Spycatcher. 10 Childcare. 11 Joan Collins. 12 Nigel Lawson. 13 Maeve Binchy. 14 Oranges. 15 Ruth Rendell. 16 Bill Bryson. 17 Agatha Christie. 18 The Godfather. 19 The English Patient. 20 John Le Carre. 21 Schindler's Ark. 22 Marie Stopes. 23 The Odessa File. 24 Edwina Currie. 25 Detective novel. 26 Jeffrey Archer. 27 Wales. 28 A Tale of Two Cities. 29 Exodus. 30 Simenon.

Quiz 94 Leisure: Books 2

LEVEL 2

Answers - see Quiz 93, page 213

1   In which university city is the Bodleian Library?
2   In which District did Beatrix Potter live?
3   Uncle Tom's Cabin was a novel which argued against what?
4   In the US what type of book is Webster famous for?
5   Who is the most famous manservant created by P.G.Wodehouse?
6   What was Muhammad Ali's autobiography called?
7   Which Dorothy L Sayers' creation was Harriet Vane's husband?
8   Which children's classic was written to encourage adults to be kinder to horses?
9   Which book by ex intelligence agent Peter Wright, did the British government try to have banned?
10   What was the subject of Benjamin Spock's most famous books?
11   Which soap star wrote Prime Time?
12   Which ex Chancellor of the Exchequer wrote a diet book?
13   Whose first successful novel was Light A Penny Candle?
14   What 'Are Not the Only Fruit' according to Jeanette Winterson?
15   Who wrote the detective novel Road Rage?
16   Who wrote A Walk in the Woods?
17   The Murder of Roger Ackroyd was an early novel by whom?
18   Which is Mario Puzo's most famous novel, first published in 1969?
19   Which Michael Ondaatje book was made into an Oscar winning film with Ralph Fiennes?
20   Who created George Smiley?
21   Which was the first Thomas Keneally book to win the Booker Prize?
22   Which birth control campaigner wrote the book Married Love?
23   What was Frederick Forsyth's follow up to The Day of the Jackal?
24   Which ex MP's first novel was A Parliamentary Affair?
25   The Woman in White is the first novel of what type in English?
26   Whose Not a Penny More, Not a Penny Less was written to clear bankruptcy debts?
27   In Colin Dexter's books where does Lewis come from?
28   Which Dickens' novel is about the French Revolution?
29   What is the second book of the Old Testament?
30   Which Georges wrote over a hundred novels featuring Jules Maigret?

Pot Luck 43   (see Quiz 93, page 213)
1 Monkey. **2** Gin. **3** James II. **4** Daily Express. **5** An acre. **6** Dauphin.
7 The Ouse. **8** Sandie Shaw. **9** Clement Attlee. **10** Scarlet Pimpernel.
11 Ray Stevens. **12** Ferdinand Marcos. **13** Menin Gate. **14** Peter Sellers.
15 Michael Barrymore. **16** Arthritis. **17** A train. **18** Boris Pasternak.
19 The Archers. **20** John Cleese. **21** Shangri-La. **22** Henry VIII.
23 Tommy Steele. **24** Jimmy Young. **25** Supertramp. **26** 1979. **27** The
Lord is my shepherd. **28** Yaks. **29** A prison camp. **30** Tony Curtis.

Quiz 95 Pot Luck 44

LEVEL 2

Answers - see Quiz 96, page 216

1 What did MGM stand for?
2 What colour is puce?
3 What is the French equivalent of the Italian race Giro D'Italia?
4 Who was the first presenter of the TV series Tomorrow's World?
5 Which cartoon character was the 'fastest mouse in Mexico'?
6 Who had 90s No 1 hits with The Power and Rhythm Is A Dancer?
7 Which US state is the second smallest?
8 According to the saying, who rush in where angels fear to tread?
9 What is Blue Vinney?
10 Who wrote Five Children and It and Wet Magic?
11 Which terrier is the largest of the breed?
12 Who was the head of the German SS?
13 What is studied by a haematologist?
14 Which county is Morganwg Ganol in Welsh?
15 What type of creature is a turnstone?
16 Which country from 1867-1914 had a governor called The Khedive?
17 In the film The Great Escape which actor played the Forger?
18 Which Egyptian President was assassinated in 1981?
19 In the TV series To The Manor Born what was the name of the butler?
20 What is Paddy Ashdown's first Christian name?
21 Who had hits with Kiss from a Rose and Crazy?
22 The town of Newcastle is in which Australian state?
23 What was Marc Bolan's real name?
24 What type of food is a bullace?
25 What is a snake's cast off skin called?
26 The holiday camp Maplins featured in which TV series?
27 Which TV Arts presenter was Director General of the BBC from 1968-75?
28 What is mineral water mixed with quinine called?
29 Cars with the international vehicle registration CDN come from where?
30 What was sought by Jason and the Argonauts?

Answers

Pop Music: Groups (see Quiz 96, page 216)
1 The Blue Flames. **2** Swedish. **3** Two. **4** Summer Love. **5** The News.
6 Chairmen of the Board. **7** Our eyes. **8** In Perfect Harmony. **9** Vic Reeves.
10 Def Leppard. **11** Live Forever. **12** Good Vibrations. **13** New York.
14 Three Lions. **15** Cream. **16** Rainbow. **17** California. **18** All Day and All
of the Night. **19** Computer Love/The Model. **20** To Trancentral. **21** Bread.
22 Jake. **23** The Bangles. **24** Clannad. **25** Moving On Up. **26** My Perfect
Cousin. **27** Elkie Brooks. **28** Heaven 17. **29** Cosmic Girl. **30** Las Vegas.

Quiz 96 Pop Music: Groups

Answers - see Quiz 95, page 215

LEVEL 2

1 What was the name of Georgie Fame's backing group?
2 What nationality were All That She Wants group Ace of Base?
3 How many Princes were in the Spin Doctors UK No 3 hit?
4 What Sensation were the Bay City Rollers singing about in 1974?
5 Huey Lewis was vocalist for which group?
6 Which Company band had a hit with Give Me Just A Little More Time?
7 What did Go West close in their No 5 from 1985?
8 What followed in brackets on I'd Like To Teach the World to Sing?
9 Who did the Wonder Stuff serve as backing group for?
10 Which heavy band took When Love and Hate Collide to No 2?
11 What was Oasis' first UK Top Ten single?
12 What was The Beach Boys' first UK No 1?
13 In Which American city was the Pogues Fairytale?
14 Which Lightning Seeds No 1 was the official song of the England Football Team in 1996?
15 Ginger, Jack and Eric formed which trio?
16 Which British group had a No 3 hit with I Surrender in 1981?
17 Which Hotel was visited by the Eagles in 1977?
18 What part of the day took the Stranglers to No 7 in 1988?
19 In 1982, what was the name of the first UK No 1 by a German group?
20 Which Last Train did KLF catch in their No 2 UK hit in 1991?
21 Singer/ songwriter David Gates led which group?
22 Who was the brother in the title of a track by Free from 1970?
23 Which girl band had hits with Manic Monday and Walk Like An Egyptian?
24 Which Irish group had a No 5 hit with the Theme from Harry's Game?
25 What action were M People doing in their No 2 UK hit from 1993?
26 What relative was Perfect according to the hit by the Undertones?
27 Who was the female artist in Vinegar Joe?
28 Which group had hits in '83 with Temptation and Come Live With Me?
29 What sort of girl took Jamiroquai to No 6 in 1996?
30 Where was ZZ Top on the No 10 hit Viva?

Answers

Pot Luck 44 (see Quiz 95, page 215)
1 Metro Goldwyn Mayer. 2 Purple brown. 3 Tour De France. 4 Raymond Baxter. 5 Speedy Gonzales. 6 Snap. 7 Delaware. 8 Fools. 9 Cheese.
10 E. Nesbit. 11 Airedale. 12 Himmler. 13 Blood. 14 Mid Glamorgan.
15 A bird. 16 Egypt. 17 Donald Pleasence. 18 Anwar Sadat.
19 Brabinger. 20 Jeremy. 21 Seal. 22 New South Wales. 23 Mark Field.
24 A fruit (plum). 25 Slough. 26 Hi De Hi. 27 Huw Wheldon. 28 Tonic water. 29 Canada. 30 The Golden Fleece.

Quiz 97 Pot Luck 45

Answers - see Quiz 98, page 218

LEVEL 2

1. Who was the first Briton to hold a world javelin record?
2. Who performed and wrote the theme for Ghostbusters?
3. How many players are there in a Canadian football team?
4. Chester Whites, Durocs and Hampshire are all types of what animal?
5. What is killed by an analgesic?
6. The Dufourspitze is the highest mountain where?
7. When do ducks always lay their eggs?
8. Which Laura had a hit with Gloria?
9. Who preceded Corazon Aquino as President of the Philippines?
10. Which test would you be taking if you underwent a polygraph test?
11. Which American city's football team is called the Bears?
12. Which vitamin deficiency causes rickets?
13. Which suspension bridge crosses the River Avon?
14. Which volcano erupted in 1883 and lies between Java and Sumatra?
15. What is the vocal tinkling sound made by a deer called?
16. Which sea surrounds Heligoland?
17. How many inches above grass should the top of a croquet hoop be?
18. The pituitary gland controls the production of what in the body?
19. Which prefix is a tenth in the metric system?
20. How many pounds does the Olympic hammer weigh?
21. What was the name of the Boswell's daughter in Bread?
22. What was a Minster originally attached to?
23. What is the popular name for the wood-hyacinth?
24. Where is Britain's National Horseracing Museum?
25. Who did James Earl Ray assassinate?
26. Who was the only female in Edward Heath's first cabinet?
27. Which fault line is San Francisco on?
28. Who won 100m gold at the 1988 Olympics after Ben Johnson's disqualification?
29. Where was the terrorist group ETA mainly active?
30. Who was called the Father of Medicine?

Answers

Sport: Who's Who? (see Quiz 98, page 218)
1 Sonny Liston. 2 Natalie Tauziat. 3 Rocky Marciano. 4 Al Joyner. 5 Joe DiMaggio. 6 Jake La Motta. 7 Silver. 8 Ray Reardon. 9 Boris Becker. 10 Mary Decker Slaney. 11 Italy. 12 Ernie Els. 13 Nick Faldo. 14 Steve Davis. 15 Goran Ivanisevic. 16 Paul Ince. 17 Chris Evert. 18 Davis. 19 Squash. 20 Denise Lewis. 21 Damon Hill. 22 Rocket. 23 John Conteh. 24 Judo. 25 Mike Tyson. 26 Conchita Martinez. 27 Bernard Gallacher. 28 Snooker. 29 Peter Fleming. 30 Nigel Benn.

Quiz 98 Sport: Who's Who?

Answers - see Quiz 97, page 217

LEVEL 2

1 Who did Muhammad Ali beat when he first became World Champion?
2 Who was runner up to Jana Novotna in the Wimbledon final in 1998?
3 Who was the first heavyweight boxing champion to retire undefeated?
4 Who was the late Flo Jo's husband?
5 Which husband of Marilyn Monroe was elected to the Baseball Hall of Fame?
6 Whose life was recorded on film in Raging Bull?
7 What colour individual medal did Sharron Davies win at the Moscow Olympics?
8 Which snooker champion was unkindly nicknamed Dracula?
9 Which German tennis player was born on Billie Jean King's 23rd birthday?
10 Who did Zola Budd trip up at the Los Angeles Olympics in 1984?
11 British born long jumper Fiona May represents which country in international athletics?
12 Which South African golfer's real first name is Theodore?
13 Which golfer split with his coach and his girlfriend in September '98?
14 Who did Stephen Hendry replace as world No 1 in the 1989-90 season?
15 Who is Croatia's No 1 tennis player?
16 Which sometime England captain is a cousin of boxer Nigel Benn?
17 Who lost most Ladies Singles finals at Wimbledon in the 80s?
18 Which surname has been shared by three world snooker champions?
19 Peter Nicol won Commonwealth gold for Scotland in which sport?
20 Who successfully defended her heptathlon title at the 1998 Commonwealth Games?
21 Who won his first Grand Prix since 1996 in Belgium in 1998?
22 Which Gladiator competed in the heptathlon in the 1998 Commonwealth Games?
23 Which Liverpudlian won the WBC Light Heavyweight Title in 1974?
24 Sharron Davies' one time fiancé Neil Adams was an international in which sport?
25 Who replaced Leon Spinks as Heavyweight Champion in 1987?
26 Who defeated Navratilova in the final at her last Wimbledon?
27 Who captained Europe to Ryder Cup success in 1995?
28 Allison Fisher is a former world champion in which sport?
29 Who did John McEnroe win five Wimbledon Doubles titles with?
30 Which boxer is nicknamed 'The Dark Destroyer'?

Pot Luck 45 (see Quiz 97, page 217)
1 Fatima Whitbread. 2 Ray Parker, Jr. 3 Twelve. 4 Pigs. 5 Pain.
6 Switzerland. 7 In the morning. 8 Branigan. 9 President Marcos. 10 A lie
detector. 11 Chicago. 12 D. 13 The Clifton. 14 Krakatoa. 15 A bell.
16 The North Sea. 17 Twelve. 18 Hormones. 19 Deci. 20 16.
21 Aveline. 22 Monastery. 23 The bluebell. 24 Newmarket. 25 Martin
Luther King. 26 Margaret Thatcher. 27 San Andreas. 28 Carl Lewis.
29 Spain. 30 Hippocrates.

Answers

Quiz 99 TV: TV Gold

LEVEL 2

Answers - see Quiz 100, page 220

1 Which Game For a Laugh presenters had the same surname?
2 Who was the subject of The Naked Civil Servant with John Hurt?
3 Which sitcom told of Tooting revolutionary Wolfie?
4 Who found fame as The Saint?
5 Who played Louie de Palma in Taxi?
6 Which spaghetti western star played in Rawhide for six years?
7 Who conducted Eric Morecambe playing Grieg's Piano Concerto?
8 Which reporter found fame during her reporting of the Iranian Embassy siege in 1980?
9 In which weekly drama slot was Cathy Come Home first shown?
10 Before WWII which was the single most watched event on TV?
11 Who was the main character on The Phil Silvers Show?
12 Who became Mrs Clayton Farlow in Dallas?
13 Which series looked back at film clips 25 years old?
14 How were Bruce Wayne and Dick Grayson better known?
15 Which Carry On regular was the star of Bless This House?
16 Who was 'lower class' on The Frost Report after John Cleese and Ronnie Barker?
17 Which soap was originally called The Midland Road?
18 Which famous singer/actor's daughter shot JR?
19 Which Corrie star joined the cast in 1961 as Miss Nugent?
20 What was the surname of Morticia and Gomez?
21 Which area of the country received TV after the area London in 1949?
22 In which sitcom did Richard Beckinsale play Alan Moore?
23 Which series told of the bizarre life of the Clampett family?
24 Which comedian played Colin in Colin's Sandwich?
25 Which show has numbered David Jacobs, Noel Edmonds and Rosemarie Ford among its presenters?
26 What was the BBC's first soap of the 60s?
27 Who was the Scottish undertaker in Dad's Army?
28 The controversial Death of a Princess caused a rift with which country in 1980?
29 Who had a long running TV show before starring in Mary Poppins?
30 Who is the only Corrie star remaining from the original cast?

Pot Luck 46 (see Quiz 100, page 220)
1 Dance. 2 Gunpowder. 3 Nebuchadnezzar. 4 Sioux. 5 Golf. 6 James I.
7 Violin. 8 In loco parentis. 9 Dublin. 10 Jersey. 11 Ealing. 12 A.E.
Housman. 13 Harvard. 14 Alessandro Volta. 15 House of Representatives.
16 A race or racial group. 17 The end of the world. 18 Lion. 19 Playboy.
20 Hitchcock. 21 Four. 22 Amelia Earhart. 23 Austria. 24 Rubber.
25 Gold, platinum, silver. 26 £1.05. 27 Bay. 28 Hyde Park. 29 Hormone replacement therapy. 30 Alimentary canal.

Answers

Quiz 100 Pot Luck 46

Answers - see Quiz 99, page 219

1 In Cuba what is a habanera?
2 Which black powder is the oldest known explosive?
3 Who condemned Shadrach, Meshach and Abednego to the Fiery Furnace?
4 Which tribe did Sitting Bull belong to?
5 Sam Snead found fame in which sport?
6 Who was king at the time of the Gunpowder Plot?
7 Which musical instrument did Jack Benny play?
8 Which Latin phrase means 'in place of a parent'?
9 Dun Laoghaire is a port and suburb of where?
10 Gerald Durrell was a director of which zoo?
11 Michael Balcon was head of which influential studios?
12 Who wrote A Shropshire Lad?
13 What is the oldest university in the USA?
14 Who was the volt named after?
15 What is the lower house of the US Congress called?
16 Genocide is the destruction of what?
17 In Scandinavian myth what is Gotterdammerung?
18 Which animals' legs did the Griffin have?
19 Which magazine was famous for its nude centrefold?
20 Which director made Blackmail, Britain's first successful talkie?
21 How many tournaments make up tennis's Grand Slam?
22 With which woman aviator did Frederick Noonan perish?
23 In which country was Hitler born?
24 What is a puck made from in ice hockey?
25 On which three metals would you see a hallmark?
26 In modern currency how much is a guinea?
27 What is the Great Australian Bight?
28 Where in London was the Great Exhibition of 1851?
29 What is HRT?
30 Which canal is also called the gut?

TV: TV Gold (see Quiz 99, page 219)
1 Matthew & Henry Kelly. 2 Quentin Crisp. 3 Citizen Smith. 4 Roger
Moore. 5 Danny De Vito. 6 Clint Eastwood. 7 Andre Previn. 8 Kate Adie.
9 The Wednesday Play. 10 George VI's coronation. 11 Bilko. 12 Miss Ellie.
13 All Our Yesterdays. 14 Batman and Robin. 15 Sid James. 16 Ronnie
Corbett. 17 Crossroads. 18 Bing Crosby's (Mary). 19 Eileen Derbyshire.
20 Addams. 21 Midlands. 22 Rising Damp. 23 The Beverly Hillbillies.
24 Mel Smith. 25 Come Dancing. 26 Compact. 27 Private Fraser.
28 Saudi Arabia. 29 Dick Van Dyke. 30 William Roache.

Quiz 101 Movies: People

LEVEL 2

1 Which actor is the son of a Poet Laureate?

2 Which 'Chinese Western' actor's real name was Lee Yuen Kam?

3 Which singer and actress was in Dick Tracy?

4 Kenneth Branagh cast which toothy comedian as Yorick in Hamlet?

5 Who played the adult Damien in The Omen films?

6 Which pop wife appeared with Robert Redford, aged four, in The Great Gatsby?

7 Which early screen comedian's real name was Louis Cristillo?

8 Who played Cruella de Vil's sidekick Jasper in 101 Dalmatians?

9 Who beat Meryl Streep for the lead role in The Horse Whisperer?

10 Which Glaswegian played a gangster in Goldeneye?

11 Which serious actress played comedy opposite Schwarzenegger in Junior?

12 Who directed, scripted, composed and starred in Yentl?

13 Which ex child star was US Ambassador to Czechoslovakia in 1989?

14 How were producers Harry, Albert, Sam and Jack known collectively?

15 What was Groucho Marx's real first name?

16 Which Cockney actor married the former Miss Guyana in 1973?

17 Which horror writer directed the film Maximum Overdrive?

18 Who had larger feet, Marilyn Monroe or Daryl Hannah?

19 Which star of Look Who's Talking Too was a regular on TV's Cheers?

20 Which Fonda starred in the remake of Nikita?

21 Who is Joely Richardson's famous mother?

22 Which comedies was Michael Balcon responsible for?

23 Which actress wrote Postcards From the Edge?

24 Who was the first Bond girl?

25 Which conductor is Woody Allen's father in law?

26 Which surname was shared by John, Lionel, Ethel and Drew?

27 Who played Batman in Batman Forever?

28 What was Ex-python Terry Gilliam's futuristic nightmare film, surreally named for a South American country?

29 Who bought the screen rights to Dick Tracy and made a film from it?

30 Which blonde actress is Mrs Alec Baldwin?

Pot Luck 47 (see Quiz 102, page 222)

1 The Pope. 2 Estate car. 3 The deaf. 4 Relate. 5 Ofwat. 6 Tibet. 7 Tax. 8 Munich. 9 Two. 10 SAS. 11 France (de Nimes). 12 Operation Desert Storm. 13 Franz Beckenbauer. 14 Leek. 15 Kite shaped. 16 Election. 17 Teeth or bone. 18 Variety Club. 19 Thames. 20 Houses of Parliament. 21 Special Branch. 22 Hospital. 23 American Revolution. 24 Sleeping policeman. 25 Nurse. 26 Merchant Navy. 27 Third degree. 28 Young children. 29 Lutine Bell. 30 Red.

Answers

Quiz 102 Pot Luck 47

Answers - see Quiz 101, page 221

LEVEL 2

1 Who would deliver an edict called a bull?

2 What is a shooting brake?

3 Who does the RNID provide help for?

4 What is the Marriage Guidance Council now called?

5 How is the Office of Water Services also known?

6 The Dalai Lama is the spiritual leader of where?

7 In English history what was danegeld?

8 What is the capital of Bavaria?

9 How many days does a decathlon event last?

10 The US Delta Force is based on which British anti terrorist force?

11 In which country did denim originate?

12 What was the codename for the operation to eject the Iraqis from Kuwait in 1991?

13 Who was the first person to manage and captain a World Cup winning soccer side?

14 David was responsible for the adoption of what as a Welsh emblem?

15 What shape is the approved mark of the British Standards Institution?

16 At what occasion do you see a returning officer?

17 Caries is the decay and deterioration of what?

18 Which Club's President is the Chief Barker?

19 On which river does swan-upping take place?

20 Where in London is the Strangers' Gallery?

21 Which police department deals with political security in the UK?

22 What sort of institution is UCH?

23 The Battle of Bunker Hill was the first major engagement of what?

24 What name is given to a bump in the road to slow down traffic?

25 What is the profession of an RGN?

26 Whose flag is the red ensign?

27 Which degree of burns is life threatening?

28 Who does a Norland nurse work with?

29 Which bell is found in the building of Lloyd's of London?

30 What colour is the ceremonial dress of a Yeoman of the Guard?

Answers

Movies: People (see Quiz 101, page 221)

1 Daniel Day-Lewis. 2 Bruce Lee. 3 Madonna. 4 Ken Dodd. 5 Sam Neill. 6 Patsy Kensit. 7 Lou Costello. 8 Hugh Laurie. 9 Kristin Scott Thomas. 10 Robbie Coltrane. 11 Emma Thompson. 12 Barbra Streisand. 13 Shirley Temple. 14 Warner Brothers. 15 Julius. 16 Michael Caine. 17 Stephen King. 18 Daryl Hannah. 19 Kirstie Alley. 20 Bridget. 21 Vanessa Redgrave. 22 Ealing. 23 Carrie Fisher. 24 Ursula Andress. 25 Andre Previn. 26 Barrymore. 27 Val Kilmer. 28 Brazil. 29 Warren Beatty. 30 Kim Basinger.

Quiz 103 Leisure: Media

Answers - see Quiz 104, page 224

LEVEL 2

1   What is Portland Place's most famous House?
2   What does CNN stand for?
3   Which listings magazine celebrated its 75th birthday in 1998?
4   What is Britain's principal world news agency?
5   Which magazine is supposedly edited by Lord Gnome?
6   Where is Grampian TV based?
7   What does the ASA control?
8   What is the magazine of the Consumer's Association?
9   Who is the Daily Mail's most famous cartoon dog?
10 Where is The People's Daily a top selling papers?
11 Which long-running futuristic comic featured Judge Dredd and Rogue Trooper?
12 Country Life was once edited by which royal photographer?
13 Red and yellow were the colours of which comic strip Rovers?
14 What is the full official title of GQ?
15 Which organisation had a magazine called "Expression!"?
16 Which daily paper founded in 1859 is devoted to horse racing?
17 In which part of the Commonwealth might you tune in to Penguin Radio?
18 Which Times Supplement is aimed at teachers?
19 How is the New Musical Express better known?
20 How does Dennis the Menace's mother always address her husband?
21 Which US based magazine was the world's best seller until the 80s?
22 How is the journalists' trade union commonly known?
23 Which famous magazine was founded by Hugh Hefner?
24 Where is Yorkshire TV based?
25 In which part of London are Richard Murdoch's newspapers based?
26 Which was the ill-fated satellite TV company that competed with Sky?
27 Which major UK daily newspaper, still in circulation, did Robert Maxwell own?
28 Which left wing faction had a newspaper called Militant?
29 Which major Murdoch UK paper has the longest name?
30 Which women's magazine did Cherie Blair guest edit?

Answers

Pot Luck 48 (see Quiz 104, page 224)
1 New Kids on the Block. 2 Juliet Bravo. 3 Smallpox. 4 Ben Hur. 5 In space.
6 Bradford City's. 7 Pat Garrett. 8 The Queen. 9 Britain's. 10 Hot and spicy.
11 Petula Clark. 12 Richard III. 13 Anglesey. 14 Bad Manners. 15 Tenerife.
16 Barry McGuigan. 17 Columbia. 18 M4. 19 An Emirate. 20 Dresden.
21 Niki Lauda. 22 Pacific. 23 The Gridiron. 24 Poetry. 25 Cambridge.
26 Prince. 27 The seahorse. 28 Manoeuvres. 29 Leather. 30 Nikita.

Quiz 104 Pot Luck 48

LEVEL 2

Answers - see Quiz 103, page 223

1 In the music world what did NKOTB stand for?
2 Hartley was the fictional town setting for which TV police serial?
3 Variola is the proper name for which killer disease?
4 Who competed against Messala in a literary chariot race?
5 Where did Laika, the first dog in space, die?
6 Which British stadium saw the worst soccer tragedy in 1985?
7 Which sheriff killed Billy the Kid?
8 Who had a well publicised conversation with Michael Fagan in 1982?
9 In a 1991 survey which country's inhabitants used the most soap per capita?
10 Is a piri-piri sauce sweet, or hot and spicy?
11 Which Swiss resident won a Grammie for singing Downtown?
12 Which Richard died at the Battle of Bosworth Field?
13 Which is largest, the Isle of Wight or Anglesey?
14 Buster Bloodvessel was a member of which Ska-revival band?
15 Which holiday island saw the worst ever air crash with 582 deaths?
16 Which former world boxing champion has the Christian name Finbar?
17 What does the "C" stand for in the musical initials "CBS"?
18 Which motorway joins with the M25 at Heathrow Airport?
19 What is controlled by an Emir?
20 In World War II which German city suffered the most civilian deaths?
21 Which living motor racing driver had been given the last rites before becoming World Champion?
22 What name is given to the most westerly time zone in America?
23 What is an American football pitch also called?
24 Thomas Hardy wrote what type of material for the last twelve years of his life?
25 Which is further east, Cambridge or Peterborough?
26 Which male pop superstar wrote the Bangles Manic Monday hit?
27 Which is the slowest moving fish?
28 What did the "M" stand for in the name of the band OMD?
29 Cordwainers mainly worked with which material?
30 Which Elton John hit was the first name of Russian leader Kruschev?

Leisure: Media (see Quiz 103, page 223)
1 Broadcasting House. **2** Cable News Network. **3** Radio Times. **4** Reuters.
5 Private Eye. **6** Aberdeen. **7** Advertising. **8** Which?. **9** Fred Basset.
10 China. **11** 2001AD. **12** Lord Snowdon. **13** Melchester.
14 Gentlemen's Quarterly. **15** American Express. **16** The Sporting Life.
17 Falkland Islands. **18** Educational. **19** NME. **20** Dad. **21** Reader's
Digest. **22** NUJ. **23** Playboy. **24** Leeds. **25** Wapping. **26** BSB. **27** Daily
Mirror. **28** Militant Tendency. **29** The News of the World. **30** Prima.

Quiz 105 Technology

Answers - see Quiz 106, page 226

LEVEL 2

1   What is Computer Assisted in the acronym CAD?
2   In which US state is the so called Silicon Glen?
3   Which bank does the CWS own?
4   In the oil industry what is the tower called which hoists the drill pipes?
5   What does the T stand for in DTP?
6   Which early adding device comes from the Latin meaning 'a flat surface'?
7   What does DERV stand for?
8   Exxon is the US's largest concern in which industry?
9   What does ICI stand for?
10 Which industry's members belong to Unison?
11 Who founded Habitat?
12 What is antiknock added to to reduce knocking?
13 What type of institution was BCCI?
14 Who founded Amstrad?
15 What does a Geiger counter measure?
16 What is the full name of CFCs?
17 For which industry is London's Wardour Street famous?
18 Where is Britain's largest North Sea oil terminal?
19 Which copying machine did Chester Carlson invent?
20 Who is the US's largest vehicle manufacturer?
21 What was the world's longest bridge when it was opened in 1980?
22 What is a country's GNP?
23 What does W stand for in the AWACS surveillance system?
24 What is the study of motion and impact of projectiles?
25 Which country has the world's largest electricity grid system?
26 Where is the BASF group based?
27 What is the world's largest packaged food company?
28 What is a computer's smallest unit of information?
29 Where did Lord Nuffield, aka William Morris, build up his car business?
30 What does the 'M' in IBM stand for?

Answers

Pot Luck 49 (see Quiz 106, page 226)
1 Jingles. 2 A stilt. 3 Horse fair. 4 1st October. 5 A mountain. 6 USA.
7 Face the Music. 8 Buddy Holly. 9 Horses. 10 Lethbridge-Stewart.
11 Billy Connolly. 12 French. 13 Barnsdale. 14 Coming Home.
15 Madrid. 16 Howard's Way. 17 The Times. 18 Demi Moore.
19 Italy. 20 Order of the Garter. 21 Ronnie Corbett. 22 Christopher Robin.
23 Two. 24 Christmas Day. 25 Mulder and Scully. 26 Snakes. 27 Bones.
28 Staffordshire. 29 Javelin. 30 Caskets.

Quiz 106 Pot Luck 49

Answers - see Quiz 105, page 225

LEVEL 2

1 What are the metal discs in the rim of a tambourine called?
2 Which word can be a pole with a foot rest or a wading bird?
3 What annual event is the Cumbrian town of Appleby noted for?
4 On what date does the pheasant shooting season legally start?
5 Who or what is Cader Idris?
6 Mr Birdseye – of frozen food fame – came from which country?
7 Richard Baker was a regular panellist on which musical TV quiz?
8 Which 1950s pop star had the first names Charles Hardin?
9 Which animals can be affected by a disease called vives?
10 Which Brigadier appeared in Dr Who?
11 Who played Mr Brown in the film Mrs Brown?
12 What is the official language of Haiti?
13 What was the name of Geoff Hamilton's garden?
14 Jane Fonda won a Best Actress Oscar for her role in which 1978 film?
15 Barajas airport is in which city?
16 Jack Rolfe and Charles Frere were characters in which TV series?
17 What is the oldest daily newspaper in England?
18 Demetria Guynes is better known as which actress?
19 Which country surrounds San Marino?
20 Which Order is the highest in the Order of Chivalry in Britain?
21 Who played the leading role in the TV series Sorry?
22 What was the name of A.A. Milne's son?
23 How many hours are there in a dog watch at sea?
24 In a calendar year what is the name given to the final quarter day?
25 Fox and Dana are the first names of which pair?
26 What did Saint Patrick rid Ireland of according to legend?
27 What are osselets and ossicles?
28 Alton Towers Leisure Park is in which county?
29 Steve Backley held the world record in which sports event?
30 In The Merchant of Venice the suitors pick one of three what?

Technology (see Quiz 105, page 225)
1 Design. 2 California. 3 Co-op Bank. 4 Derrick. 5 Top. 6 Abacus.
7 Diesel Engine Road Vehicle. 8 Oil. 9 International Chemical Industries.
10 Health industry. 11 Terence Conran. 12 Petrol. 13 Bank. 14 Alan Sugar. 15 Radioactivity. 16 ChloroFluoroCarbons. 17 Film industry.
18 Sullom Voe. 19 Xerox photocopier. 20 General Motors. 21 Humber Bridge. 22 Gross National Product. 23 Warning. 24 Ballistics. 25 Britain.
26 Germany. 27 Nestle. 28 Bit. 29 Oxford. 30 Machines.

Quiz 107 The Royals

Answers - see Quiz 108, page 228

LEVEL 2

1 What was Diana's official title at the time of her death?
2 Who is the oldest in line to the throne after Prince Charles?
3 Which Prince was a guest on the Des O'Connor Show in 1998?
4 On which island was Princess Margaret when she suffered a stroke?
5 Who was older, Princess Diana's mother or her stepmother?
6 In which country did the former Edward VIII marry Mrs Simpson?
7 Albert succeeded Baudouin in which country?
8 In which country did Fergie's mother spend the latter part of her life?
9 What does the Queen's only nephew do for a living?
10 At which sport did Harry excel in his first few weeks at Eton?
11 Who is the only child of the Queen not to have been divorced?
12 Who is third in line to the throne?
13 Who survived the crash in which Princess Diana died?
14 Which cavalryman co wrote A Princess In Love with Anna Pasternak?
15 Seven kings of which country have been called Haakon?
16 Which Princess is the mother of Viscount Linley?
17 Which Princess is known by her husband's name?
18 Which former Royal residence was damaged by fire in 1986?
19 'Tiggy' Legge-Bourke was PA to which Prince for three years?
20 Which Princess is the mother of Marina Mowatt?
21 Who was Princess Diana's chauffeur on her final fatal car journey?
22 Which Royal companion is the great granddaughter of Edward VII's mistress Alice Keppel?
23 Which grand child of the Queen had her tongue pierced?
24 Which Royal in law was dubbed 'Fog' because he was thick and wet?
25 Who took the official engagement photos of Charles and Diana?
26 Who is Lady Sarah Chatto's aunt on her mother's side?
27 Which Princess married the son of a director of Walls sausages?
28 In which royal castle is St George's Chapel?
29 Which musical instrument does Princess Margaret play?
30 In 1994 Diana took an advisory role for which organisation?

Pot Luck 50 (see Quiz 108, page 228)
1 Chester. 2 Sixpence. 3 Steal. 4 Laughing gas. 5 Florence Nightingale.
6 Liverpool. 7 1977. 8 A pack of tarot cards. 9 December 25th. 10 Arnold Palmer. 11 Loyd Grossman. 12 Lou Reed. 13 Bailey. 14 Wigan Pier.
15 You have a bite. 16 Manchester. 17 Avalon. 18 Kingston Upon Hull.
19 MCC. 20 Steve Davis. 21 Andrew. 22 Beethoven. 23 X rays.
24 Three. 25 Rudolf Nureyev. 26 Barbara Cartland. 27 Saddle. 28 Zambia. 29 17th. 30 Four.

Quiz 108 Pot Luck 50

LEVEL 2

Answers - see Quiz 107, page 227

1   Deva was a Roman city now known as what?
2   What was the top price for goods in the first British Woolworth's?
3   What does a kleptomaniac do?
4   What is the popular name for the anaesthetic nitrous oxide?
5   Who was the first woman to be awarded the Order of Merit?
6   The doomed ship Titanic was registered in which English city?
7   In which year did Marc Bolan die?
8   What is made up of the minor arcana and the major arcana?
9   The Romanian dictator Ceausescu was executed on which day in 1989?
10 Who was the last playing Ryder Cup captain, in the 60s?
11 Which food show presenter once played in a band called Jet Bronx and the Forbidden?
12 Which Lou was vocalist with the Velvet Underground?
13 Which shipping forecast area is due north of Rockall?
14 Which pier featured in a George Orwell book title?
15 If you are an angler why are you pleased if your monkey starts to climb?
16 In which city was painter LS Lowry born?
17 Where was King Arthur taken after his last battle?
18 What is Hull's full name?
19 Which all male bastion allowed women members for the first time in September 1998?
20 Who made the first televised 147 in snooker, in 1982?
21 Which Prince's childhood nickname was 'The Sniggerer'?
22 Who wrote the Emperor Concerto?
23 For which medical breakthrough did Roentgen win the Nobel Prize in 1901?
24 How many Inns of Court are there in London?
25 Which ballet dancer died on the same day as Dizzy Gillespie?
26 Whose codename was 'Pink' before she was surprised on This Is Your Life?
27 What is a pommel a part of?
28 Cars with the international vehicle registration Z come from where?
29 In which century was the Battle of Naseby?
30 How many pecks are there in a bushel?

The Royals (see Quiz 107, page 227)
Answers

1 Diana, Princess of Wales. 2 Prince Andrew. 3 Edward. 4 Mustique.
5 Stepmother. 6 France. 7 Belgium. 8 Argentina. 9 Make furniture.
10 Football. 11 Prince Edward. 12 Prince Harry. 13 Trevor Reece Jones.
14 James Hewitt. 15 Norway. 16 Margaret. 17 Michael of Kent. 18 Hampton Court. 19 Charles. 20 Alexandra. 21 Henri Paul. 22 Camilla Parker Bowles. 23 Zara Phillips. 24 Mark Phillips. 25 Lord Snowdon. 26 The Queen. 27 Anne. 28 Windsor. 29 Piano. 30 International Red Cross.

Quiz 109 Who Was Who?

LEVEL 2

1. Who was Chancellor, Foreign Secretary and PM between 1964 and 1979?
2. Which nation introduced chocolate to Europe?
3. Which American was known as Ike?
4. Which future President organised the Free French Forces in WWII?
5. What was Indira Gandhi's maiden name?
6. Who became US Vice President in 1993?
7. Which title did Hitler take as Nazi leader?
8. Who was the last Tsarina of Russia?
9. Who was Soviet Foreign Minister from 1957 to 1985?
10. Whose resignation on 1st November 1990 began Thatcher's downfall?
11. Whose 1963 Report led to the closure of many railway stations?
12. Who was famous for his pictures of Campbell's Soup cans?
13. Who was British Prime Minister during the abdication crisis?
14. For how long were Hitler and Eva Braun married?
15. In 1996 who had served longer continuously as a Minister, John Major or Kenneth Clarke?
16. Which athlete became MP for Falmouth and Cambourne in 1992?
17. Which world leader celebrated his 80th birthday in July 1998?
18. Who was the first Archbishop of Canterbury?
19. Which US President publicly pardoned ex President Nixon?
20. Who had the title Il Duce?
21. Which US evangelist asked his flock to make a "decision for Christ"?
22. In 1990 which ex PM went to Iraq to try to secure the release of British hostages?
23. Who was the youngest queen of Henry VIII to be beheaded?
24. Which Prime Minister introduced the Citizen's Charter?
25. Who became Defence Secretary in May 1997?
26. What was the name of Horatio Nelson's daughter by Emma Hamilton?
27. Who said her boss Michael Howard had "something of the night about him"?
28. What was the religion of a French Huguenot?
29. Whose Report formed the basis for the British welfare state?
30. In which category did Einstein win his Nobel prize in 1921?

Pop Who's Who? (see Quiz 110, page 230)

Answers

Pop Who's Who?
1 Bay City Rollers. 2 Barbra Streisand. 3 Bill Tarmey. 4 Shakin' Stevens
5 Kate Bush. 6 Chris De Burgh. 7 Two. 8 The Spice Girls. 9 Bono.
10 Richard Clayderman. 11 George Michael. 12 Emerson, Lake & Palmer.
13 Judith Durham. 14 Meatloaf. 15 Celine Dion. 16 Michael Caine.
17 Bill Medley. 18 Ken Hutchinson - Hutch. 19 Right Said Fred. 20 David
Bowie. 21 Lily the Pink. 22 George Michael. 23 Rod Stewart. 24 Shirley
Bassey. 25 Morgen. 26 Coco Hernandez. 27 Jarvis Cocker. 28 The Kemp
Brothers. 29 Victoria 'Posh'. 30 Nick Berry.

Quiz 110 Pop Who's Who?

LEVEL 2

Answers - see Quiz 109, page 229

1   The Longmuir brothers were in which 70s teeny bop group?
2   Who partnered Don Johnson on the Goya theme Till I Loved You?
3   Which Coronation Street star had a hit in '94 with Wind Beneath My Wings?
4   Which UK male vocalist's real name is Michael Barratt?
5   Who duetted with Peter Gabriel on Don't Give Up?
6   Christopher John Davidson is the real name of which Irish vocalist?
7   How many members are there in D:Ream?
8   Who launched the British Legion Poppy Appeal with Dame Vera Lynn in 1997?
9   Who featured on the 1986 Clannad hit In a Lifetime?
10 Which pianist and instrumentalist's real name is Philippe Pages?
11 Who was the younger of the two Wham! members?
12 Keith, Greg and Carl were the Christian names of which 70s trio?
13 Who was lead female singer with 60s group The Seekers?
14 Marvin Lee Aday is better known as which dead ringer vocalist?
15 Who had a No 5 UK hit with the theme song Because You Loved Me?
16 Which actor shares his name with a 1984 hit by Madness?
17 Who sang the theme tune to Dirty Dancing with Jennifer Warnes?
18 Which TV detective had a No 1 hit with Don't Give Up On Us in 1976?
19 Which group share their name with a Bernard Cribbins 1962 hit?
20 Who joined with Queen in the 1981 No 1 hit Under Pressure?
21 Who invented Medicinal Compound according to the 1968 No 1?
22 Which superstar has an autobiography called Bare?
23 Which pop legend said, "I really wanted to be a soccer star"?
24 Who partnered Chris Rea on the 1996 hit 'Disco' La Passione?
25 Complete the A-ha trio - Pal, Mags and ....?
26 Which character was played by Irene Cara in Fame?
27 Who interrupted Michael Jackson's Earth Song at the 1996 Brit Awards?
28 Which brothers were members of Spandau Ballet?
29 Who was the first Spice Girl to get engaged?
30 Who links the '86 hit Every Loser Wins and the '92 hit Heartbeat?

Answers

TV Who's Who? (see Quiz 111, page 231)
1 Ben Elton. 2 Michael Barrymore. 3 Julia Carling. 4 Cookery books.
5 Harry Enfield. 6 Jimmy Tarbuck. 7 Susan Hampshire. 8 Nigel. 9 Eamonn
Holmes. 10 James Naughtie. 11 Gaby Roslin. 12 Birmingham. 13 Lynda
Bellingham. 14 Mark Porter. 15 Airport. 16 Judi Dench. 17 Mr Motivator.
18 Melanie Stace. 19 Gloria Hunniford. 20 Frost. 21 Trisha Goddard.
22 Vet. 23 Carol Smillie. 24 Peak Practice. 25 Ann Jones. 26 Jonathan
Ross. 27 Dale Winton. 28 Herself. 29 Maureen Reece. 30 Peter Snow.

Quiz 111 TV Who's Who?

Answers - see Quiz 110, page 230

LEVEL 2

1 Which comedian wrote Blackadder with Richard Curtis?
2 Who hosted the talent spotting show My Kind of People?
3 Who replaced Anneka Rice on Carlton TV's Capital Woman?
4 David Dimbleby's first wife wrote what type of books?
5 Which comedian created the character Stavros?
6 Who has the car number plate COM 1C?
7 Which star of The Grand is President of the Dyslexia Institute?
8 Which first name is shared by subsequent stars of Dangerfield?
9 Who told Noel Edmonds live that co presenter Anthea Turner's interviews sent him to sleep?
10 Which radio name replaced Richard Baker presenting The Proms?
11 Which blonde first presented Big Breakfast with Chris Evans?
12 Julie Walters hails from which city?
13 Who replaced Carol Drinkwater as Helen in All Creatures Great and Small?
14 Which Doctor is a regular on Newsnight?
15 In which docu soap did Jeremy Spake find fame?
16 Who is actor Michael Williams' wife?
17 How is Derrick Evans better known?
18 Who became Jim Davidson's regular assistant on The Generation Game?
19 Which ex Radio 2 presenter moved to Open House on Channel 5?
20 Who could you regularly have Breakfast With... on Sunday mornings?
21 Who replaced Vanessa on ITV's morning talk show?
22 What did Trude Mostue train to be on TV?
23 Who first presented Changing Rooms?
24 In which drama series did the character Dr Beth Glover appear?
25 Who was the first woman tennis player to be BBC Sports Personality of the Year?
26 Who was the interviewer on C4's The Last Resort?
27 Who presented the National Lottery's fourth birthday show in 1998?
28 Who did Fergie play in Friends?
29 Who was the woman driver from hell in BBC's docu soap?
30 Who moved from Newsnight to Tomorrow's World?

Answers

Who Was Who? (see Quiz 109, page 229)
1 James Callaghan. 2 Spain. 3 President Eisenhower. 4 De Gaulle.
5 Nehru. 6 Al Gore. 7 Fuhrer. 8 Alexandra. 9 Andrei Gromyko. 10 Sir
Geoffrey Howe. 11 Beeching. 12 Andy Warhol. 13 Baldwin. 14 One day.
15 Kenneth Clarke. 16 Sebastian Coe. 17 Nelson Mandela. 18 St Augustine.
19 Gerald Ford. 20 Mussolini. 21 Billy Graham. 22 Edward Heath. 23
Catherine Howard. 24 John Major. 25 George Robertson. 26 Horatia. 27
Ann Widdecombe. 28 Protestant. 29 Beveridge. 30 Physics.

Hard Questions

Ah yes, the hard questions. Cackle fiendishly, and take just a moment to stroke your white, diamond-collared cat before rubbing your hands together gleefully, because these questions are the real McCoy. The posers in this selection will sort the men out from the boys, and no mistake. If you do find any boys in the public bar by the way, be sure to let the landlord know, so he can give them a packet of crisps and a bottle of coke and send them outside. The quizzes in this section will make even the most dedicated trivia hound quake with fear. No-one is going to get many of them correct, so if someone turns out an incredible score on these questions, search their coat for a copy of this book.

When you're setting a quiz, use these questions sparingly, like hot chilli powder. Even for teams, they're going to be decidedly tricky. You'll need to allow plenty of time for people to think about each question. What you don't want to do is make an entire night's quizzing out of this section, because you'll only make people feel stupid, and everyone hates a smart alec who makes them look dumb. A few of these questions, strategically placed, can go a long way.

Quiz 1 Pot Luck 1

Answers - see Quiz 2, page 234

LEVEL 3

1 Asuncion is the capital of which country?

2 In the 1980s the town of Spitak was destroyed in which disaster?

3 Who had hits with Take Your Time and Got To Have Your Love?

4 What is a paravane used for?

5 Dr James Naismith devised which game?

6 In which decade was Jeremy Paxman born?

7 Which world wide magazine was conceived by DeWitt Wallace?

8 To within two years, when were postcodes introduced to the UK?

9 Waterways Airways operates from which country?

10 Who is the elder – Rowan Atkinson or Clive Anderson?

11 What is prase?

12 Who, in 1890, composed the music for the opera Ivanhoe ?

13 A poniard is a type of what?

14 Who led the Expedition of the Thousand in 1860?

15 Which 60s No 1 was written by Madden and Morse in 1903?

16 Which part of the body is affected by thlipsis?

17 Who was found dead in the first episode of EastEnders?

18 Which Mel Brooks' film was a spoof of Hitchcock movies?

19 Which road was part of the title of the TV series based on the true story of the Cavendish Hotel?

20 What did Princess Diana once describe as "hard work and no pay"?

21 Antonio Salazar was dictator for many years in which country?

22 Which US anti-terrorist force is based at Fort Bragg?

23 William Benting was an English pioneer of what?

24 By volume, what makes up about 21% of our atmosphere?

25 Who starred with his wife in the film Mr and Mrs Bridge?

26 Whose one and only hit was I've Never Been To Me in 1982?

27 Whose codename was Pink for This Is Your Life?

28 To which Court are US Ambassadors to Britain officially credited?

29 Which US poet had the middle names Weston Loomir?

30 Which was the first African team to compete in the Cricket World Cup?

Answers

TV Detectives (See quiz 2, page 234)
1 Lynda La Plante. 2 Maisie Raine. 3 Liverpool One. 4 Adrian Kershaw. 5 Reginald Hill. 6 Eddie Shoestring. 7 Charlie's Angels. 8 R.D.Wingfield. 9 CIB. 10 David Renwick. 11 Rupert Davies. 12 Reilly - Ace of Spies. 13 The Rockford Files. 14 Crime Traveller. 15 Denise Welch. 16 Cadfael. 17 Imogen Stubbs. 18 Jasper Carrott. 19 Taggart. 20 Stanton. 21 Van der Valk. 22 Sexton Blake. 23 Gideon's Way. 24 Cordelia Gray. 25 Chief Inspector Haskins. 26 Hercule Poirot. 27 The Body in the Library. 28 Paul Usher. 29 Henry Crabbe. 30 Simon Templar.

Quiz 2 TV Detectives

Answers - see Quiz 1, page 233

LEVEL 3

1 Which playwright created the character Jane Tennison?
2 Which TV detective was played by Pauline Quirke?
3 In which series was Samantha Janus transferred from the Met to Merseyside?
4 Who was Morse's sidekick in The Wench is Dead?
5 Which novelist created the characters of Dalziel and Pascoe?
6 Which detective worked for Radio West?
7 Which series centred on Townsend Investigations?
8 Which novelist created Jack Frost?
9 Which acronymic part of the Met did Tony Clark work for in Between The Lines?
10 Which writer created off beat sleuth Jonathan Creek?
11 Who introduced the very first series of Detective?
12 In which series did Inspector Tsientsin appear?
13 Which famous series was introduced with a message on an answering machine?
14 In which series was Slade assisted by Holly?
15 Who played Frances Spender in the Jimmy Nail series?
16 Whose investigations are based in Shrewsbury but often filmed in central Europe?
17 Who played mini skirted detective Anna Lee?
18 Whose real-life daughter plays a nanny in The Archers?
19 Which long running series began with a pilot called Killer in 1983?
20 Where did The Cops take place?
21 What was the full name of TV's most famous Dutch detective?
22 Who had Rolls Royce called The Grey Panther?
23 Which 60s series had Chief Inspector Keen aiding his Commander?
24 Who is the detective in An Unsuitable Job for a Woman?
25 Who was Regan's boss in The Sweeney?
26 Which detective lived at Whitehaven Mansions?
27 Which was the first Miss Marple adaptation to star Joan Hickson on TV?
28 Which actor linked Brookside with Liverpool One?
29 Who had retired from Barstock CID?
30 Claude Eustace Teal was invariably beaten in his dealings with whom?

Answers

Pot Luck 1 (See quiz 1, page 233)
1 Paraguay. 2 Armenian earthquake. 3 Mantronix. 4 Mine-sweeping.
5 Basketball. 6 1950s. 7 Reader's Digest. 8 1968. 9 New Zealand.
10 Clive Anderson. 11 A type of quartz. 12 Sir Arthur Sullivan. 13 Dagger.
14 Garibaldi. 15 Two Little Boys. 16 The blood vessels. 17 Reg Cox.
18 High Anxiety. 19 Duke Street. 20 Motherhood. 21 Portugal. 22 Delta
Force. 23 Slimming diet. 24 Oxygen. 25 Paul Newman. 26 Charlene. 27
Barbara Cartland. 28 St. James. 29 Ezra Pound. 30 East Africa (in 1975).

Quiz 3 Pot Luck 2

LEVEL 3

1 Phil Read won several World Championships in which sport?
2 What did an alchemist use an alembic for?
3 What was Eternal's first UK Top Ten hit?
4 In Hindu mythology who was goddess of destruction and death?
5 In which country is the Mackenzie River?
6 Which instrument did Lionel Hampton play?
7 Which character was played by June Allyson in the film The Glenn Miller Story?
8 What was President Carter's wife's first name?
9 Who won the first squash World Open Championship?
10 Where is England's national hockey stadium?
11 Who is the elder – Dame Judi Dench or Barbara Taylor Bradford?
12 Who wrote the novel Rodney Stone?
13 How many times is Annie mentioned in the lyrics of Annie's Song?
14 In Swift's novel what was Gulliver's first name?
15 To which part of the body does the adjective 'cutaneous' refer?
16 In which sport were Hildon and Black Bears British Champions?
17 Whose first Top Ten hit was What A Waste in 1978?
18 Who was James I of England's father?
19 Which record label did Geri Halliwell sign up with when she left the Spice Girls?
20 What was the old name for stamp collecting?
21 In which decade was the Earl of Lichfield born?
22 Alfredo di Stefano of Real Madrid fame was born in which country?
23 What is the name of the police officer in West Side Story?
24 Which language's name means 'one who hopes'?
25 Which public figure resigned over dealings concerning prostitute Monica Coghlan?
26 In The Old Testament which two books are named after women?
27 The Prix Goncourt is awarded for what?
28 Who joined Patrick Macnee on the 1990 No 5 UK hit Kinky Boots?
29 Who or what is a dourousouli?
30 Which broadcaster died in June, 1988, at a Leeds hospital from hepatitis?

Books 1 (See quiz 4, page 236)
1 John Cleese. 2 Full Disclosure. 3 Diana Rigg. 4 Martin Amis. 5 Dame Barbara Cartland. 6 Ronnie Spector. 7 Six. 8 Pat Conroy. 9 Clare Francis. 10 Madonna. 11 Isaac Asimov. 12 Ordeal. 13 Pig. 14 Sussex. 15 Richard Noble. 16 Torvill & Dean. 17 South Africa. 18 Her Majesty's Stationery Office. 19 Stephen Hawking. 20 Jilly Cooper. 21 Octaves. 22 Noah Webster. 23 Styles. 24 The Rainbow. 25 The Highway Code. 26 Set. 27 Winston Churchill. 28 Guinness Book of Records. 29 Bridget Jones's. 30 Agatha Christie.

Quiz 4 Books 1

Answers - see Quiz 3, page 235

LEVEL 3

1 Which comedian wrote Families and How to Survive Them with psychiatrist Robin Skynner?

2 What was Andrew Neil's autobiography called?

3 Who wrote an anthology of critics' anecdotes called No Turn Unstoned?

4 Whose first novel was The Rachel Papers in 1974?

5 Which novelist recorded an Album of Love Songs in 1978?

6 Which pop celebrity wrote Be My Baby?

7 How many Barchester Chronicles are there?

8 Who wrote the novel on which the movie Prince of Tides was based?

9 Who went from Deceit and Betrayal to A Dark Devotion?

10 Whose book Sex, coincided with a dance album Erotica?

11 Which science fiction writer wrote the Foundation Trilogy?

12 In the title of the largely autobiographical 1957 Evelyn Waugh novel, what does the main character experience?

13 Who or what was PG Wodehouse's Empress of Blandings?

14 The founder of Wisden played for which English county?

15 Whose quest for speed is recorded in his book Thrust?

16 Which sports stars' autobiography was called Facing the Music?

17 Rider Haggard's colonial service where influenced his books?

18 Who publishes Hansard?

19 Whose 1998 best seller argued that our universe is a part of a super universe?

20 Which novelist's great great grandfather founded The Yorkshire Post?

21 What did Compton Mackenzie refer to each individual volume of his autobiography as?

22 Whose 19th century dictionary standardised US English?

23 Where was the Mysterious Affair in the first Agatha Christie in Penguin paperback?

24 Which colourful DH Lawrence book was banned because of its sexual content along with Lady Chatterley and Women in Love?

25 First appearing in 1931, what sold out of its new edition in three months in 1996?

26 In the Oxford English Dictionary which word has the longest entry?

27 Whose biography already has 22 volumes and is still being written?

28 What is the best-selling copyright book of all time?

29 Whose Diary was written by Helen Fielding?

30 Who wrote romantic novels as Mary Westmacott?

Answers

Pot Luck 2 (See quiz 3, page 235)
1 Motor Cycling. 2 To distil liquids. 3 Stay. 4 Kali. 5 Canada. 6 Vibraphone. 7 Glenn Miller's wife. 8 Rosalyn. 9 Geoff Hunt. 10 Milton Keynes. 11 Barbara Taylor Bradford. 12 Sir Arthur Conan Doyle. 13 Never. 14 Lemuel. 15 Skin. 16 Polo. 17 Ian Dury & The Blockheads. 18 Lord Darnley. 19 Chrysalis. 20 Timbrology. 21 1930s. 22 Argentina. 23 Officer Krupke. 24 Esperanto. 25 Jeffrey Archer. 26 Ruth and Esther. 27 Literature (in France). 28 Honor Blackman. 29 A monkey. 30 Russell Harty.

Quiz 5 Pot Luck 3

Answers - see Quiz 6, page 238

LEVEL 3

1 Who designed the tapestry behind the altar in Coventry Cathedral?

2 An odalisque is a female what?

3 Who founded the record label Maverick Records?

4 Who won the southern junior and senior cross country titles on the same day?

5 Which English poet had the middle name Chawner?

6 The Russian Revolution began in which year?

7 Which King of Hollywood died on the same day as broadcaster Gilbert Harding?

8 Who is the elder – Zoe Ball or Gary Barlow?

9 In the 1980s Greg Lemond became the first American to do what?

10 Whose one and only hit was Little Things Mean A Lot?

11 Who created the Statue of Zeus about 430 BC?

12 What did Lee Marvin throw in Gloria Grahame's face in The Big Heat?

13 What was film star Edward G Robinson's real name?

14 Who was the husband of cellist Jacqueline du Pre?

15 What is the drink kumiss made from?

16 Who came up with The Book of Heroic Failures?

17 What was discovered in 1930 by Clyde Tombaugh?

18 In The Bible, who was King David's father?

19 In 1865, where did the Confederates surrender?

20 Wellesley is the family name of which Dukes?

21 What is a dhole?

22 Norman Parkinson made his name in which field of art?

23 How many times did Steve Donoghue win the Derby?

24 What was Paula Abdul's first UK Top Ten hit from 1989?

25 Lynn Ripley shone under which name as a pop singer?

26 Which theory was formulated by the German physicist Max Planck?

27 Which poet wrote, "She was a phantom of delight"?

28 Which England soccer manager was born in Burnley, Lancashire?

29 The Haber Process manufactures which gas?

30 Who was Banquo's son in Macbeth?

Albums (See quiz 6, page 238)
1 Simon & Garfunkel. 2 If U Can't Dance. 3 Mystery Girl. 4 Vertigo. 5 Innuendo. 6 Alison Moyet (Essex). 7 American Pie. 8 Frank Sinatra. 9 All Things Must Pass. 10 Help! - The Beatles. 11 Sheer Heart Attack. 12 A black dog. 13 Face Value. 14 Tinita Tikaram. 15 Blue. 16 Mark Coyle. 17 The Police. 18 The Sound of Music. 19 Goodbye Yellow Brick Road. 20 As a soloist, with Style Council and the Jam. 21 Chris De Burgh. 22 Fleetwood Mac. 23 Saturday Night Fever. 24 A postal strike. 25 Postcard. 26 Atom Heart Mother. 27 WEA. 28 Transformer. 29 Never For Ever. 30 South Pacific.

Quiz 6 Albums

Answers - see Quiz 5, page 237

LEVEL 3

1 Who released the biggest-selling album in Britain in the 70s?
2 What was the final track on Spice?
3 Which 1988 album confirmed a comeback by Roy Orbison?
4 Dire Straits first albums came out on which label?
5 Which 6.5 minute hit was the title track of Queen's 7th No 1 album?
6 Who charted with an album named after an English county?
7 Don McLean's Vincent came from which album?
8 Which superstar first charted with Come Fly With Me?
9 What was George Harrison's first solo album after the Beatles?
10 What was the first album to make its debut into the UK chart at No 1?
11 Which album contains the line, "My kingdom for a horse"?
12 Who is not on the front cover of Urban Hymns, but features on an inside cover shot?
13 What was Phil Collins' first solo No 1 album?
14 Whose debut album was Ancient Heart?
15 What was the main colour on the cover of Enya's Shepherd Moons?
16 Who along with Oasis gets production credits on Definitely Maybe?
17 Which group had five consecutive No 1 albums from 1979 to 1986?
18 Which original film soundtrack was on the charts for a staggering 382 weeks?
19 Which album first featured Candle In the Wind?
20 Paul Weller has topped the charts in which three guises?
21 Who was the first artist to enter the Swiss album charts at No 1?
22 What was the last Fleetwood Mac album released before the world smash Rumours?
23 Which double-album film soundtrack was a 30 million seller in 1978?
24 Why weren't the album charts published in 1971 for eight weeks?
25 What was the name of Mary Hopkin's debut album?
26 What was Pink Floyd's first album to top the UK charts?
27 Tubular Bells launched the Virgin label, but which label put out Tubular Bells II?
28 Which album originally featured Perfect Day?
29 Which Kate Bush album featured a song about Delius?
30 Which film soundtrack topped the first UK chart in November 1958?

Answers

Pot Luck 3 (See quiz 5, page 237)
1 Graham Sutherland. 2 Slave. 3 Madonna. 4 David Bedford. 5 Rupert Brooke. 6 1917. 7 Clark Gable. 8 Zoe Ball. 9 Win the Tour de France. 10 Kitty Kallen. 11 Phidias. 12 Boiling coffee. 13 Emmanuel Goldenberg. 14 Daniel Barenboim. 15 Milk. 16 Stephen Pile. 17 Pluto. 18 Jesse. 19 Appomattox. 20 Wellington. 21 An Asian wild dog. 22 Photography. 23 Six. 24 Straight Up. 25 Twinkle. 26 Quantum theory. 27 Wordsworth. 28 Ron Greenwood. 29 Ammonia. 30 Fleance

Quiz 7 Pot Luck 4

LEVEL 3

Answers - see Quiz 8

1. Who was 'The Radio Doctor' in the 1940s and 50s?
2. What was Golden Earring's first UK Top Ten hit?
3. Started in 1850, what were Children's Temperance Societies called?
4. Which motorcyclist appeared in the film Space Riders?
5. Gravure is a term connected with which industry?
6. Who played the leading role in the film The Stone Killer?
7. To the nearest hundred how many islands make up the Maldives?
8. Who was Prime Minister during the General Strike?
9. What does a mendicant do?
10. Mycology is the study of what?
11. What was the Carla Rosa, existing from 1875 to 1958?
12. Who was the last King of Troy according to legend?
13. What was George Burns real name?
14. The word Ombudsman comes from which language?
15. In which decade was Lord Rothschild born?
16. Who wrote the play The Homecoming?
17. Who was writer and producer for New Kids On the Block?
18. In which American state were Bonnie and Clyde killed in an ambush?
19. The Statue of Liberty's 100th birthday was celebrated in which year?
20. Who is the elder – Jeremy Beadle or Christopher Biggins?
21. What is studied by a pedologist?
22. Spencer Gore was the first winner of what?
23. George Galvin performed in music-hall under what name?
24. Placido Domingo studied music at which National Conservatory?
25. Who was the last Prime Minister during the reign of Queen Victoria?
26. The star Betelgeuse is in which constellation?
27. What does the Thomas Hardy novel The Dynasts deal with?
28. Who was the first woman to be Canadian Prime Minister?
29. What do a tinchel of men do?
30. Ahmed Sukarno was President of which country from 1945-62?

Answers

Cricket (See quiz 8, page 240)
1 Vengsarkar. 2 Mark Taylor. 3 Leeward Islands. 4 Swansea, Glamorgan. 5 Old Trafford. 6 West Indies. 7 Geoff Boycott. 8 Old Trafford. 9 Cigarettes & Alcohol by Oasis. 10 Warren Hegg. 11 Imperial. 12 Australia. 13 Shell Shield. 14 Sunday Express. 15 New Zealand & India. 16 Charlton Athletic. 17 Steve Bucknor. 18 Ivon. 19 India v New Zealand. 20 India & Pakistan. 21 Bob Taylor. 22 No one. 23 Mike Gatting. 24 Wayne Larkins. 25 Mike Atherton. 26 Six. 27 Alec Stewart. 28 Victoria. 29 Craig McDermott. 30 Surrey.

Quiz 8 Cricket

Answers - see Quiz 7, page 239

LEVEL 3

1 Who was the first overseas batsman to score three Test centuries at Lord's?
2 Which Aussie equalled Don Bradman's batting record in October 1998 but declared rather than beat it?
3 Which West Indian islands did Viv Richards play for?
4 Where did Sobers hit his 36 runs in one over and against whom?
5 Where did Dennis Amiss score the first century in a one day international?
6 Against whom did Mike Atherton make his first international one-day century?
7 Who deputised for Mike Brearley as England skipper four times in 1977-8?
8 Where did Lance Gibbs take most of his wickets in England?
9 Which song did Phil Tufnell choose to escort him on to the field in the New Zealand test tour?
10 Who scored a maiden first class century in his fourth match in 1987?
11 Until 1965 what did 'I' stand for in ICC?
12 Which was the first women's side to win the World Cup in successive occasions?
13 Which competition in the West Indies was replaced by the Red Stripe Cup?
14 David Gower became which newspaper's cricket correspondent when he retired?
15 Graham Gooch became the first player to score 1000 Test runs in an English summer against which sides?
16 Which football team did Alec Stewart's father play for?
17 Who was the first overseas umpire to umpire a Test Match in England?
18 What is David Gower's middle name?
19 Who was playing when the first hat trick by a bowler was scored in a World Cup?
20 Where was the first World Cup outside England played?
21 In '95 Jack Russell broke whose record for dismissals in a Test match?
22 Who sponsored what became the AXA Equity & Law League in '92?
23 Whose autobiography was called Leading From the Front?
24 Who was the first batsman to score centuries against all the counties?
25 Who was the youngest Lancastrian to score a Test century, in 1990?
26 How old was Graeme Hick when he scored a century for his school?
27 Who was the first Englishman to score a century in each innings against the West Indies in 1994?
28 Which Australian state did Ben Holioake's father play for?
29 Who was Australia's leading wicket taker on the 1994-5 Ashes tour?
30 Who won the first ever county championship?

Answers

Pot Luck 4 (See quiz 7, page 239)
1 Charles Hill. **2** Radar Love. **3** Bands of Hope. **4** Barry Sheene. **5** Printing (platemaking). **6** Charles Bronson. **7** 1200 (1196). **8** Stanley Baldwin. **9** Begs. **10** Fungi. **11** An Opera Company. **12** Priam. **13** Nathan Birnbaum. **14** Swedish. **15** 1930s. **16** Harold Pinter. **17** Maurice Starr. **18** Louisiana. **19** 1986. **20** Jeremy Beadle. **21** Soils. **22** Men's singles, Wimbledon. **23** Dan Leno. **24** Mexico. **25** Marquis of Salisbury. **26** Orion. **27** The war with Napoleon. **28** Kim Campbell. **29** Hunt. **30** Indonesia.

1   Who was the letter which revealed the Gunpowder Plot addressed to?
2   Which lecturer in philosophy wrote The Second Sex?
3   Which non-metallic element has the atomic number 6?
4   What was Marc Almond's first solo UK Top Ten hit?
5   Made in 1975 with George Segal The Black Bird was a spoof of which screen classic?
6   In surveying, how long is a Gunter's Chain in feet?
7   Susan Godfrey was the first victim of which atrocity?
8   In which city was the infamous Gatting and Rana Test Match flare up?
9   Who was older when they died Jimi Hendrix or Marc Bolan?
10 In which film did Chaplin first tackle dialogue?
11 How did Bruce Lee die?
12 What was a lamia in ancient mythology?
13 What date was the Stock Market's Black Monday of the 1980s?
14 Which saint was shot dead in 288 AD by arrows?
15 In TV's The Six Wives of Henry VIII who played wife number one?
16 The European Economic Community was established in which year?
17 In poetry what was hung around the neck of the Ancient Mariner?
18 In which decade was Greta Scacchi born?
19 Who was the first man to win a Grand Prix in a car he designed himself?
20 Whose one and only hit was Turtle Power in 1990?
21 The sword is the symbol of which of the twelve apostles?
22 Which artist painted Bubbles used by Pears to advertise their soap?
23 What can be a unit of length or a small island in Scotland?
24 Who is the elder – Kenneth Branagh or Rory Bremner?
25 What is the name of America's National Cemetery?
26 Where would you have found Zoroastrianism?
27 Robert, Grattan and Emmett were which famous Wild West outlaw gang?
28 Who wrote the play Old Times?
29 In 1941 which American defined the Four Freedoms?
30 What does Zymurgy magazine deal with?

Battle Stations (See quiz 10, page 242)
1 Auchinleck. 2 Panmunjom. 3 Madras. 4 Mohne & Eder. 5 Vidkun Quisling. 6 Right arm. 7 MacArthur. 8 Reims. 9 Richthofen's Flying Circus. 10 Gavrilo Princip. 11 Treaty of Sevres. 12 Switzerland & Luxembourg. 13 Anzio. 14 Second Battle of the Somme. 15 Major Johnny Paul Koroma. 16 29. 17 Contras. 18 Dien Bien Phu. 19 American. 20 Ardennes. 21 Japanese. 22 Tobruk. 23 Near Kiev, Ukraine. 24 Spanish Civil War. 25 Michel Aoun. 26 Boer War. 27 Tutsi v Hutu. 28 Passchendaele. 29 Von Moltke. 30 Vichy France.

Quiz 10 Battle Stations

Answers - see Quiz 9, page 241

1 Who led the British forces in the First Battle of El Alamein?
2 Where was the peace treaty signed after the Korean War?
3 What was the only place in India attacked by foreign forces in WWI?
4 Which dams were destroyed by bouncing bombs in 1943?
5 Which Norwegian leader aided the 1940 invasion of his country through non resistance?
6 Which part of his body did Lord Raglan lose at Waterloo?
7 Who was commander of the US forces in the Pacific from March '42?
8 In which city did the German High Command formally surrender to General Eisenhower?
9 What was the German 11th Chasing Squadron known as in WWI?
10 Who assassinated Archduke Franz Ferdinand in 1914 thus precipitating WWI?
11 What was the last of the treaties which ended WWI?
12 Which countries were on either end of the Maginot Line?
13 Which birthplace of Nero was the site of an Allied beachhead invasion in WWII?
14 How is the battle at St Quentin in 1918 also known?
15 Who led the military coup in Sierra Leone's Civil War in 1997?
16 How many countries made up the coalition v Iraq in the Gulf War?
17 In the Nicaraguan Civil War which faction had US support?
18 Where was France's defeat which brought about the division of Vietnam along the 17th parallel?
19 Hitler's plan 'Watch on the Rhine' was aimed at which troops?
20 In which area of Belgium/Luxembourg was the Battle of the Bulge?
21 Which navy was defeated at the Battle of Midway Island in 1942?
22 The retreat by the British from which port brought about the replacement of Auchinleck by Montgomery?
23 Where is Babi Yar, where 100,000 people were slaughtered in 1941?
24 In which war did the Battle of Ebro take place?
25 Which General declared a 'war of liberation' against Syrian occupation of Lebanon in 1989?
26 Which war was ended with the Peace of Vereeniging?
27 Who were the two opposing factions in the Ruandan Civil War in the mid 90s?
28 How is the third battle of Ypres in WWI also known?
29 Who was in charge of the German troops in the First Battle of the Marne?
30 What name was given to that part of France not occupied by the Germans until 1942?

Pot Luck 5 (See quiz 9, page 241)

1 Lord Monteagle. 2 Simone de Beauvoir. 3 Carbon. 4 The Days of Pearly Spencer. 5 The Maltese Falcon. 6 66. 7 Hungerford Massacre. 8 Lahore. 9 Marc Bolan. 10 The Great Dictator. 11 Aneurism. 12 A snake-bodied female demon. 13 October 19th. 14 Sebastian. 15 Annette Crosbie. 16 1957. 17 An albatross. 18 1960s. 19 Jack Brabham. 20 Partners In Kryme. 21 St Paul. 22 Millais. 23 Inch. 24 Kenneth Branagh. 25 Arlington. 26 Ancient Persia. 27 The Daltons. 28 Harold Pinter. 29 FD Roosevelt. 30 Brewing.

Quiz 11 Pot Luck 6

LEVEL 3

Answers - see Quiz 12, page 244

1 What was the original family business of Shell Oil developer Marcus Samuel?

2 What was the middle name of Wallis Simpson, later Duchess of Windsor?

3 Which greedy giant was created by Rabelais?

4 Who is the elder – Tony Blair or Pierce Brosnan?

5 What is sorghum?

6 From what is the writing material true vellum made?

7 What is separated by the oval window and the round window?

8 Whose presidential hopes were ended by model Donna Rice?

9 What fraction of a gold object is a carat as a proportional measure?

10 What is a killick?

11 Which country hosted the first women's world angling championship?

12 What was the name of the cat which retired from 10 Downing Street in 1987?

13 What name is given to an animal that may be slaughtered to provide. food under Moslem law?

14 In which county did the Tolpuddle Martyrs form a trade union?

15 What is a bowyang ?

16 Which politician said that northerners die of "ignorance and crisps"?

17 In which decade was actress Kristin Scott Thomas born?

18 Which American duo had a Top Ten 8 hit in 1977 with Oh Lori?

19 Where did Alexander the Great die?

20 What relation was Queen Victoria to George IV?

21 Who won the first WBC cruiserweight title in boxing?

22 Why were the Piccard brothers famous in the 1930s?

23 Which Roman god was the god of beginnings and doors?

24 What is gneiss?

25 What was Florence Nightingale the first woman to receive in 1907?

26 What was a 'quod' in old slang?

27 Who preceded David II as King of the Scots?

28 What was Rainbow's first UK Top Ten hit?

29 The Purple Rose of Cairo was written and directed by which actor?

30 Nim was a type of what?

Answers

Quiz and Games (See quiz 12, page 244)
1 Chris Tarrant. 2 The Moment of Truth. 3 Patrick Kielty. 4 Alan Coren.
5 Kenny Everett. 6 Fern Britton. 7 Carry on Campus. 8 Vincent Price. 9
Countdown (OED). 10 Ally McCoist. 11 Richard Wilson. 12 Blockbusters.
13 Magnus Magnusson kept it. 14 Pass the Buck. 15 Max Robertson. 16
John Leslie. 17 Gaby Roslin. 18 Newspaper – day of birth. 19 Matthew Kelly.
20 Princess Diana. 21 Blind Date. 22 Max Bygraves. 23 Armand Jammot.
24 Ed Tudor-Pole. 25 Double Your Money. 26 Paul Daniels. 27 Round the
World. 28 Leslie Crowther. 29 The Great Garden Game. 30 Anthea Redfern.

Quiz 12 Quiz and Games

Answers - see Quiz 11, page 243

1 Who hosted the show which offered a million pound first prize?
2 Which show has a Dream Directory?
3 Who joined Anthea Turner on The National Lottery's Big Ticket?
4 Who opposed Sandi Toksvig in the 90s Call My Bluff?
5 Who was the first male team captain in That's Showbusiness?
6 Who hosts Ready Steady Cook?
7 Which student quiz was produced by Ginger Productions?
8 Which horror movie actor was on the first Celebrity Squares?
9 In which show might Mark Nyman adjudicate?
10 Who was the footballing A Question of Sport team captain when Sue Barker took over on a regular basis?
11 Who was the Reverend Green in the second series of Cluedo?
12 In which show were you pleased to be on the Hot Spot?
13 What happened to the black chair after the final Mastermind?
14 Which weekday elimination quiz is hosted by Fred Dinenage?
15 Who presented the original Going For a Song?
16 Which Blue Peter presenter took over Wheel of Fortune?
17 Who presented the show which had a Status Quo hit as its theme tune?
18 What do contestants receive at the end of Today's The Day?
19 Who hosted You Bet before Darren Day?
20 Who was the subject of an entire show of 100% in August 1998?
21 Sue Middleton and Alex Tatham famously followed a TV win on which show with marriage?
22 Who presented Family Fortunes immediately prior to Les Dennis?
23 Who created Countdown?
24 Who replaced Richard O'Brien on The Crystal Maze?
25 The Sky's The Limit was a variation of which show?
26 Who did Bob Monkhouse replace on Wipeout?
27 Where were contestants figuratively taken on the quiz show Anthea Turner presented after leaving GMTV?
28 Who first asked contestants to "Come on down"?
29 What was Channel 5's first gardening quiz called?
30 Who was the female half of the first husband and wife team to present The Generation Game?

Answers

Pot Luck 6 (See quiz 11, page 243)
1 Importing sea shells. 2 Warfield. 3 Gargantua. 4 Tony Blair. 5 A cereal crop. 6 Calf skin. 7 Middle ear and inner ear. 8 Gary Hart. 9 1/24th. 10 A small anchor. 11 Italy. 12 Wilberforce. 13 Halal. 14 Dorset. 15 String tied to the knee to hitch trousers up. 16 Edwina Currie. 17 1960s. 18 Alessi. 19 Babylon. 20 Niece. 21 Marvin Camel. 22 Balloonists. 23 Janus. 24 A type of rock. 25 The Order of Merit. 26 A prison. 27 Robert the Bruce. 28 Since You've Been Gone. 29 Woody Allen. 30 An ancient game.

Quiz 13   Pot Luck 7

Answers - see Quiz 14, page 246

LEVEL 3

1   Who led the British force in 1898 at Omdurman?
2   What was Adam Ant's first UK Top Ten hit?
3   How many cubic centimetres in a cubic metre?
4   In which decade was Selina Scott born?
5   Which real island, famed in fiction, is some 25 miles south of Elba?
6   Who would use a fyke?
7   Who was the first Irish cyclist to win the Tour de France?
8   What first did Bernard Harris achieve when he did his space walk?
9   Who or what is Katherine Gorge?
10   Which two countries are separated by the Kattegat?
11   In which decade did Picasso die?
12   Houses in Sherwood Crescent were destroyed in which disaster?
13   Which classic film was billed as "The Eighth Wonder of the World"?
14   Which Royal House ruled from 1461 to 1485 in England?
15   What is a gribble?
16   How many books are there in The New Testament?
17   Who narrated the TV series The World at War?
18   Which city is the capital of Tibet?
19   In No Way to Treat a Lady what did the killer leave on the brow?
20   What is bohea?
21   The Greek goddess Nyx was the personification of what?
22   What was Telly Savalas' Christian name?
23   What form did the Yahoos have in Gulliver's Travels ?
24   Who is the elder – Tamara Beckwith or Naomi Campbell?
25   Which Rumanian tennis star appeared in the film Players?
26   Whose one and only hit was First Time in 1988?
27   Which place is in Berkshire in England and Pennsylvania in America?
28   Where did the Great Britain rugby league team tour for the first time in 1984?
29   When George Bush was elected president who was his Democrat opponent?
30   Which rock star has children called Rufus Tiger and Tiger Lily?

50s Films (See quiz 14, page 246)

Answers

1 Giant. **2** St Swithin's. **3** Robert Morley. **4** Kim Novak. **5** Darby O'Gill and the Little People. **6** Richard Burton. **7** George Cole. **8** Danny Kaye. **9** Mount Rushmore. **10** Carry On Nurse. **11** Operation Petticoat. **12** Dorothy Dandridge. **13** George Sanders. **14** High Noon. **15** Mike Todd. **16** Viva Zapata!. **17** Jack Lemmon. **18** Anastasia. **19** The Trouble With Harry.
20 The Swan. **21** Yul Brynner. **22** No Way Out. **23** 1915. **24** The Long Hot Summer. **25** Bewitched Bothered and Bewildered. **26** Green Grow the Rushes. **27** William Wyler. **28** Yves Montand. **29** Larry Adler. **30** Judy Garland.

Quiz 14 50s Films

LEVEL 3

Answers - see Quiz 13, page 245

1　James Dean died during the filming of which film in 1955?

2　In which hospital would you find Sir Lancelot Spratt?

3　Who played George III in Beau Brummell ?

4　Who played the blonde that James Stewart was hired to follow in Vertigo?

5　In which 50s film did Sean Connery sing?

6　Which actor wins Christ's robe in a dice game in The Robe?

7　Who played the younger Scrooge in the classic with Alistair Sim?

8　Who replaced Astaire for the Holiday Inn remake White Christmas?

9　Where does the climax of North By Northwest take place?

10　What was the second Carry On film?

11　What was the only film where Tony Curtis and Cary Grant starred together?

12　Whose voice was dubbed by Marilyn Horne in Carmen Jones?

13　Who won Best Supporting Actor for All About Eve?

14　Which film was based on The Tin Star by John W Cunningham?

15　Which one time husband of Elizabeth Taylor produced Around the World in 80 Days?

16　What was the second of Brando's four consecutive Oscar nominations for. between 1951 and 1954?

17　Who contributed a song for his 1957 film Fire Down Below?

18　Ingrid Bergman won a second Oscar for which film, marking her return from Hollywood exile?

19　What was Shirley Maclaine's debut film in 1955?

20　What was the last film Grace Kelly made before becoming a princess?

21　Who played the Pharaoh in The Ten Commandments?

22　What was Sidney Poitier's first film, in 1950?

23　The African Queen, made in 1951, is about events in which year?

24　What was the first film in which Paul Newman and Joanne Woodward appeared together?

25　Which song did Rita Hayworth famously sing in Pal Joey?

26　What was Richard Burton's last UK film before turning to Hollywood?

27　Who won his third Best Director for his third Best Picture in 1959?

28　Which French superstar was the husband of the 1959 Oscar-winning Best Supporting Actress?

29　Who composed and played the music for Genevieve?

30　Who was replaced by Betty Hutton in Annie Get Your Gun?

Pot Luck 7 (See quiz 13, page 245)

1 Lord Kitchener. **2** Dog Eat Dog. **3** One million. **4** 1950s. **5** Monte Cristo. **6** A fisherman. **7** Stephen Roche. **8** First black man to walk in space. **9** National Park in Australia. **10** Denmark and Sweden. **11** 1970s. **12** Jumbo jet crash, Lockerbie. **13** King Kong. **14** York. **15** A crustacean. **16** 27. **17** Laurence Olivier. **18** Lhasa. **19** A lipstick kiss. **20** Tea. **21** Night. **22** Aristotle. **23** Human. **24** Tamara Beckwith. **25** Ilie Nastase. **26** Robin Beck. **27** Reading. **28** Papua New Guinea. **29** Michael Dukakis. **30** Roger Taylor.

Answers

1 The Euroroute E24 is from Birmingham to which county town?
2 Which Scottish university was named after a jeweller and an inventor?
3 Which polo ground is in the park of a burnt down former country house?
4 What is the smallest theatre at the Barbican in London called?
5 Where is Grimsetter Airport?
6 Which inlet of the Clyde was used as a US submarine base from the early 60s?
7 In which part of London is Kenwood?
8 Which shipping area is due north of Trafalgar?
9 In which county was the Open University founded?
10 Where in Berkshire is the Atomic Weapons Research Establishment?
11 How many national parks does the Pennine Way pass through?
12 Which wall runs from the river Forth in the east to Clyde in the west?
13 What is the real name of 'Petticoat Lane'?
14 Which county is due north of Buckinghamshire?
15 Where is the Post Office's main sorting office?
16 What name is given to someone born east of the Medway?
17 Which county is due South of Tyne and Wear?
18 Which colloquial name of the main church in Boston serves as a landmark for ships?
19 Who or what was London's Liverpool Street station named after?
20 Where is the official London residence of the Foreign Secretary?
21 What is the administration centre of Wiltshire?
22 How is London's Collegiate Church of St Peter better known?
23 Which House has an Egyptian Hall for banqueting?
24 Which important collection was given to the city of Glasgow in 1944?
25 Which World Heritage Site was built for the Duke of Marlborough?
26 Which house is headquarters and home to the BBC World Service?
27 What is MOMI on London's South Bank?
28 Which famous House is the only surviving part of Whitehall Palace?
29 Where is Scatsa Airport?
30 Which county is due south of Shropshire?

Pot Luck 8 (See quiz 16, page 248)

Answers

1 Groove between nose and lip. 2 1940s. 3 Architecture. 4 Joseph Black.
5 Benjamin Britten. 6 The bowie knife. 7 Russia. 8 Family Plot. 9 Baikonur, Tyuratam. 10 Flushing Meadow, New York. 11 Madonna. 12 A Fairy.
13 Winston. 14 A warship. 15 Lynn Anderson. 16 Marsh Marigold.
17 100-30. 18 Henry Miller. 19 Rudolf Nureyev. 20 The Road to Hell (Part 2). 21 Julia Carling. 22 Arthur. 23 T S Eliot. 24 Annika Sorenstam.
25 Corpuscles. 26 Stewart Copeland. 27 Edwin Land. 28 Neil Simon.
29 Communism. 30 Thomas Edison.

Quiz 16 Pot Luck 8

Answers - see Quiz 15, page 247

LEVEL 3

1. Where on your body is your philtrum?
2. In which decade was Delia Smith born?
3. Inigo Jones was famous in which profession?
4. Who discovered carbon dioxide in 1754 and called it "fixed air"?
5. Who was the first musician to be made a life peer?
6. What was the Iron Mistress in the film of the same name?
7. Who defeated Sweden's forces at Poltava in 1709?
8. What was the last film directed by Alfred Hitchcock?
9. Where does Russia launch their space missions from?
10. Where is the Louis Armstrong Stadium?
11. Who wrote Gary Barlow's second solo No 1?
12. What is a peri?
13. What was John Lennon's middle name?
14. The opera Billy Budd is set on what?
15. Whose only UK Top Ten hit from 1971 was called Rose Garden?
16. What is the more common name for the flower called the Kingcup?
17. What odds is a horse if it is "Burlington Bertie" in rhyming slang?
18. Who wrote Tropic of Cancer and Tropic of Capricorn?
19. Which ballet dancer died on the same day as Dizzy Gillespie?
20. What was Chris Rea's first UK Top Ten hit?
21. Who is the elder – Julia Carling or Helena Bonham-Carter?
22. What was Sir John Gielgud's first name?
23. Which poet wrote, "I have measured out my life with coffee spoons"?
24. Who was the first woman golfer to head the money lists in Europe and the US, in 1995?
25. Plasma in blood consists of platelets and red and white what?
26. Who was the drummer in the group Police?
27. Who invented the Polaroid camera in 1947?
28. Barefoot in the Park was written by which US playwright?
29. What is opposed by the John Birch Society in the USA?
30. Which famous inventor had the middle name Alva?

Answers

Around the UK (See quiz 15, page 247)
1 Ipswich. 2 Heriot-Watt. 3 Cowdray Park. 4 The Pit. 5 Orkney. 6 Holy Loch. 7 Hampstead. 8 Finisterre. 9 Buckinghamshire. 10 Aldermaston. 11 Three. 12 Antonine Wall. 13 Middlesex Street. 14 Northamptonshire. 15 Mount Pleasant. 16 Man of Kent. 17 Durham. 18 The Boston Stump. 19 PM Earl of Liverpool. 20 Carlton House Terrace. 21 Trowbridge. 22 Westminster Abbey. 23 Mansion House. 24 The Burrell Collection. 25 Blenheim Palace. 26 Bush House. 27 Museum of the Moving Image. 28 Banqueting House. 29 Shetlands. 30 Hereford and Worcester.

1   Which TV presenter published his Unreliable Memoirs in 1980?
2   Whose novel A Time to Dance was adapted into a controversial TV drama?
3   In From One Charlie to Another, who did Charlie Watts write about?
4   Which singer wrote the book Tarantula?
5   What was the colour of the first Penguin paperback?
6   Which blonde wrote The Constant Sinner?
7   Which John Grisham book had a record initial print run of 2.8 million?
8   To be considered for the Booker Prize a book has to be published where first?
9   What according to Dickens was "the best of times, the worst of times"?
10 Whose only novel won the Pullitzer Prize in 1937?
11 Which PM wrote Sybil?
12 For which novel did Tom Clancy receive an advance of $14 million?
13 Which joint 1992 Booker Prize winner had his book made into an Oscar winning film?
14 Which Ian Fleming novel has the shortest title?
15 What was Hercule Poirot's last case called?
16 What did J.M. Barrie give the royalties from Peter Pan to?
17 Who received a record breaking advance of £17 million for three novels in 1992?
18 What was the sequel to D.H. Lawrence's The Rainbow?
19 Who created Pomeroy's wine bar for his hero?
20 Whose early thriller include The Eye of the Needle?
21 Who wrote The House of Stairs under a pseudonym?
22 Which detective novelist wrote the screenplay for Strangers on a Train?
23 What was Charles Dickens second novel, after Pickwick Papers?
24 Who wrote The Exorcist which was made into a successful film?
25 How are Patrick Dannay and Manfred B Lee better known?
26 Who produced The Truth That Leads to Eternal Life?
27 Who wrote the historical romance Micah Clarke?
28 Which novelist once owned a Rolls registration number ANY 1?
29 Whose early novels were Bella, Harriet and Prudence?
30 How is the wife of author Eric Siepmann better known?

Answers

Pot Luck 9 (See quiz 18, page 250)
1 The Zulus. 2 Phyllis Nelson. 3 Jose Maria Olazabal. 4 Aldeburgh. 5 Jess Yates. 6 Varicella. 7 Baseball. 8 Robbie Coltrane. 9 National Theatre. 10 Georgie Fame. 11 Soot. 12 The tennis Grand Slam. 13 Lloyd Grossman. 14 Toulouse Lautrec. 15 A hangman. 16 Paul Gauguin. 17 Hero. 18 Wear it. 19 Picture Post. 20 Turner. 21 1970s. 22 Battle of Naseby. 23 1860 . 24 New Zealand. 25 A hoofed mammal. 26 Ipswich. 27 Love In Bloom. 28 Kim Appleby. 29 Margaret Atwood. 30 Land's End.

Quiz 18 Pot Luck 9

LEVEL 3

1 Cetewayo, Dingaan and Chaka have all led which people?
2 Whose one and only hit was Move Closer in 1985?
3 Which injured player did Ian Woosnam replace in the 1995 European Ryder Cup team?
4 Which Suffolk town was the first in Britain to have a woman mayor?
5 Which 1970s presenter of Stars on Sunday was nicknamed 'The Bishop'?
6 What is the correct name for chickenpox?
7 The film The Stratton Story featured which sport?
8 Who is the elder – Phil Collins or Robbie Coltrane?
9 In the 80s which building did Prince Charles compare to a "nuclear power station"?
10 Under what name did musician Clive Powell find fame and fortune?
11 The brown pigment bistre is prepared from what?
12 Maureen Connolly was the first female to perform what?
13 Which food show presenter once played in a band called Jet Bronx and the Forbidden?
14 Which character was played by Jose Ferrer in the film Moulin Rouge?
15 What did Jack Ketch do for a living?
16 Van Gogh's Sunflowers used to hang in the bedroom of which other famous artist?
17 In mythology, who did Leander swim the Hellespont nightly to see?
18 What would you do with a filibeg?
19 Bert Hardy was a staff photojournalist for which periodical?
20 Who painted Snow Storm – Steamboat off a Harbour's Mouth?
21 In which decade was Mandy Smith born?
22 Which battle was the decisive one in the English Civil War?
23 To ten years, when was the National Rifle Association of Great Britain formed?
24 In which country are the Sutherland Falls?
25 What is an alpaca?
26 At which Crown Court was Lester Piggot's tax evasion case?
27 What was American comedian Jack Benny's signature tune?
28 Who had UK Top Ten hits in the 90s with Don't Worry and G.L.A.D.?
29 Who wrote The Handmaid's Tale?
30 What did businessman Peter de Savray buy for £6.7 million in 1987?

Books 2 (See quiz 17, page 249) **1** Clive James. **2** Melvyn Bragg. **3** Charlie Parker. **4** Bob Dylan. **5** Blue. **6** Mae West. **7** The Rainmaker. **8** Britain. **9** French Revolution (Tale of Two Cities). **10** Margaret Mitchell. **11** Disraeli. **12** Without Remorse. **13** Michael Ondaatje. **14** Dr No. **15** Curtain. **16** Children's Hospital. **17** Barbara Taylor Bradford. **18** Women in Love. **19** John Mortimer (Rumpole). **20** Ken Follett. **21** Ruth Rendell as Barbara Vine. **22** Raymond Chandler. **23** Oliver Twist. **24** William Blatty. **25** Ellery Queen. **26** Jehovah's Witnesses. **27** Conan Doyle. **28** Jeffrey Archer. **29** Jilly Cooper. **30** Mary Wesley.

Quiz 19   Musical Greats

LEVEL 3

Answers - see Quiz 20, page 252

1   Which Pete Ham and Tom Evans song has been at No 1 with two different artists?
2   The Isley Brothers and which other Motown act recorded Grapevine before Marvin Gaye?
3   To the nearest year, how long was there between Sinatra's first and second UK No 1s?
4   Where is the singer's home in the lyrics of On The Dock Of The Bay?
5   What was the first song to be Christmas No 1 in two different versions?
6   Which hit for Sweet was the longest running No 1 of 1973?
7   Which 1970 seven week No 1 was best selling UK single of the year?
8   Who did Billy Joel dedicate his 1983 version of Uptown Girl to?
9   What was Elvis Presley's closing number in his Las Vegas stage act?
10 What was Cliff Richard's first self-produced No 1?
11 What was the chief of the Diddymen's only UK No 1?
12 Which standard has the line, "I see friends shaking hands saying how do you do"?
13 Which Beatles hit stayed in the UK Top 50 for 33 weeks in 1963?
14 Who had the first UK No 1 with Unchained Melody?
15 Which film theme was the biggest selling single of 1979?
16 Who took Led Zeppelin's Stairway To Heaven into the singles charts?
17 Who wrote You'll Never Walk Alone?
18 Which heavenly body is mentioned in the title of the song that gave George Michael his 4th solo and Elton John his 3rd No 1?
19 Who played Buddy Holly in the 1978 movie The Buddy Holly Story?
20 Who wrote Aretha Franklin's first UK hit Respect?
21 Which classic was the Walker Brothers second No 1 hit from 1966?
22 Which 1967 No 1 recorded the longest-ever stay in the UK Top 50?
23 Who is the only French solo male singer to reach No 1?
24 How many weeks in total did Whitney Houston top the US and UK charts with I Will Always Love You?
25 Which hit is the only No 1 for writers Gerry Goffin and Carole King?
26 Which song includes the line, "nothing to kill or die for"?
27 What was the colour mentioned in the title of Tom Jones' final No 1 in the 1960s?
28 What is the biggest international hit from Eurovision Song Contest?
29 What was Sam Cooke's real name?
30 What was the Beatles first No 1 in America?

Answers

Pot Luck 10 (See quiz 20, page 252)
1 Richard. 2 Physics. 3 Alexander Selkirk. 4 US President. 5 The Strand Magazine. 6 The Verve. 7 Chamonix, France. 8 Albert Reynolds. 9 A fusil. 10 Judge Dredd. 11 Have A Go. 12 Room At The Top. 13 Liquids. 14 Shiny Happy People. 15 Gliders. 16 Sean Connery. 17 Royal Flying Corps. 18 Morgan. 19 Grasmere. 20 The skin that separates the nostrils. 21 Anderson. 22 Ian Woosnam. 23 A seal. 24 Prince Andrew of Greece. 25 Troon. 26 Debussy. 27 1930s. 28 Paul Channon. 29 Average White Band. 30 St Dominic. Answers Music 2: All Time Greats.

Quiz 20 Pot Luck 10

Answers - see Quiz 19, page 251

LEVEL 3

1   Which christian name derives from the Germanic for 'strong ruler'?
2   What did the Italian Amedeo Avogadro study?
3   The novel Robinson Crusoe was based on whose experiences?
4   What important post did Millard Fillmore hold?
5   Which magazine serialised The Adventures Of Sherlock Holmes in the 1890s?
6   Which group features Peter Salisbury on drums and Simon Jones on bass?
7   Where were the first Winter Olympics held in 1924?
8   Who preceded John Bruton as Prime Minister of Ireland?
9   What can be a type of musket or a type of rhomboid?
10 Walter, the robot with a lisp, featured in which comic strip?
11 Which long running radio quiz show was hosted by Wilfred Pickles?
12 In which John Braine book is Joe Lampton the central character ?
13 What does a manometer measure the pressure of?
14 What was R.E.M's first UK Top Ten hit?
15 Otto Lilienthal was associated with what form of transport?
16 Who is the elder – Sean Connery or Sir Terence Conran?
17 What amalgamated in 1918 with the Royal Naval Air Service to form the RAF?
18 What did the M stand for in E M Forster's middle name?
19 Where is the poet Wordsworth buried?
20 What is your columella?
21 Which Anna claimed to be Anastasia?
22 Who was the first UK golfer to win the World Match-Play Championship?
23 In folktales a silkie was half man and half what?
24 Who was Prince Philip's father?
25 Which British golf course has a hole called the 'Postage Stamp'?
26 Who composed Clair De Lune?
27 In which decade was the Earl of Snowdon born?
28 Who was Transport Secretary at the time of the King's Cross tube fire disaster?
29 Whose only UK Top Ten hit was Pick Up The Pieces in 1975?
30 Black Friars are members of the religious order established by whom?

Muscial Greats (See quiz 19, page 251)

Answers
1 Without You. 2 The Miracles. 3 12 years. 4 Georgia. 5 Mary's Boy Child.
6 Blockbuster. 7 In The Summertime. 8 Christie Brinkley. 9 Can't Help Falling
In Love. 10 Mistletoe and Wine. 11 Tears. 12 What A Wonderful World.
13 She Loves You. 14 Jimmy Young. 15 Bright Eyes. 16 Far Corporation.
17 Rodgers and Hammerstein. 18 Sun. 19 Gary Busey. 20 Otis Redding.
21 The Sun Ain't Gonna Shine Anymore. 22 Release Me. 23 Charles Aznavour.
24 24 weeks. 25 I'm Into Something Good. 26 Imagine. 27 Green.
28 Waterloo by Abba. 29 Cook without an 'e'. 30 I Wanna Hold Your Hand.

Quiz 21 Football

LEVEL 3

Answers - see Quiz 22, page 254

1 Who preceded Frank O'Farrell as Man Utd manager?
2 How did Joan Bazely make history in 1976?
3 Who were the opponents in Peter Shilton's last game for England?
4 Who coached Cameroon to the latter stages of the 1990 World Cup?
5 Who offered the England and Scotland squads a week on his Caribbean island if they won the World Cup in 1998?
6 Which Mexican player in France 98 ran a chain of sandwich shops?
7 Which club's motto is 'Nil Satis Nisi Optimum'?
8 What was the name of the horse jointly owned by Liverpool's Fowler & McManaman?
9 Apart from Preson, which other team did Alan Ball's father play for?
10 Ray Wilkins was sent off while playing for England against which country?
11 Who did Denis Law play for immediately before Man Utd?
12 Who was the only side to beat England over 90 minutes when Venables was manager?
13 Who appeared in a TV ad for bacon before the 1998 World Cup?
14 Who is Sweden's most capped player of all time?
15 Who led Naples to their first ever Italian championship?
16 Which of the Italian sides David Platt played for had the shortest name?
17 Angus Deayton had a trial with which soccer club?
18 Who was fourth in the 1994 World Cup?
19 Roy Hodgson joined Blackburn Rovers from which club?
20 What was Arsenal tube station called before it was called Arsenal?
21 Who was the first Dutchman to play in an FA Cup Final?
22 Who were Man Utd playing when George Best made his debut?
23 Which sides competed in the first all British UEFA Cup Final?
24 Who were the first winners of the Inter Toto Cup?
25 How many times did Bobby Moore captain England in 108 internationals?
26 Which soccer side does Bank of England Governor Eddie George support?
27 Where did Paul Ince captain England for the first time?
28 Which club side were the first to win the South American Cup?
29 Which two members of the '98 Nigerian squad released rap albums?
30 Who won Olympic gold in Barcelona?

Pot Luck 11 (See quiz 22, page 254)
1 James Fenimore Cooper. 2 Monkey. 3 Ailurophobia. 4 Turkey. 5 Rudyard Kipling. 6 One. 7 Senegal. 8 Theme from Harry's Game. 9 John Prescott. 10 Fruits. 11 E102. 12 Catalan. 13 Darby & Joan. 14 Princetown. 15 Newport Jazz Festival. 16 From the beginning. 17 Winston Churchill. 18 Eagle. 19 Azerbaijan. 20 With fire. 21 Black eagle. 22 A. 23 J Danforth Quayle. 24 Newton St Boswells. 25 North and South Islands of New Zealand. 26 1945. 27 Clout. 28 Equatorial Guinea. 29 Belgium. 30 Dot.

Answers

1. Who wrote the novel The Red Rover ?
2. Which creature is represented in the year the Chinese call hou?
3. A fear of cats is known as what?
4. Which country ruled Greece until 1830?
5. Who wrote the line: 'The female of the species is more deadly than the male'?
6. How many species of ostrich are there?
7. Dakar is the capital of which country?
8. Which theme gave Clannad their first UK Top Ten hit?
9. Who is the elder – John Prescott or Trevor McDonald?
10. The spice allspice is made from which part of a plant?
11. Which 'E' number is used to represent Tartrazine in products?
12. What is the main language of Andorra?
13. Which elderly couple were immortalised in a poem by Henry Woodfall?
14. Where on Dartmoor is Dartmoor prison?
15. Which jazz festival is held annually in Rhode Island?
16. What does the Latin ab initio mean?
17. Which Prime Minister was offered a dukedom when he retired in '55?
18. The constellation Aquila has which name in English?
19. In which country is the city of Baku?
20. What does the musical term 'con fuoco' mean?
21. Which bird appears with two heads on the Albanian flag?
22. Which letter in Braille comprises a single raised dot?
23. Who was Vice President when George Bush was President of the USA?
24. What is the administrative centre for the Scottish Borders region?
25. What are separated by the Cook Straits?
26. In which year did the UK become a member of the UN?
27. Whose one and only UK hit was Substitute in 1978?
28. Which country has the Ekuele and centimos as units of currency?
29. Prime Minister Wilfried Martens was leader of which country?
30. How would the letter E be formed in Morse Code?

Answers

Football (See quiz 21, page 253)
1 Wilf McGuinness. 2 First woman ref of men's soccer. 3 Italy (1990). 4 Valeri Nepomaniachi. 5 Richard Branson. 6 Jorge Campos. 7 Everton. 8 Some Horse. 9 Halifax Town. 10 Morocco. 11 Torino. 12 Brazil. 13 Peter Schmeichel. 14 Thomas Ravelli. 15 Diego Maradona. 16 Bari. 17 Crystal Palace. 18 Bulgaria. 19 Inter Milan. 20 Gillespie Road. 21 Arnold Muhren. 22 West Brom. 23 Spurs v Wolves. 24 Ajax. 25 90. 26 Aston Villa. 27 Boston, USA. 28 Santos. 29 Amokachi & Okocha. 30 Australia.

Quiz 23 TV Sitcoms

LEVEL 3

Answers - see Quiz 24, page 256

1 Who of the elderly trio in the first episode of Last of the Summer Wine is no longer in the cast?

2 Thirtysomething was set in which US state?

3 Who did Casualty's George play in May to December?

4 What were Private Godfrey's sisters called in Dad's Army?

5 Which bookie did Vince Pinner work for?

6 Who had a wife, daughter and mother in law who were witches?

7 Which sit com star made the album What Is Going To Become of Us All in 1976?

8 Who sang the theme music for You Rang M'Lord with Bob Monkhouse?

9 What was Richard's mother called in To The Manor Born?

10 Which lead character had the nickname Privet?

11 In which series did George, Kramer and Elaine appear?

12 Which TV husband and wife lived in Lanford Illinois?

13 Who was the first manager of the Bayview Retirement Home?

14 Who in his later years had a black home help called Winston?

15 What was the US series on which The Upper Hand was based?

16 Which property was left to Jim Davidson in Up The Elephant and Round the Castle?

17 In which hospital did Sheila Sabatini work?

18 Which sitcom was first called You'll Never get Rich in the US?

19 What was Reg Varney's character called in On the Buses?

20 What was Thelma's surname before she married Likely Lad Bob?

21 Elaine Nardo was the only female cabbie in which company?

22 In which advertising agency did Caroline work in The Upper Hand?

23 What was Harold Steptoe's middle names?

24 Which character in Soap was later given his own series?

25 Who wrote the original series of Shine on Harvey Moon?

26 Which sit com star played Vera Hopkins in Coronation Street?

27 Who was Roger's wife in Outside Edge?

28 Who was the barman of the Nag's Head as frequented by the Trotters?

29 Who created the theme music for One Foot in the Grave?

30 Which show centred round the 1-2-1 Club?

Answers

Pot Luck 12 (See quiz 24, page 256)

1 Charles Blondin. 2 Vectis. 3 Mike Swain. 4 Fish. 5 Welcome to my World. 6 Emma Thompson. 7 John Williams. 8 Nineveh. 9 July 23rd. 10 The Queen. 11 Mazo De La Roche. 12 Cyril Fletcher. 13 A ship's timber. 14 Fred Astaire. 15 Pewter. 16 1960s. 17 Nine. 18 Arthur. 19 1992. 20 The Greek alphabet. 21 Bend. 22 Ruff. 23 Shirley Bassey. 24 Westminster Abbey. 25 Fairground Attraction. 26 Architecture. 27 Yellow River. 28 James Buchanan Brady. 29 To spout rainwater from roof gutters to stop it running down the walls. 30 Frank Capra.

1   Who crossed Niagara Falls in 1859 on a tightrope?
2   What did the Romans call the Isle of Wight?
3   Mike Swain was the first male American World title winner in which sport?
4   What are gar, wrasse, alewife and blenny?
5   What was Jim Reeves' first UK Top Ten hit?
6   Who is the actress daughter of actress Phillida Law?
7   Who composed the music for Jaws and Star Wars?
8   What was the capital of the ancient empire of Assyria?
9   On what date in 1986 did Prince Andrew marry Fergie?
10 Which part did Prunella Scales play in A Question of Attribution?
11 Who wrote the series about the Whiteoak family?
12 Which presenter of That's Life was famous for his odd odes?
13 What is a futtock?
14 Which film star married Robyn Smith in 1980?
15 Which alloy contains 2% antimony, 8% copper and 90% tin?
16 In which decade was Tomasz Starzewski born?
17 How many No 1 singles did Take That have?
18 Which son of Henry VII married Catherine of Aragon in 1501?
19 In what year did Classic FM begin?
20 What are Lambda, Omicron and Tau all found in?
21 Charing, as in Charing Cross comes from an Old English word meaning what?
22 What can be a trump at cards or a type of sandpiper?
23 Who is the elder – Jilly Cooper or Shirley Bassey?
24 Where is English actor David Garrick buried?
25 Who followed up a No 1 with Find My Love?
26 Walter Gropius was famous in what field?
27 What is the natural water form which the Chinese call Huang Ho?
28 Which American speculator and philanthropist had the nickname Diamond Jim?
29 What is the practical purpose of a gargoyle?
30 Who directed the film You Can't Take It With You?

TV Sitcoms (See quiz 23, page 255)
1 Michael Bates. **2** Philadelphia. **3** Hilary. **4** Dolly & Cissy. **5** Eddie Brown's. **6** Darrin Stephens (Bewitched). **7** John Le Mesurier. **8** Paul Shane. **9** Mrs Polouvicka. **10** Bernard Hedges. **11** Seinfeld. **12** Roseanne & Dan Conner. **13** Harvey Bains. **14** Alf Garnett. **15** Whose the Boss?. **16** 17 Railway Terrace. **17** The Gillies Hospital. **18** The Phil Silvers Show. **19** Stan Butler. **20** Chambers. **21** The Sunshine Cab Company. **22** Blake & Hunter. **23** Albert Kitchenere. **24** The butler Benson. **25** Marks & Gran. **26** Kathy Staff. **27** Mim. **28** Mike. **29** Eric Idle. **30** Dear John.

Quiz 25 Animal World

LEVEL 3

1 What is the only mammal to live as a parasite?
2 How is a Sibbald's rorqual also known?
3 For how many hours in a period of 24 does a giraffe sleep?
4 What is the world's largest rodent?
5 What gives the sloth its greenish appearance?
6 Which mammal lives at the highest altitude?
7 Which animals are famously sold at Bampton Fair?
8 The mammal which can live at the greatest depth is a species of what?
9 From which part of a sperm whale is ambergris obtained?
10 Where does a cane toad squirt poison from?
11 What is the longest type of worm?
12 Where would you find a shark's denticles?
13 What does the male mouse deer have that no other deer has?
14 Where does a browser find food?
15 What is the only bird which can fly backwards?
16 A Clydesdale was originally a cross between a Scottish draught horse and a what?
17 What colour is a mandrill's beard?
18 The wisent is native to where?
19 Lemurs are only found in their natural habitat where?
20 What is the oldest indigenous breed of cat in the US?
21 What is a koikoi?
22 What is the average life expectancy of the mayfly?
23 Which protein is cartilage made up of?
24 The term monkey refers to all primates except apes, humans and what?
25 Why were Samoyeds originally bred?
26 Falabellas are native to where?
27 What is another name for the aye-aye?
28 Which animal has the longest tail?
29 What name is given to the smaller of a rhino's horns?
30 What does it mean if an animal is homoiothermic?

Pot Luck 13 (See quiz 26, page 258)
1 Bowden. 2 Plumber. 3 Vladimir and Estragon. 4 Syphilis. 5 Scotland. 6 1950s. 7 J.J. Barrie. 8 Rocks. 9 Mozambique. 10 Comet. 11 The Agricultural Hall. 12 Scottish Euro 96 single. 13 A diesel engine. 14 Goat Island. 15 Richard Bacon. 16 Painting. 17 Mexico. 18 Bronze. 19 Cloudesley Shovell. 20 He was a horse. 21 Irving Berlin. 22 Belgium. 23 After childbirth. 24 Peter Grimes. 25 Enemy Coast Ahead. 26 Michael Crawford. 27 James and John. 28 Call Up The Groups. 29 Sean Kelly. 30 China.

1 What was Arthur Askey's middle name?
2 What was the trade of John Galliano's dad?
3 In the Beckett play which characters were Waiting for Godot?
4 Which disease is diagnosed by the Wasserman Test?
5 The King of Alba ruled in which country?
6 In which decade was Sting born?
7 Whose one and only hit was No Charge in 1976?
8 What does a petrologist study?
9 Which African country lies between the sea and Zimbabwe?
10 What are Temple-Tuttle and Kohoutek both types of?
11 In which London hall was England's first official showjumping event held in 1869?
12 Rod Stewart donated the royalties from which single to the Dunblane fund?
13 The ship Petit Pierre was the first to be driven by what in 1902?
14 Which island is in the middle of Niagara Falls?
15 Who was the first Blue Peter presenter to be sacked?
16 For what did John Singer Sargent achieve fame?
17 In which country is the majority of the Yucatan Peninsula?
18 The statue of Albert opposite the Albert Hall is made from what?
19 Which admiral was thrown ashore from his flagship Association in 1707?
20 Why was the Roman consul Incitatus unusual?
21 Who composed God Bless America?
22 Violinist Arthur Grumiaux came from which country?
23 When can a woman suffer puerperal fever?
24 Which George Crabbe poem was made into an opera?
25 The Dambusters film was based on which book?
26 Who is the elder – Michael Crawford or Eric Clapton?
27 Which of Jesus' disciples were sons of Zebedee?
28 What was the Baron Knights' first UK Top Ten hit?
29 Who won the first cycling World Cup?
30 By tonnage, which country is the world's top fishing nation?

Answers

Animal World (See quiz 25, page 257)
1 Vampire bat. 2 Blue whale. 3 One. 4 Capybara. 5 Algae which grow on it. 6 Mount Everest pika. 7 Exmoor ponies. 8 Bat. 9 Intestine. 10 Behind its eyes. 11 Bootlace worm. 12 On its skin. 13 Canine teeth. 14 Anywhere above ground. 15 Hummingbird. 16 Flemish horse. 17 Yellow. 18 Europe (bison). 19 Madagascar. 20 Maine coon. 21 Poisonous frog. 22 Couple of hours. 23 Collagen. 24 Tarsiers. 25 Herd reindeer. 26 Argentina. 27 Lemur. 28 Asian elephant. 29 Forehead horn. 30 Warm blooded.

1 In which 60s film did Richard Attenborough sing?
2 Who became head of production at EMI in 1969?
3 Between which two cities is The Great Race set?
4 Who directed the Civil War sequences of How the West Was Won?
5 Who was Camembert in Carry On – Don't Lose Your Head?
6 Who inspired the David Hemmings role in Antonioni's Blow Up?
7 What is unusual about Christopher Lee's terrifying role in Dracula – Prince of Darkness?
8 What was the sequel to A Million Years BC?
9 Who devised the dance routines in Half A Sixpence?
10 Who is the only American in King Rat?
11 Who was the Doctor in the big screen Doctor Who and the Daleks?
12 Which film classic inspired Billy Wilder to make The Apartment?
13 In which film did Peter Sellers first head the cast as Clouseau?
14 Who took over directing Cleopatra mid way through production?
15 Who was the singing voice of Tony in West Side Story?
16 Who wrote the music for Lawrence of Arabia?
17 In which film of her father's did Anjelica Huston make her screen debut?
18 Which golf course featured in Goldfinger?
19 What was Tracy and Hepburn's final movie together?
20 Which pop star starred in Rag Doll in 1960?
21 Which '62 Best Actor studied medicine at the University of California?
22 Who was Oscar nominated for Pasha in Doctor Zhivago?
23 Which 60s Oscar winner was narrated by Michael MacLiammoir?
24 Who killed Ronald Reagan in his last film The Killers?
25 Who did John Wayne play in North to Alaska?
26 For which film did Elizabeth Taylor win her second Oscar?
27 For which role was Dustin Hoffman nominated in 1969?
28 Which of the Redgrave clan appeared in A Man For All Seasons?
29 Who played opposite then wife Claire Bloom in The Illustrated Man?
30 Who was the older winner of the shared Best Actress Oscar in 1968?

Food & Drink 1 (See quiz 28, page 260)

1 Liebfraumilch. 2 Warm. 3 Salsa. 4 Stomach remedy. 5 Ice cream.
6 Tomatoes. 7 Crescent shaped (roll). 8 Steen. 9 Stum. 10 Browned at the edges due to age. 11 Sicily. 12 Semi sparkling, fully sparkling. 13 Calzone.
14 Maize. 15 Grapes are partly sun dried before use. 16 San Lorenzo.
17 Portugal. 18 Barsac, Bommes, Fargues, Preignac. 19 Britain. 20 Jennifer Paterson. 21 Canary Islands. 22 Wine and methylated spirits. 23 Salsify.
24 Remuage. 25 Pomerol. 26 Wine award in Germany. 27 Bechamel. 28 Oenology. 29 Escoffier. 30 Mirin.

Answers

Quiz 28 Food & Drink 1

Answers - see Quiz 27, page 259

LEVEL 3

1 Which wine comes from Worms?
2 How is sake usually drunk?
3 Which food shares its name with Latin American big band music?
4 What were angostura bitters originally used for?
5 In the US if a dessert is served 'a la mode' what is served with it?
6 Which vegetable is a passata made from?
7 What shape is a rugelach?
8 What is chenin blanc wine known as in South Africa?
9 Which term describes the fermented grape juice added to wine that has lost its strength to perk it up?
10 If a wine is madeirized what has happened to it?
11 Where is Marsala, famed for its fortified wine?
12 In wine terms what is the difference between frizzante and spumante?
13 Which folded pizza dough dish takes its name from the Italian for trouser leg?
14 Which cereal is polenta made from?
15 How does Malaga wine achieve its dark colour?
16 Which Kensington restaurant was co founded by Mara Berni in 1963?
17 Where does Dao wine come from?
18 In addition to Sauternes itself which four communes can call their wine Sauternes?
19 Where did balti cooking originate?
20 Who has cooked lunches for The Spectator magazine and written for The Oldie?
21 Other than Spain and Portugal where does sack come from?
22 What is a red biddy?
23 Which food is also called the vegetable oyster?
24 In wine making which term describes turning the bottles so the sediment collects at the cork end?
25 In which district of Bordeaux is Chateau Petrus produced?
26 What is pradikat?
27 Which classic French sauce was named after a courtier of Louis XIV?
28 What is the study of wine called?
29 Which chef created the Bombe Nero and the peche melba?
30 Which sweet rice wine is used in Japanese cookery?

60s Films (See quiz 28, page 259)
Answers
1 Doctor Dolittle. 2 Bryan Forbes. 3 New York & Paris. 4 John Ford.
5 Kenneth Williams. 6 David Bailey. 7 He has no dialogue. 8 When Dinosaurs Ruled the Earth. 9 Gillian Lynne. 10 George Segal. 11 Peter Cushing. 12 Brief Encounter. 13 A Shot in the Dark. 14 Joseph Mankiewicz. 15 Jimmy Bryant. 16 Maurice Jarre. 17 A Walk With Love and Death. 18 Stoke Poges. 19 Guess Who's Coming to Dinner. 20 Jess Conrad. 21 Gregory Peck. 22 Tom Courtenay. 23 Tom Jones. 24 Lee Marvin. 25 Big Sam. 26 Who's Afraid of Virginia Woolf?. 27 Ratso Rizzo. 28 Corin. 29 Rod Steiger. 30 Katherine Hepburn.

Quiz 29 Pot Luck 14

Answers - see Quiz 30, page 261

LEVEL 3

1. A zinfandel is used for making what?
2. What separates Alaska from the other 48 US states?
3. How many times is 'Um' sung in the chorus of 60s hit Um Um Um Um Um Um?
4. Which TV personality launched the 1998 poppy appeal?
5. On which island which is also a country is Adam's Peak?
6. In which year did London Underground's Bakerloo Line open?
7. Who won Best Actor Oscar for his part in the musical film Amadeus?
8. If you have comedos, what are you suffering from?
9. What is the third largest city in Britain?
10. Who is the elder – David Bowie or Edwina Currie?
11. What is Warwickshire's county motif?
12. What was Cat Stevens' first UK Top Ten hit?
13. What kind of weapon was an arbalest?
14. Which Austrian physicist gave his name to perceived frequency variations under certain conditions?
15. Imran Khan played cricket for which two English counties?
16. From 1957 to 1985, who was the Russian Foreign Minister?
17. Which optical aid was invented by Benjamin Franklin?
18. What was the Bay City Rollers' first UK Top Ten hit?
19. Where are the ethmoid, vomer and zygomatic bones in your body?
20. In which decade was Peter Stringfellow born?
21. The capital of Japan is an anagram of which former capital?
22. Who rode both Toulon and Moonax to St Leger triumphs?
23. Who wrote All Quiet on the Western Front?
24. Where did John McGregor found the first Canoe Club in 1866?
25. What is the main colour on the cover of Celine Dion's album Let's Talk About Love?
26. Who wrote The Sea Wolf?
27. Which European country lost the battle of Ulm in 1805?
28. Who had hits in the 70s with Love Me and If I Can't Have You?
29. Which country has Guyana to the east and Colombia to the west?
30. How did Emiliano Zapata, the Mexican revolutionary, die in 1919?

Answers

Kings and Queens (See quiz 30, page 262)
1 17 Bruton St, London. 2 The Delhi Durbar. 3 Edward VII. 4 Adelaide.
5 George I. 6 Hit with a cricket ball. 7 George V. 8 Henry II's wife Eleanor of Aquitaine. 9 Edward I (19). 10 It was his second. 11 The Pope.
12 Dunfermline. 13 Square, she was so obese. 14 Richard II. 15 River Soar.
16 Tax collectors. 17 Charles II. 18 St Stephen's Abbey Caen. 19 Henry I.
20 Edward VIII. 21 George I. 22 William IV. 23 Edward VII. 24 Christian IX of Denmark. 25 William II. 26 Opening Blackfriars Bridge. 27 Norfolk.
28 Two. 29 Jane Seymour & Catherine Parr. 30 Gloucester Cathedral.

Quiz 30 Kings and Queens

Answers - see Quiz 29, page 261

LEVEL 3

1. At which address was Elizabeth II born?
2. Where were George V and Queen Mary crowned Emperor and Empress of India?
3. Who was the only British monarch from the House of Wettin?
4. Who was William IV's queen?
5. Which monarch's mother was Sophia of Bohemia?
6. How did George II's eldest son die?
7. Who was the first British monarch to make a Christmas Day broadcast?
8. Which English king's wife was a former wife of Louis VII of France?
9. Which British monarch produced the most legitimate children?
10. What was notable about Henry VI's coronation in 1470?
11. Who made Henry VIII Fidei Defensor?
12. Where was Charles I born?
13. What shape was Queen Anne's coffin and why?
14. Which English king is reputed to have invented the handkerchief?
15. Where were Richard III's bones thrown when his grave was desecrated?
16. Why was Henry VIII's execution of Richard Empson and Edmund Dudley a popular move?
17. Who was threatened by the Rye House Plot?
18. Where is William the Conqueror buried?
19. Which king founded the first English zoo?
20. Who was the penultimate Emperor of India?
21. The Duchess of Kendal was mistress of which king?
22. Who was the first monarch born in Buckingham Palace?
23. Who was the first Emperor of India?
24. Who was Edward VII's father in law?
25. Which English king was killed by Walter Tyrel?
26. What was Victoria's only public ceremony in 1870?
27. In which county did George V die?
28. How many shirts did Charles I wear for his execution?
29. Who were Henry VIII's two oldest wives?
30. Where was Henry III crowned?

Pot Luck 14 (See quiz 29, page 261)
Answers
1 Wine. 2 British Columbia. 3 24. 4 Des Lynam. 5 Sri Lanka. 6 1906. 7 F. Murray Abraham. 8 Blackheads. 9 Glasgow. 10 Edwina Currie. 11 A standing bear next to a ragged staff. 12 Matthew and Son. 13 A giant crossbow. 14 Christian Doppler. 15 Worcestershire and Sussex. 16 Gromyko. 17 Bifocal lenses. 18 Keep On Dancing. 19 Skull. 20 1940s. 21 Kyoto. 22 Pat Eddery. 23 Erich Remarque. 24 Richmond, Surrey. 25 Black. 26 Jack London. 27 Austria. 28 Yvonne Elliman. 29 Venezuela. 30 Assassinated.

Quiz 31 Pot Luck 15

Answers - see Quiz 32, page 264

1 Who directed the1930s film Mr Deeds Goes To Town?
2 Which disease did Prince Albert die from?
3 Shogi is a Japanese form of which game?
4 Who wrote The Seven Pillars of Wisdom?
5 Which bird would you find in a squab pie?
6 Who played the lead character in the film The Loneliness of the Long Distance Runner?
7 In which decade was the Marquis of Tavistock born?
8 What was Rolf Harris' first UK Top Ten hit?
9 Which famous actor played Philo Beddoe in two films?
10 Who did Australia beat when they first won cricket's World Cup?
11 What is the legendary ship The Flying Dutchman doomed to do?
12 Which queen of England had most fingers?
13 Who wrote the novel Fair Stood the Wind for France?
14 Who is the elder – Joan Collins or Michael Caine?
15 Whose one and only hit was Eye Level in 1973?
16 To three years, when did the M1 motorway open?
17 What was found in 1939 at Sutton Hoo, in Suffolk?
18 What is of interest to a thanatologist?
19 Where would you find calderas?
20 Who wrote The Lost World?
21 If something is napiform which vegetable shape is it?
22 What part of the body is studied by a myologist?
23 Which song features the words, "Here am I floating round my tin can"?
24 What was the Triangular Trade mainly concerned with?
25 What, in America, is a cayuse?
26 How many strokes underwater may a competitive breast-sroke swimmer make at the start and turn?
27 The town of Carrara in Italy is famous for what?
28 Who wrote humour books naming Mussolini and Hitler in the titles?
29 Who is thought to be the author of the Acts of the Apostles?
30 The Battle of Antietam was in which war?

Classic No 1s (See quiz 33, page 264)

Answers
1 Wet Wet Wet. 2 Unchained. 3 My Sweet Lord. 4 Wooden Heart. 5 Maggie May. 6 Frankie Laine. 7 Love. 8 Ticket To Ride. 9 Peter Cetera. 10 Herbert Kretzmer. 11 Girls' School. 12 Elton John. 13 The Fly (U2). 14 The Fleet's In. 15 Slade. 16 I Know Him So Well. 17 Whatever Will Be Will Be. 18 Do They Know It's Christmas? 19 Hello Goodbye. 20 Careless Whisper. 21 Bridge over Troubled Water. 22 Who's Sorry Now? 23 Three Times A Lady. 24 John Travolta. 25 You Wear It Well. 26 Claudette. 27 Mike Read. 28 I'm Not In Love. 29 Bohemian Rhapsody. 30 Living Doll.

Quiz 32 Classic No 1s

Answers - see Quiz 31, page 263

LEVEL 3

1　Who were the first Scottish group to have three No 1s?

2　Which 1955 American movie had Unchained Melody as theme tune?

3　Which No 1 was the first solo single by George Harrison?

4　Which Elvis hit made him the first artist with three consecutive British No 1s?

5　Which Rod Stewart hit was originally the B-side of Reason to Believe?

6　Who was on top of the charts the week Everest was first climbed?

7　What word appears three times in the title of the Gary Glitter No 1 that was covered by Joan Jett in America?

8　What was the first No 1 from the Beatles' second film Help!?

9　Who wrote Chicago's No 1 classic If You Leave Me Now?

10　Which lyricist of Aznavour's She was a writer on Les Mis?

11　What was on the other side of the double A No 1 Mull of Kintyre?

12　Who co-wrote a No 1 duet song under the pseudonym Ann Orson?

13　What finally knocked (Everything I Do) I Do It For You off the No 1 spot?

14　Which film did Frank Ifield's I Remember You originally come from?

15　Which group holds the record for the most consecutive years in which a songhas charted?

16　What became the all time best UK selling single by a female duo?

17　Which Doris Day Oscar-winning song was from The Man Who Knew Too Much in 1956?

18　What was the first debut single to enter straight at No 1?

19　Which No 1 hit by the Beatles equalled 7 weeks at the top with From Me To You?

20　What is the only George Michael song for which Andrew Ridgeley takes equal writing credit?

21　Which album title track gave Simon and Garfunkel their biggest hit?

22　Which 1920s standard gave Concetta Franconero a 6 week No 1 hit?

23　Which Commodores classic became Motown's best UK seller?

24　Who is the male half of the duo that have spent most weeks at No 1?

25　Which No 1 mentions Jackie Onassis?

26　Apart from Cathy's Clown, which other No 1 for the Everly Brothers had a girl's name in the title?

27　Which Radio 1 DJ banned Frankie Goes to Hollywood's Relax?

28　Which 10cc hit was covered by Johnny Logan in 1987?

29　Which 1975 megahit remained at No 1 for 9 weeks?

30　Which No 1 hit was Cliff Richard's first million seller?

Pot Luck 15 (See quiz 31, page 263)

1　Frank Capra. **2**　Typhoid Fever. **3**　Chess. **4**　Lawrence of Arabia. **5**　Pigeon. **6**　Tom Courtenay. **7**　1940s. **8**　Tie Me Kangaroo Down Sport. **9**　Clint Eastwood. **10**　England. **11**　Sail forever. **12**　Anne Boleyn (11). **13**　H.E.Bates. **14**　Michael Caine (by 2 months). **15**　Simon Park Orchestra. **16**　1959. **17**　A Saxon ship. **18**　Death. **19**　Volcanoes (They are craters). **20**　Sir Arthur Conan Doyle. **21**　Turnip. **22**　Muscles. **23**　Space Oddity. **24**　Slaves. **25**　A horse. **26**　One. **27**　White marble. **28**　Spike Milligan. **29**　St Luke. **30**　American Civil War.

Quiz 33 Pot Luck 16

LEVEL 3

Answers - see Quiz 34, page 266

1   What is Kyzyl Kum in Russia?
2   Neville Cardus was associated with which sport?
3   Who played Paul Henreid's wife in the film Casablanca?
4   What was the first woman's magazine to be published in 1693?
5   Where did the Dryad nymphs live in Greek mythology?
6   What sort of creature is a killdeer?
7   What type of music is Ira D Sankey particularly noted for composing?
8   How old was Louis Braille when he invented his reading system for the blind?
9   Which actor starred in the silent films Robin Hood, The Three Musketeers and The Black Pirate?
10 What was Five Star's first UK Top Ten hit?
11 Ficus Elastica is the Latin name for which plant?
12 In which sport is there a bonspiel?
13 Arch, loop and whorl are all parts of what?
14 What is pishogue a form of?
15 Permission was given to whom in 1988 to rebuild London's Globe Theatre?
16 In which decade was Emma Thompson born?
17 A fylfot is better known as a what?
18 Alton Byrd was famous in which sport?
19 Who played the magical Supergran in the 1985 TV series?
20 Whose one and only UK Top Ten hit was called Tarzan Boy?
21 Which actor was The Virginian on TV?
22 Who is the elder – Timothy Dalton or Charles Dance?
23 Richard Meade won Olympic gold in which sport?
24 What is the main difference between squash and rackets?
25 In which year was the CBI set up?
26 Whose first Top Ten hit was House of Love?
27 Where is the Caledonian market held?
28 Which battle in 1813 was the last battle of the Peninsular War?
29 Who would use a trochee?
30 Who wrote the play called A Taste of Honey?

Answers

TV Soaps (See quiz 34, page 266)
1 Sid Owen. 2 Where Will You Be. 3 General Hospital. 4 Ross Kemp.
5 E20. 6 Jean Alexander. 7 Gordon Clegg. 8 Peggy Mitchell. 9 Brookside.
10 Seven network. 11 Southworth, Ewing, Farlow. 12 Ali and Sue Osman.
13 The Banned. 14 Ida and Frank. 15 Los Barcos. 16 Rodney Harrington.
17 JR & Kristin. 18 Commercial Inn. 19 Desmond Carrington. 20 George
Peppard. 21 Braddock County. 22 When I Need You. 23 Mark Torrance.
24 Jacob Sugden. 25 Albion Market. 26 The Fowlers. 27 Larry Hagman.
28 1942. 29 Michael Grade. 30 Helicopter accident in South America.

Quiz 34 TV Soaps

Answers - see Quiz 33, page 265

LEVEL 3

1 How is David Sutton better known?
2 Sue Nicholls alias Audrey in Coronation Street made which record?
3 Which soap did Demi Moore appear in?
4 Who played Graham Lodsworth in Emmerdale?
5 What is the post code of the London Borough of Walford?
6 Which former soap star played Christine Keeler's mother in Scandal?
7 Which role did impresario Bill Kenwright play in Coronation Street?
8 Jo Warne played which Albert Square character?
9 Which soap featured the 'Free George Jackson' campaign?
10 On which Australian network was Neighbours first shown?
11 In Dallas what three surnames did Miss Ellie have?
12 Who ran the cafe when EastEnders started?
13 Sharon and Kelvin in EastEnders made a record under what name?
14 What were Ken Barlow's parents called?
15 In which village was the BBC's ill fated Eldorado set?
16 Which role did Ryan O'Neal play in Peyton Place?
17 In Dallas who were the parents of baby Christopher?
18 When Emmerdale was filmed at Esholt which pub was used as The Woolpack?
19 Which Radio 2 regular played Chris Anderson in Emergency Ward 10?
20 Who played Blake Carrington in the pilot for Dynasty?
21 In which county was Southfork ranch?
22 Jambo from Hollyoaks recorded which song as Will Mellor?
23 In Dynasty what name did Blake's supposed son Adam use when he first arrived on the scene?
24 Whose funeral was seen in the first episode of Emmerdale Farm?
25 Where was there a pub called The Waterman's Arms?
26 Who lived at 45 Albert Square?
27 Which soap star directed Son of Blob in 1972?
28 A one off 'prequel' about Albert Square was set in which year?
29 Which BBC 1 controller was responsible for moving Neighbours to a prime time viewing slot?
30 In Dallas, how and where did Jock Ewing die?

Pot Luck 16 (See quiz 33, page 265)

Answers

1 A desert. 2 Cricket. 3 Ingrid Bergman. 4 The Ladies' Mercury. 5 In trees.
6 A bird (Type of plover). 7 Hymns. 8 15. 9 Douglas Fairbanks. 10 System
Addict. 11 Rubber plant. 12 Curling. 13 Fingerprints. 14 Sorcery.
15 Sam Wanamaker. 16 1950s. 17 Swastika. 18 Basketball. 19 Gudrun
Ure. 20 Baltimora. 21 James Drury. 22 Timothy Dalton. 23 3 Day
Eventing. 24 Squash uses a softer ball. 25 1965. 26 East 17. 27 East end of
London. 28 Battle of Vittoria. 29 A poet . 30 Shelagh Delaney.

Quiz 35 Pot Luck 17

LEVEL 3

Answers - see Quiz 36, page 268

1　With which police identification system is Francis Galton associated?
2　Which trees mainly produced the fossilised resin which becomes amber?
3　Who is the elder – Sarah Brightman or Jill Dando?
4　If a ship is careened, what has happened to it?
5　What did Henry Segrave break at Daytona in 1927 and 1929?
6　What was the Beautiful South's first UK Top Ten hit?
7　Which event is the first in a Decathlon?
8　Which US President died on the same day as Aldous Huxley?
9　When is Haley's Comet predicted to make its next visit in Earth's vicinity?
10　Who wrote the Gormenghast Trilogy?
11　In which county is Chequers?
12　The King of which country was the Prisoner of Zenda?
13　Who was the first jockey to record three consecutive Derby wins?
14　What relation to King Arthur was Mordred?
15　Who designed the first lightning conductor?
16　In which decade was Vivienne Westwood born?
17　What is matzo?
18　Which actor played Captain Bligh, Quasimodo and Henry VIII in films?
19　Which Archbishop of Canterbury was burnt at the stake in 1556?
20　Who is the most capped English hockey player?
21　Which country did Frenchman Patrick Juvet love in his 70s UK hit?
22　Who played King Arthur in First Knight?
23　Whose one and only hit was Michelle in 1966?
24　What can be grapnel, sheet and bower?
25　A trudgen is used in which sport?
26　Which river was first explored by Mungo Park, a Scottish surgeon?
27　To five years, when were Nobel Prizes first awarded?
28　In the poem Beowulf, what kills Beowulf?
29　What would you do with a gigot?
30　The sitcom in which Warren Mitchell made his name took its title from which book?

Answers

Golf (See quiz 36, page 268)
1　South Africa. 2　Gene Sarazen. 3　Gentleman Golfers of Edinburgh. 4　Sandy Lyle. 5　1989 PGA. 6　Nick Price. 7　John Jacobs. 8　Nick Faldo. 9　Greg Norman. 10　Ivan Lendl. 11　Carnoustie. 12　Royal Lytham. 13　John Daly in 1991. 14　Worcester, Massachusetts. 15　Willie Park. 16　Bobby Jones (in perpetuity). 17　David Leadbetter. 18　Mark Calcavecchio. 19　Nick Faldo. 20　Walter Hagen. 21　20 22.　Troon. 23　The Walrus. 24　Seven. 25　British Open. 26　Great Britain & Ireland. 27　Twice. 28　Fred Couples. 29　Laura Davies. 30　Royal Portrush.

Quiz 36 Golf

Answers - see Quiz 35, page 267

LEVEL 3

1   Who retained golf's Dunhill Cup in 1998?

2   Who was the first man to with the US PGA and the US Open in the same year?

3   What was the world's first golf club called?

4   Which golfer was born on Bernard Gallacher's ninth birthday?

5   What was Payne Stewart's first. victory in a major?

6   In 1986 Greg Norman equalled whose record low score of 63 in the US Masters?

7   Who did Tony Jacklin replace as Ryder Cup captain?

8   Who was only the second person after Jack Nicklaus to win two successive US Opens?

9   Who did Nick Faldo sensationally beat to win his third US Masters?

10 In August 1996 who made his debut as a pro in the Czech Open?

11 In 1968 what became the longest course ever used for the British Open?

12 Where did Tom Lehman win his first major?

13 When Steve Jones first won the US Open he was the first qualifier to win a Major since who?

14 Where did the very first Ryder Cup take place?

15 Who won the first ever British Open?

16 Who is the President of Augusta National Golf Club?

17 Who did Nick Faldo sack as his coach at the same time as divorcing wife number two?

18 Who was the last American to win the British Open before John Daly in 1995?

19 Who was the first European to win the US Masters in the 90s?

20 Who was the first US born winner of the British Open?

21 How old was Nick Faldo when he was first in a Ryder Cup team?

22 Which golf course boasts a Postage Stamp?

23 What was Craig Stadler's nickname?

24 By how many strokes did Tony Jacklin win his first US Open?

25 Gary Player won all the Majors but which did he win first?

26 Who were the USA's opponents in the Ryder Cup from '73 to '77?

27 How many times did Jack Nicklaus win the US Amateur title before turning pro?

28 Who was the first American to win the US Masters in the 90s?

29 Who admitted losing half a million gambling in 1996?

30 What is the only Irish course to have staged the British Open?

Answers

Pot Luck 17 (See quiz 35, page 267)
1 Fingerprints. **2** Coniferous trees. **3** Sarah Brightman. **4** Turned on one side for cleaning. **5** Land Speed record. **6** Song for Whoever. **7** 100 metres. **8** J. F. Kennedy. **9** 2061. **10** Mervyn Peake. **11** Buckinghamshire. **12** Ruritania. **13** Steve Donoghue. **14** Nephew. **15** Benjamin Franklin. **16** 1940s. **17** Unleavened bread. **18** Charles Laughton. **19** Thomas Cranmer. **20** John Potter. **21** America. **22** Sean Connery. **23** Overlanders. **24** Anchors. **25** Swimming. **26** River Niger. **27** 1901. **28** A dragon. **29** Eat it. **30** The Book of Common Prayer.

Quiz 37 Pot Luck 18

Answers - see Quiz 38, page 270

LEVEL 3

1 What was discovered by Garcia Lopez de Cardenas in 1540?

2 Whose first Top Ten hit was titled September?

3 In the Seven Years War who were Britain's two allies?

4 In which decade was Paula Yates born?

5 Who was the first player to score 100 points in a NBA basketball game?

6 Rose Louise Hovick achieved fame under what name?

7 Who is the father of Marsha Hunt's daughter Karis?

8 What is the final line in the film Gone With the Wind?

9 Which newspaper was featured in the TV series Hot Metal?

10 The gemstone ruby is associated with which month?

11 What is the name of Phil and Jill Archer's farm?

12 Who directed the film It Happened One Night?

13 What was the Tote originally known as?

14 Where on your body are the Mounts of the Sun, Mercury and Venus?

15 Which fungal disease has the name Ceratostomella Ulmi?

16 Who created the cartoon character Colonel Blimp?

17 Where is the village of Skara Brae?

18 Who won the 1989 Best Actor Oscar for the film My Left Foot?

19 Who is the elder – Ian Botham or Jim Davidson?

20 Which actor played the title role in the TV series Dear John?

21 Whose theme was a No 4 UK hit in 1959 for Elmer Bernstein?

22 If you are an encratic person, what do you possess?

23 Who said, "There never was a good war, nor a bad peace"?

24 David Beckham made his league debut on loan at which club?

25 Who wrote The White Company?

26 Which general was the youngest in the American Civil War?

27 What was the Fine Young Cannibals first UK Top Ten hit?

28 With which profession is the organisation RIBA associated?

29 Who founded the record label Respond?

30 Who in 1632 painted The Anatomy Lesson of Dr Tulip?

Famous Celebs (See quiz 38, page 270)
1 Marianne Faithfull. 2 Terry O'Neill. 3 Ivana Trump. 4 A handbag.
5 Great grand daughter. 6 Pat van den Hauwe. 7 John Aspinall. 8 Sir
Anthony Buck. 9 Tavistock. 10 John Galliano. 11 The Queen Mother. 12
Victor Edelstein. 13 Paula Yates. 14 Countess of Dartmouth. 15 Camilla
Parker Bowles. 16 Bianca & Mason. 17 Marquess of Bath. 18 Geri Halliwell.
19 The Earl of Lichfield. 20 Alexandra. 21 Salford. 22 Debbie Moore. 23
David Bailey. 24 Architect. 25 Victoria Lockwood. 26 Barbara Cartland. 27
Camilla Parker Bowles. 28 Stella Tennant. 29 John Galliano. 30 Paula.

Answers

Quiz 38 Famous Celebs

Answers - see Quiz 37, page 269

LEVEL 3

1 Whose first husband was John Dunbar when she was 18?
2 Which photographer married Faye Dunaway in 1981?
3 Who announced her engagement to Riccardo Mazzucchelli in 1995?
4 What did Tara Palmer Tomkinson use to hide her modesty when posing nude with three friends?
5 What relation is Camilla Parker Bowles to Edward VII's mistress Mrs Keppel?
6 Who was Mandy Smith's second husband?
7 Who owns the private zoos, Howletts and Port Lympne?
8 Which Tory MP did Maria-Bienvenida Perez Blanco marry?
9 Former deb Henrietta Tiarks became which Marchioness?
10 Who designed the deep blue, lingerie style dress Diana wore in New York in 1996?
11 Who was Duchess of York before Fergie?
12 Who designed Diana's dress when she danced with John Travolta at the White House?
13 Heller Toren is the mother of which blonde celeb?
14 Which title did Raine have before she married the late Earl Spencer?
15 Whose Regency home is Ray Mill House in Wiltshire?
16 What were Regan Gascoigne's step siblings called?
17 Who is famous for his 'wifelets'?
18 Who is Watford Grammar School's most famous old girl?
19 Who was Mick Jagger's best man when he married Bianca?
20 What is Tiggy Legge-Bourke's real first name?
21 Fergie was appointed Chancellor of which University?
22 Who founded the Pineapple Dance Studios in 1979?
23 Who discovered Jean Shrimpton in the 60s?
24 Queen Noor of Jordan studied for what profession before her marriage?
25 Who was the first wife of the ninth Earl Spencer?
26 Whose husbands were Alexander McCorquodale then his cousin Hugh?
27 Who was the most famous daughter of Major Bruce Shand?
28 Who replaced Claudia Schiffer as the face of Chanel?
29 Who became Dior's chief designer in 1996?
30 Which model Hamilton co founded the elephant charity Tusk Force?

Answers

Pot Luck 18 (See quiz 37, page 269)
1 The Grand Canyon. **2** Earth, Wind & Fire. **3** Hanover and Prussia.
4 1960s. **5** Wilt Chamberlain. **6** Gypsy Rose Lee. **7** Mick Jagger.
8 "Tomorrow is another day." **9** Daily Crucible. **10** July. **11** Brookfield.
12 Frank Capra. **13** Paris Mutuel. **14** Your hand. **15** Dutch Elm Disease.
16 David Low. **17** The Orkneys. **18** Daniel Day-Lewis. **19** Jim Davidson.
20 Ralph Bates. **21** Staccato's Theme. **22** Self-control. **23** Benjamin
Franklin. **24** Preston. **25** Sir Arthur Conan Doyle. **26** George A Custer.
27 Johnny Come Home. **28** Architects. **29** Paul Weller. **30** Rembrandt.

Quiz 39 Pot Luck 19

Answers - see Quiz 40, page 272

1　Who died in the avalanche in Klosters in 1988 involving Prince Charles' party?

2　Who was chairman of the Joint Chiefs of Staff during the Gulf War?

3　How many hours are there in a fortnight?

4　Which modern day explorer has Twisleton-Wykeham as part of his name?

5　In whose reign was the Chelsea Hospital founded?

6　Who was Elizabeth I's State Secretary from 1573 to 1590?

7　Edward Whymper is associated with which leisure activity?

8　What did alchemists call the imaginary object that would turn base metals to gold?

9　What was the surname of the Lord in the TV series The Buccaneers?

10　Who designed and built the world's first iron bridge?

11　Who took her Toot Toot into the pop charts in the 80s?

12　Who is the elder – Sean Bean or Daniel Day-Lewis?

13　What was Michel Platini's club when he was three times European Footballer of The Year?

14　On the Chinese calendar, what is the only bird?

15　Where are the Padang Highlands?

16　What are you if you are described as being an ectomorph?

17　Where did Indian ink originally come from?

18　In which town is Channel TV based?

19　In which decade was Catherine Zeta Jones born?

20　What bird was the symbol of Persia's monarchy from 1739 to 1979?

21　What is the metal zinc extracted from?

22　Which game uses the expression 'J'adoube'?

23　In London what was the Tyburn?

24　Who attempted the programme of social reform called Fair Deal?

25　Where in England might you do a Furry Dance?

26　What are measured in hadal, abyssal and bathyl zones?

27　The Australian Aborigines' creation legend is told in what stories?

28　The word Eskimo means the eaters of what?

29　If you were banting, what would you be doing?

30　What was the Michael Bolton's first UK Top Ten hit?

Answers

Communications (See quiz 40, page 272)
1　Atlanta, Georgia. **2**　Stephen Wozniak & Steven Jobs. **3**　Olympic Games in Atlanta. **4**　Fibre-optic Link Around the Globe. **5**　Puerto Rico. **6**　The Branch Mall. **7**　Hand held fax machine. **8**　Grote Reber. **9**　MERLIN. **10**　Analogue Digital Converter. **11**　13. **12**　So drivers will concentrate. **13**　Siding Spring Mountain. **14**　1866. **15**　British Library. **16**　Tim Berners-Lee. **17**　The Confederation Bridge. **18**　The Times. **19**　Japan. **20**　1940. **21**　BBC & ITV. **22**　Betamax. **23**　Deep Blue. **24**　Leslie Ibsen Rogge. **25**　Isaac Newton. **26**　Nuffield. **27**　The Met Office. **28**　Water. 29 Catadioptric. **30**　Decca.

Quiz 40 Communications

Answers - see Quiz 39, page 271

LEVEL 3

1 Where is the HQ of CNN?
2 Who founded the Apple Computer Company?
3 Why was the Bellsouth telephone exchange the world's busiest in 1996?
4 What is FLAG?
5 In which country is the world's largest single dish radio telescope?
6 What was the first shopping mall on the Internet called?
7 What sort of communications device is "Pagentry"?
8 Who built the only purpose built radio telescope before WWII?
9 The Lovell Telescope is part of which network?
10 What is an ADC?
11 On household goods how many lines are there on a bar code?
12 Why was the Confederation Bridge built with so many curves?
13 Which mountain is the site of the Anglo Australian telescope in New South Wales?
14 In which decade of which century was the first transatlantic telegraph cable sent?
15 Where is BLAISE used?
16 Who was the World Wide Web originally created by?
17 Which bridge links Prince Edward Island with New Brunswick?
18 Marconi began a regular news service between the UK and US for which newspaper?
19 Where did the world's first major ISDN centre begin operating in '88?
20 When were the first experimental transmissions of colour TV in the US?
21 Who introduced the world's first teletext systems?
22 What was Sony's video cassette system for domestic viewers called?
23 What was the name of the first computer to beat a world chess champion?
24 Who was the first man to be arrested after having his picture on the Internet?
25 The telescope on La Palma in the Canary Islands is named after which scientist?
26 As which Radio Astronomy Laboratory is Jodrell Bank also known?
27 Who owns the Cray Supercomputer?
28 The New York City West Delaware tunnel is used to supply what?
29 What name is given to a telescope which uses lenses and mirrors?
30 Which company in Britain pioneered the videodisc?

Pot Luck 19 (See quiz 39, page 271)
1 Major Hugh Lindsay. **2** Colin Powell. **3** 336. **4** Sir Ranulph Fiennes. **5** Charles II. **6** Sir Francis Walsingham. **7** Mountaineering. **8** Philosopher's Stone. **9** Brightlingsea. **10** Abraham Darby. **11** Denise La Salle. **12** Daniel Day-Lewis. **13** Juventus. **14** Cockerel. **15** Sumatra. **16** Thin. **17** China. **18** St Helier. **19** 1960s. **20** Peacock. **21** Sphalerite. **22** Chess. **23** A stream. **24** President Truman. **25** Helston, Cornwall. **26** Ocean depths. **27** Dreamtime Stories. **28** Raw Meat. **29** Dieting. **30** How Am I Supposed To Live Without You.

Answers

Quiz 41 Pot Luck 20

Answers - see Quiz 42, page 274

LEVEL 3

1 What is a line joining any two points on a curve called in geometry?
2 What was Suzi Quatro's first UK Top Ten hit?
3 Which battle is remembered in the USA in April on Patriots' Day?
4 Who directed the films Marathon Man and Billy Liar?
5 Who was the eldest son of Henry III?
6 Who preceded Douglas Hurd as Foreign Secretary?
7 Which part of the body is affected by chorea?
8 Who was William Shakespeare's mother?
9 Which pop singing duo had the real first names of Reg and Pauline?
10 Who founded the Outward Bound Trust?
11 In which decade was Gary Rhodes born?
12 How old was Klaus Barbie when he was sentenced to life for wartime atrocities?
13 What would you do with a kaki?
14 What are Purple Laver and Devil's Apron types of?
15 Where would ichor supposedly have flowed?
16 Which singing twins were Hal and Herbert?
17 In The Bible, what did Job suffer with?
18 Which straits separate India from Sri Lanka?
19 Who referred to international financiers as "gnomes of Zurich"?
20 Who was the second oldest Goon?
21 What was author John Buchan's real title?
22 Which country do the Hausa people live in?
23 What was the name of Don Quixote's horse?
24 Who wrote the opera The Love for Three Oranges?
25 Christopher Nolan was a Whitbread Book of the Year winner with what?
26 Which fur comes from the coypu?
27 Whose only UK Top ten hit was called Shake You Down. in 1986?
28 Who became Minister of Defence when Churchill became PM in 1940?
29 In which Asian country is there an edition of the FT printed?
30 Who is the elder – Paddy Ashdown or Lord Archer?

Food & Drink 2 (See quiz 42, page 274)

Answers

1 Type of grape. 2 Buck's Club in London. 3 Doner kebab. 4 Belgium.
5 The Dorchester. 6 Caraway seeds. 7 Australia. 8 Salt cod. 9 John Tovey.
10 Chocolate. 11 Top. (garnish). 12 Chile. 13 Ullage. 14 Madame Harel, a
French farmer's wife. 15 Chocolate. 16 Greece. 17 Bucket. 18 VDQS.
19 Cinzano, apricot brandy & angostura bitters. 20 Butter made from coconut.
21 Maths. 22 Biscuit. 23 Asparagus. 24 Tarragon, chervil. 25 Plums. 26
Geese or ducks. 27 Lime juice. 28 Mixed green salad. 29 Kebab. 30 Filled
tortilla or pancake.

1 What is hanepoot?
2 Who or what was Buck's Fizz named after?
3 Which snack's name comes from the Turkish for rotating?
4 Where is the yeastless beer faro made?
5 Where was Anton Mosimann's first position as chef in the UK?
6 Kummel is a Russian liqueur extracted from what?
7 The macadamia is native to where?
8 What is the main ingredient of a brandade?
9 Who opened the Miller Howe restaurant in 1971?
10 In his diary what did Pepys call 'jucalette'?
11 Where in a dish would you put gremolata?
12 Which country has a wine growing area called O'Higgins?
13 Which term indicates the amount of wine by which a container falls short of being full?
14 Who is credited with creating camembert cheese in about 1790?
15 What is the base of a florentine biscuit made from?
16 Where did malmsey wine originate?
17 Balti is the Indian word for what?
18 Which abbreviation indicates wine between the qualities of vin de pays and appellation controle?
19 What are the ingredients of a Mr Callaghan?
20 What is cocose?
21 What did TV cook Sophie Grigson study at university?
22 In Swiss cooking what is a leckerli?
23 What is added to an omelette to make an omelette Argenteuil?
24 Which herbs are put in a béarnaise sauce?
25 Which fruit is used to make slivovitz?
26 Foie gras is the liver of which creatures?
27 In ceviche raw fish is marinated in what?
28 What is a mesclun?
29 A brochette is another name for what?
30 In Mexican cookery what is a quesadilla?

Answers

Pot Luck 20 (See quiz 41, page 273)
1 Chord. 2 Can The Can. 3 Lexington. 4 John Schlesinger. 5 Edward I.
6 John Major. 7 The central nervous system. 8 Mary Arden. 9 Elton John and Kiki Dee. 10 Kurt Hahn. 11 1960s. 12 73. 13 Eat it . 14 Seaweed.
15 In the veins of Greek gods. 16 Kalin Twins. 17 Boils. 18 Palk Straits.
19 Harold Wilson. 20 Harry Secombe. 21 Lord Tweedsmuir. 22 Nigeria.
23 Rosinante. 24 Prokofiev. 25 Under the Eye Of The Clock. 26 Nutria fur.
27 Gregory Abbot. 28 Churchill. 29 Japan. 30 Lord Archer.

1 What was Sting's debut movie?

2 What was Justin Henry's surname in a 70s Oscar winner?

3 In which film does railwayman Cleavon Little become sheriff?

4 That's Entertainment was a compilation of clips from which studio?

5 Who played Siegfried to Simon Ward's James in All Creatures Great and Small?

6 Which music plays in the background in 10?

7 What was Alan Parker's first feature film?

8 Who starred in and produced The China Syndrome?

9 What was Tom Selleck's first film, in 1970?

10 Who played Winston's father in Young Winston?

11 Whose was the disembodied voice narrating Agatha Christie's And Then There Were None?

12 Who wrote the music for Shaft?

13 Who was the landlord of 10 Rillington Place?

14 Who sang the title song in The Aristocats?

15 For the trailer of which Hitchcock film was the director seen floating in then Thames?

16 Stacy Keach starred in Fat City after who turned it down?

17 Who directed Death Wish?

18 Who was the first director to cast Goldie Hawn in a non comedy film?

19 Who did Jane Fonda play in Julia?

20 Why did Peter Finch not collect his Oscar for Network?

21 Whose music did Malcolm McDowell like in A Clockwork Orange?

22 Who was the only female Oscar winner for One Flew Over the Cuckoo's Nest?

23 Who played the editor of the Washington Post in All the President's Men?

24 Which club features in Cabaret?

25 Who played the brother in The Railway Children?

26 Who was Maid Marian opposite Sean Connery in Robin and Marian?

27 What was the first film in which Julie Christie and Warren Beatty starred together?

28 What was Peter Ustinov's first film as Hercule Poirot?

29 What was the sequel to Love Story?

30 Which film of a Frederick Forsyth novel starred Jon Voight?

Pot Luck 21 (See quiz 44, page 276)
1 Anything (omnivore). 2 Bankers. 3 Areas of equal rainfall. 4 Maria (Seas).
5 Kingston, Ontario. 6 Paranoid. 7 Britain. 8 The Order of the Thistle. 9
Bran. 10 Diphtheria. 11 Woody Harrelson. 12 Smoke it (It's a strong cigar).
13 Hecuba. 14 The Go Between (L. P. Hartley). 15 Copper & nickel. 16
White. 17 1920s. 18 Ethiopia. 19 The Hopman Cup, Perth, Australia. 20
Cuban Rebel Girls. 21 1930s. 22 Tivoli gardens in Copenhagen. 23 Officer
Barraclough. 24 Gamophobia. 25 Army Of Me. 26 Janet Street-Porter. 27 A
ship. 28 Euphemism. 29 Lynsey de Paul. 30 Harley Street doctor.

Quiz 44 Pot Luck 21

Answers - see Quiz 43, page 275

LEVEL 3

1   What is eaten by a pantophagist?
2   Who were the Fuggers?
3   What do isohyet lines indicate on a map?
4   What are the dark, lowland plains on the moon known as?
5   Where, in 1855, is ice hockey thought to have originated?
6   What was the only UK Top Ten hit for the group Black Sabbath?
7   In which country was musician Leopold Stokowski born?
8   Which Scottish order has the motto 'Nemo me impune lacessit'?
9   What was the name of Fingal's dog in Gaelic legend?
10 The Schich Test can be used to test for which disease?
11 In the Oliver Stone film Natural Born Killers, who played Mickey?
12 What do you do with a maduro?
13 Who was Hector's mother in mythology?
14 Which novel starts "The past is a foreign country: they do things differently there"?
15 Which metals is a 50p piece made from?
16 What is the main colour on the cover of the album Spice?
17 In which decade was Betty Boothroyd born?
18 Coptic Christians are found in Egypt and which one other country?
19 Which 1996 tennis tournament saw the debut of a fluorescent ball?
20 What was Errol Flynn's last film in 1959?
21 In which decade was playwright Sir Alan Ayckbourn born?
22 The Festival Garden in Battersea Park are based on which continental gardens?
23 Which part did Brian Wilde play in the TV series Porridge?
24 Which phobia describes a fear of marriage?
25 What was Bjork's first UK Top Ten hit from 1995?
26 Which female media personality has been President of the Ramblers Association?
27 What was a carrack?
28 What term describes using a gentler expression to soften a hard one?
29 Who is the elder – Lynsey de Paul or Noel Edmonds?
30 What was the profession of Jane Asher's father?

Answers

70s Films (See quiz 43, page 275)
1 Quadrophenia. 2 Kramer. 3 Blazing Saddles. 4 MGM. 5 Anthony Hopkins.
6 Ravel's Bolero. 7 Bugsy Malone. 8 Michael Douglas. 9 Myra Breckinridge.
10 Robert Shaw. 11 Orson Welles. 12 Isaac Hayes. 13 John Reginald Christie.
14 Maurice Chevalier. 15 Frenzy. 16 Marlon Brando. 17 Michael Winner.
18 Spielberg (The Sugarland Express). 19 Lilian Hellman. 20 He died shortly
after it was made. 21 Beethoven. 22 Louise Fletcher. 23 Jason Robards. 24 The
Kit Kat Club. 25 Gary Warren. 26 Audrey Hepburn. 27 McCabe and Mrs Miller.
28 Death on the Nile. 29 Oliver's Story. 30 The Odessa File.

Quiz 45 TV Gold

Answers - see Quiz 46, page 278

LEVEL 3

1 Who played Emperor Nero in I, Claudius?
2 Who was the female presenter of Tiswas?
3 Which presenter once played Sir Julius Berlin in Corrie?
4 Which future Oscar nominee played Samantha Briggs in Dr Who?
5 Who was the only female on the first Top of the Pops?
6 In which TV pub did Vince Hill find fame?
7 On The Golden Shot who famously always got her sums wrong?
8 Who was the housekeeper in All Creatures Great and Small?
9 Who was the first presenter of World of Sport on ITV?
10 What was the booby prize on Crackerjack?
11 Who were the trio in Take Three Girls?
12 Who had the role of George Starling written for him in 1963?
13 Who originally shared a flat with Sandra in The Liver Birds?
14 Which comedian starred as himself in the Northern town of Woodbridge?
15 Who played the shop treasurer in The Rag Trade?
16 The lead singer of Herman's Hermits played whose son on TV?
17 Who was the first Teenage Mutant Hero Turtle alphabetically?
18 Who played Yosser in Boys From the Blackstuff?
19 Who was doing the asking in Ask the Family?
20 Who frequently appeared as Nymphia in Up Pompeii?
21 Who starred as Charley Farley, partner of Piggy Malone?
22 Who was the author played by Elaine Stritch in Two's Company?
23 Which sitcom began with a one off play called The Offer?
24 Who played Nancy Astor's husband in the 80s series Nancy Astor?
25 As which character did David Cassidy shoot to fame in the 70s?
26 In My Wife Next Door which sitcom doyenne played George's mother?
27 Who was the only person the horse Mr Ed would talk to?
28 Which character shot Alan Rickman to fame in The Barchester Chronicles?
29 Who played Tom the tap dancing pimp in Pennies From Heaven?
30 Which corporal in M*A*S*H took to wearing women's clothes in order to be discharged?

Pot Luck 22 (See quiz 46, page 278)
1 A group hired to applaud. 2 1982. 3 A torture device. 4 Fabrics.
5 Margaret Atwood. 6 Japan. 7 A crash. 8 A.J. Cronin. 9 His wife
Clytemnestra. 10 Kenya. 11 Daddy Cool. 12 Conscription. 13 Ernest
Hemingway. 14 Dawn French. 15 Blucher. 16 Trial of the Pyx. 17 Jennie
Lee. 18 Newcastle-upon-Tyne. 19 Goldsbrough Orchestra (after its founder).
20 1868. 21 Princess Yashara. 22 Tiger. 23 1970s. 24 Veterinary Surgeon.
25 Big Ben. 26 Blow Monkeys. 27 Lord Nolan. 28 Groucho Marx. 29
Massaging you. 30 The farthing.

Answers

Quiz 46 Pot Luck 22

Answers - see Quiz 45, page 277

1 What is a claque?
2 In which year did Channel 4 start to broadcast?
3 What was the Scavenger's Daughter used for in the 16th century?
4 What can be sornick, nainsook and samite?
5 Who wrote Life Before Men and The Edible Woman?
6 Which country launched a strike against Russia's fleet in 1904 at Port Arthur?
7 What is the collective name for a group of rhinoceroses?
8 Who created the character Doctor Finlay?
9 In mythology, who murdered the Greek king Agamemnon?
10 The Flame Trees of Thika was set in which country?
11 What was Boney M's first UK Top Ten hit from 1976?
12 What was the Derby Scheme of 1915?
13 Who wrote A Farewell to Arms?
14 Who is the elder – Dawn French or Jennifer Saunders?
15 What name was given to George Stephenson's first locomotive?
16 At which ceremony are coins of the realm tested?
17 Who was Britain's first Minister for the Arts in 1967?
18 Which Northern city was given the Latin name Pons Aelius?
19 What was the English Chamber Orchestra originally called?
20 When was Exchange & Mart first published?
21 Who did Buddha marry before searching for enlightenment?
22 Alphabetically what is the last of the Chinese Zodiac signs?
23 In which decade was actress Dervla Kirwan born?
24 What was the profession of the pneumatic tyre patentee John Dunlop?
25 What, on 31st December 1923, gave its first broadcast?
26 Whose only UK Top Ten hit was It Doesn't Have To Be This Way?
27 Which Lord headed the investigating committee into 'sleaze' in public life in 1995?
28 Who said, "Don't point that beard at me: it might go off"?
29 If someone was Rolfing you, what would they be doing?
30 What ceased to be legal at midnight, December 31st, 1960?

TV Gold (See quiz 45, page 277)

Answers
1 Christopher Biggins. 2 Sally James. 3 Leonard Sachs. 4 Pauline Collins.
5 Dusty Springfield. 6 Stars and Garters. 7 Anne Aston. 8 Mrs Edna Hall.
9 Eamonn Andrews. 10 Cabbage. 11 Kate, Avril & Victoria. 12 Richard
Briers. 13 Dawn. 14 Harry Worth. 15 Sheila Hancock. 16 Len Fairclough's
son in Corrie. 17 Donatello. 18 Bernard Hill. 19 Robert Robinson.
20 Barbara Windsor. 21 Ronnie Corbett. 22 Dorothy McNab. 23 Steptoe &
Son. 24 Pierce Brosnan. 25 Keith Partridge. 26 Mollie Sugden. 27 Wilbur
Post. 28 Obadiah Slope. 29 Christopher Walken. 30 Maxwell Klinger.

Quiz 47 Girl Power

LEVEL 3

1   What are Celine Dion's first two words on My Heart Will Go On?
2   What is Tina Turner's highest ever UK solo singles chart position?
3   What did Geri write by her signature on the cover notes of Spice?
4   Which sisters gave Stock/Aitken/Waterman their first No1 hit?
5   In which year was Diana Ross's first UK solo Top Ten hit?
6   Which hit made Helen Shapiro the youngest British artist to reach No 1?
7   Who sang female vocals on the Beautiful South's first No 1?
8   Belinda Carlisle and Bonnie Tyler both covered which 1970 No 1?
9   Who partnered Janet Jackson on her UK No 3 hit Scream ?
10 Who was the first British female soloist to have three chart No 1 hits?
11 Whose first UK Top Ten hit as a solo artist was Light of My Life?
12 Which character was played by Kylie Minogue in The Delinquents?
13 What is Enya's full name?
14 Which Bananarama star went on to join Shakespear's Sister?
15 What was Madonna's first UK No 1?
16 Whose first UK Top Ten hit was Love Resurrection ?
17 When did Shirley Bassey first reach the UK Top Ten?
18 Formed in 1981, girl band The Colours charted under which name?
19 What was Dina Carroll's first solo Top Ten hit?
20 Which UK vocalist released an album in 1974 called Ma?
21 Which film featured the Eternal hit Someday in 1996?
22 Whose first UK Top Ten hit was My One Temptation?
23 Which UK No 3 for Stacy Lattisaw was a No 8 for Dannii Minogue?
24 Which lady recorded the original Midnight Train To Georgia?
25 Which lady was Rockin' Around The Christmas Tree in 1987?
26 What did Belinda Carlisle want in her UK No 6 hit from 1990?
27 Which female star first reached No 1 29 years after her first hit?
28 What was the No 3 hit by Youssou N'Dour featuring Neneh Cherry?
29 What type of girl gave Tori Amos her first UK Top Ten hit in 1994?
30 Who was the first solo female to enter the UK charts at No 1?

Pot Luck 23 (See quiz 48, page 280)
1 In a road accident. 2 Jehovah's Witnesses. 3 1940s. 4 A Lizard. 5 Cain.
6 Laurence Sterne. 7 The Rain. 8 Israel. 9 Virginia. 10 Apollo Creed.
11 Seat placed on the back of an elephant. 12 Velasquez. 13 Amazon.
14 Mariah Carey. 15 A sucker. 16 Chemistry. 17 Max Schmeling (German).
18 Ben Elton. 19 Ted Danson. 20 Mont Blanc. 21 Duke of York.
22 Cheese. 23 Beestings. 24 Mexico. 25 Evelyn Waugh. 26 Estelle.
27 London to Penzance. 28 U-boats. 29 Go Wild In The Country.
30 Tennyson.

Answers

Quiz 48 Pot Luck 23

Answers - see Quiz 47, page 279

LEVEL 3

1　How did Marie Curie's husband Pierre die?

2　Which group of people were once known as Millennial Dawnists?

3　In which decade was musician Mark Knopfler born?

4　What are you like if you are described as being saurian?

5　Who was the father of Enoch in The Bible?

6　Who created the character Tristram Shandy?

7　What was the title of Oran 'Juice' Jones only UK hit from 1986?

8　In which country is there a political party called Likud?

9　What was Tammy Wynette's real first name?

10　Which part did Carl Weathers play in the Rocky movies?

11　Where is a howdah normally found?

12　Which Spaniard painted the picture The Rokeby Venus?

13　Which River mouth was discovered by Amerigo Vespucci in 1499?

14　Who joined Boyz II Men in their 1995 No 6 UK hit One Sweet Day?

15　What did P.T. Barnum allegedly say is born every minute?

16　Richard Kuhn, Jutus Liebig and Harold Urey were famous in which scientific field?

17　Who was the first undisputed heavyweight world champion boxer to be European?

18　Who is the elder – Ben Elton or Harry Enfield?

19　Who played the lead male role in the 1995 film Loch Ness ?

20　Horace Saussure made the first ascent of where in 1787?

21　Which title is traditionally given to the second son of the monarch?

22　What sort of food is Dunlop?

23　What is a cow's first milk after calving called?

24　Which country celebrates the National holiday, the 'Day of the Dead'?

25　Who wrote A Handful of Dust?

26　What's Geri Halliwell's middle name?

27　The train the Cornish Riviera ran from where to where?

28　In the Second World War what did the Germans send out in 'wolf packs'?

29　What was Bow Wow Wow's first UK Top Ten hit?

30　Who wrote the poems Maud and Locksley Hall?

Girl Power (See quiz 47, page 279)
1　Every Night. 2　Three. 3　Girl Power. 4　Mel and Kim Appleby. 5　1970.
6　You Don't Know. 7　Briana Corrigan. 8　Freda Payne's Band of Gold.
9　Michael Jackson. 10　Sandie Shaw. 11　Louise. 12　Lola Lovell. 13　Eithne
Ni Bhraonain. 14　Siobhan Fahey. 15　Into The Groove. 16　Alison Moyet.
17　1957. 18　The Bangles. 19　Don't Be A Stranger. 20　Lena Zavaroni.
21　Hunchback of Notre Dame. 22　Mica Paris. 23　Jump To The Beat.
24　Cissy Houston. 25　Kim Wilde. 26　(We want) The Same Thing. 27　Lulu.
28　7 Seconds. 29　Cornflake Girl. 30　Mariah Carey.

Quiz 49 Sport Moments

Answers - see Quiz 50, page 282

1　Which Grand National winner was the first to be trained by a woman?
2　David Broome was the first British showjumping champion on which horse?
3　Who was the only player to kick the ball when the crowd sang "There's only one team in Tallinn"?
4　Who broke the world 5,000m by 11 seconds in 1995?
5　Jesse Owens was part of which university team when he set his three world records?
6　Who was the second player to hit a maximum 36 runs off one over?
7　In which road in Oxford did Roger Bannister run his four minute mile?
8　How many people witnessed Brazil's defeat by Uruguay in the 1950 World Cup Final?
9　Who was the first athlete to break 13 minutes for the 5,000m?
10　Who made Chris Boardman's winning bicycle in Barcelona?
11　Which famous pacemaker founded the London Marathon?
12　Which Grand National horse was the first to cross the line the year the race was abandoned?
13　By what score did Steve Davis lose the World Professional Championship Final in 1985?
14　Who was the first man to break one minute for 100m breaststroke in a 25m pool?
15　With whom did Steve Redgrave take the second of his four Olympic golds?
16　Which British man ran the fastest mile in the 80s?
17　Why did Susan Brown make history in 1981?
18　Which was the last horse before Lammtarra in 1995 to win the classic triple?
19　How many times did Nadia Comaneci score a perfect 10 at Montreal in 1976?
20　To the nearest 10 minutes, how long did it take Brian Lara to score his record 501 against Durham in 1994?
21　Who caddied for Tiger Woods on his first US Masters victory?
22　How many races out of the 16 did Nigel Mansell win to become World Champion?
23　Who was the first player since WWII to score more than 30 goals in three consecutive seasons?
24　Where was Harvey Smith when he made his infamous V sign?
25　Who did Virginia Wade beat to win her Wimbledon Singles title?
26　How many League games had Stanley Matthews played before his final match aged 50?
27　Seb Coe simultaneously held three world records, at which distances?
28　To the nearest 100 what were the odds against Frankie Dettori's seven Ascot wins?
29　Who broke the 1500, 3000 and 5000m records in 1994?
30　Who did Mike Tyson beat to become the youngest WBC champion?

Pot Luck 24 (See quiz 50, page 282)
1　50. 2　Polio. 3　A plant. 4　Jack London. 5　Roads. 6　Hobson - the butler/valet. 7　An ornamental hanging in a church. 8　He was shot dead. 9　King Crabbs. 10　Chris Evans. 11　Vanessa Redgrave. 12　A small barrel. 13　Eight. 14　Cliff Richard. 15　Insects. 16　Priests. 17　Four. 18　Win golf's British and US Opens. 19　Toni Braxton. 20　Harold Wilson. 21　29th February. 22　Donald Coggan. 23　A rainbow bridge. 24　Michael Foot. 25　Parsec. 26　Sir Matt Busby. 27　A silken fabric. 28　Artillery. 29　Athenia. 30　1940s.

Quiz 50 Pot Luck 24

Answers - see Quiz 49, page 281

LEVEL 3

1   How many chapters are in the book of Genesis in The Bible?
2   The Salk vaccine was developed against which disease?
3   What is a Venus's Looking Glass?
4   Who wrote White Fang?
5   What were constructed in the Highlands by General Wade in 1724?
6   What was the name of the John Gielgud character in the film Arthur?
7   What is a dossal?
8   What happened in Northern Ireland to Bananarama's road manager?
9   What was the Royal name of the band formed by Jimmy Nail?
10 Who is the elder – Chris Evans or Paul Gascoigne?
11 In the film Isadora who played the role of Isadora Duncan?
12 What is a barrico?
13 How many American colleges and universities are in the Ivy League?
14 Who played the lead role in the film Take Me High?
15 Cicada are types of what?
16 Who are in charge in a theocracy?
17 How many lines has a clerihew?
18 What was Patty Sheehan the first woman to do in the same year?
19 Breathe Again was the first UK Top Ten hit for which female vocalist?
20 Who had been Britain's youngest cabinet member before William Hague?
21 Frederick is born on which day in The Pirates Of Penzance?
22 Who was Archbishop of Canterbury from 1974 to 1980?
23 What was Bifrost in Norse mythology?
24 Which Labour leader was accused by The Sunday Times of being a Russian agent?
25 Which unit of measurement is equal to 3.2616 light years?
26 Which Man Utd manager appeared in a film called Cup Fever?
27 What was sendal?
28 What is a firearm called if it has a calibre over 20mm?
29 Which British liner was the first to be sunk by a U-boat on the first day of the Second World War?
30 In which decade was actor David Jason born?

Answers

Sport Moments
1 Corbiere. 2 Beethoven. 3 Billy x. 4 Haile Gebreselassie. 5 Ohio State University. 6 Ravi Shastri. 7 Iffley Road. 8 200,000. 9 Said Aouita.
10 Lotus. 11 Chris Brasher (pacemaker for Bannister). 12 Esha Ness.
13 18-17. 14 Adrian Moorhouse. 15 Andrew Holmes. 16 Steve Cram.
17 First woman to take part in the boat race. 18 Mill Reef (1971). 19 Seven.
20 7hr 54 mins. 21 Mike 'Fluff' Cowan. 22 Nine. 23 Alan Shearer.
24 Hickstead. 25 Betty Stove. 26 700. 27 800m, 1000m, 1500m.
28 25,095-1. 29 Noureddine Morceli. 30 Trevor Berbick.

Quiz 51 20th Century

LEVEL 3

1 What was the last ruling dynasty of China?
2 Which oil field blow-out caused an 8.2 million gallon spill in April 1977?
3 Who became Europe's youngest head of state at 28 in 1993?
4 Where was Archbishop Makarios exiled by the British in the mid 50s?
5 Which Deputy Ministerial post did Winnie Mandela hold in Nelson Mandela's first government?
6 Which German Chancellor achieved post war reconciliation with France in the 50s and early 60s?
7 Who became the youngest ever member of the GLC in 1969?
8 Which political parties linked in the UK in the 80s to form the Alliance?
9 Which Middle East leaders were awarded the Nobel Peace Prize in 1994?
10 Which film studio released the first talking film?
11 In the Watergate scandal, who or what was CREEP?
12 What was the occupation of Jean Bertrand Aristide of Haiti?
13 Wembley Stadium was completed for which event?
14 Harold Wilson became Baron of where on his elevation to the peerage?
15 Which quotation from Richard III was used to describe the end of 1978 and beginning of 1979?
16 What was nicknamed 'The Flapper Vote' in 1928?
17 Who succeeded the Ayatollah Khomeini as political leader of Iran?
18 Who was the first president of an independent Mozambique?
19 J Arthur Rank entered films in the 30s to promote which cause?
20 In 1987, what did the Tower Commission investigate in the US?
21 Where was the Recruit Scandal of 1988?
22 Which minister in Thatcher's government shared his name with Henry VIII's chaplain?
23 What did the initials of film company RKO stand for?
24 Whose gang did Al Capone's men massacre on Valentine's Day 1929?
25 A shortage of which commodity was a major issue in the 1998 Indian election?
26 At what number Cromwell Street did Rose and Fred West live?
27 King Michael abdicated which throne in 1947?
28 Who did Jacques Santer replace as President of the European Commission?
29 The 1964 Rivonia Trial involved those opposed to what?
30 What was the name of Franco's fascist party in Spain?

Pot Luck 25
1 Vanessa Feltz. 2 Dublin. 3 Bookbinding. 4 Sculling. 5 James Joyce.
6 New York. 7 The flying shuttle. 8 Ken Boothe. 9 Cultivation of plants
without soil. 10 Charles II. 11 A whip. 12 Mark Twain. 13 Handsome.
14 Stalin. 15 The Zaire. 16 Four. 17 Horses. 18 Dr Michael Stroud.
19 1940s. 20 The Victoria Falls. 21 A pine cone. 22 Troops. 23 Muirfield.
24 King Baudouin (Belgium). 25 Esther. 26 September. 27 Ground-hog Day.
28 End Of The Road. 29 Poetry. 30 Salmon.

Quiz 52   Pot Luck 25

Answers - see Quiz 51, page 283

LEVEL 3

1   Who is the elder – Paul McKenna or Vanessa Feltz?

2   In which city in 1882 were the Phoenix Park murders?

3   What is Roxburghe a style of?

4   Actor Thomas Doggett is remembered by an award in which sport?

5   Which writer died in Zurich after an operation for an ulcer in 1941?

6   Which city's underground has more stations than any other?

7   Which weaving invention was invented by John Kay?

8   Who was first to take Everything I Own to No 1 ?

9   What is hydroponics?

10   The Rye House Plot of 1683 was aiming to assassinate which king?

11   What is a quirt?

12   Who wrote A Connecticut Yankee in King Arthur's Court?

13   The Christian name Kenneth derives from the Gaelic for what?

14   Which Soviet dictator died on the same day as composer Prokofiev?

15   What is the unit of currency in The People's Republic of Congo?

16   How many No 1 albums did Take That have?

17   Which animals can suffer the disease strangles?

18   Who went with Ranulph Fiennes on his trek across Antarctica in '95?

19   In which decade was Gloria Hunniford born?

20   What were discovered by David Livingstone in 1855?

21   What is a strobilus another name for?

22   The name Commandos comes from an Afrikaans word for what?

23   Where did Nick Faldo win his first British Open?

24   Which European King died in 1993?

25   Which Biblical woman is the Jewish festival Purim a celebration to?

26   In which month is Prince Harry's birthday?

27   In America what is the 2nd February called?

28   What was Boyz II Men's first UK Top Ten hit?

29   Bragi was the Norse god of what?

30   Grilse, Alevins and Kelts are all forms of what?

Past Times 3: 20th Century (See quiz 51, page 283)
1 Manchu or Qing ('Ching'). **2** Ekofisk. **3** Mario Frick of Liechtenstein.
4 Seychelles. **5** Arts & Science. **6** Konrad Adenauer. **7** Jeffrey Archer. **8** Liberals and SDP. **9** Arafat, Rabin, and Peres. **10** Warner Brothers. **11** Committee to RE-Elect the President. **12** Priest. **13** British Empire Exhibition 1924. **14** Rievaulx. **15** Winter of discontent. **16** Vote to women over 21. **17** Rafsanjani. **18** Samora Machel. **19** Methodism. **20** Irangate. **21** Japan. **22** Nicholas Ridley. **23** Radio Keith Orpheum. **24** Bugs Moran. 25 Onions. **26** **25** 27. Romania. **28** Jacques Delors. **29** Apartheid. **30** Falange.

1   Who owns the Sydney Harbour Casino?
2   Which eating house did Ruthie Rogers found?
3   What was the name of the board game launched by Terry Venables?
4   1949 saw what innovation in the game of badminton?
5   Who founded the Harlem Globetrotters?
6   How many tiles are there in a game of mah-jong?
7   Who designs clothes for younger people under the Emporio label?
8   What type of art was known as Jugenstil in Germany?
9   How long is the rope in water skiing?
10   In the early days of cinema how long would a 'two reeler' last?
11   Serigraphy is also known as what?
12   What name is given to the style of skiing on a single broad ski?
13   Which type of outdoor spectacular was created by Paul Houdin and first shown at the Chateau de Chambord in 1952?
14   Which craft takes its name from the Arabic for 'striped cloth'?
15   Where did canasta originate?
16   What are the two winning numbers made with two dice in craps?
17   Who opened Les Quat' Saisons in 1977?
18   If you follow FINA rules which sport do you practise?
19   How many dominoes are there in a double six set?
20   Southampton boast of having the first sports area of what type in the country?
21   Which sport would interest you if you followed the work of the ACS?
22   Ellem in Scotland is the oldest club of what type?
23   In the Role-Playing Game known as D&D, what does the second D stand for?
24   Where do cycle races called criteriums take place?
25   If you spent your leisure time in a sulky where would you. be?
26   If you were spelunking in the US what would you be doing?
27   In 1976 the NBA and the ABA merged in which sport?
28   In sepek takrow you can hit the ball with any part of the body except which?
29   General Choi Hong Hi is responsible for the development of which martial art?
30   What position does the canoeist adopt in Canadian canoeing?

Pot Luck 26 (See quiz 54, page 286)
1 Smetana. 2 Mary Peters. 3 Pool. 4 Nine years old. 5 John Wesley.
6 Ballet. 7 Heliopolis. 8 The Mediterranean. 9 T. Rex. 10 Bernard Bresslaw.
11 Second sight. 12 Robin Williams. 13 Robert McClure. 14 Gary Lineker.
15 Nicaragua. 16 Scotland. 17 It is haunted. 18 The Futhark. 19 The eyes.
20 My Prerogative. 21 On the Thames. 22 Ronald Searle. 23 Tannenburg.
24 Horse. 25 1960s. 26 Clergy. 27 Pact of Steel. 28 Clint Eastwood.
29 Mary O'Brien. 30 Fox.

Answers

Quiz 54 Pot Luck 26

LEVEL 3

Answers - see Quiz 53, page 285

1 Who composed the opera The Bartered Bride?
2 Who won the 1972 Olympic pentathlon title?
3 In the film The Baltimore Bullet which game was featured?
4 How old was Henry III when he became King?
5 Who said, "I look upon the world as my parish"?
6 In which performing art was Beryl Grey famous?
7 Where in Egypt did Cleopatra's needle originally stand?
8 The Silk Road ancient trade route ran between China and where?
9 Micky Finn played bongos in which pop group?
10 Whose only UK Top Ten Hit was Mad Passionate Love from 1958?
11 Deuteroscopy is the common name for what?
12 Which actor links Awakenings, Toys and Cadillac Man?
13 Who was the first admiral to pass through the Northwest Passage?
14 Who is the elder – Nicholas Lyndhurst or Gary Lineker?
15 Daniel Ortega was President of which country from 1981-1990?
16 Where was the Encyclopaedia Britannica first published?
17 Why is Chinge Hall in Lancashire famous?
18 What name is given to the Runic alphabet?
19 What are affected by nystagmus?
20 What was Bobby Brown's first UK Top Ten hit?
21 Where were Frost Fairs held in London until 1831?
22 Which illustrator created the girls of St Trinians?
23 Where were the Russians defeated by the Germans from 26-30th August 1914?
24 Which creature is represented in the year the Chinese call 'ma'?
25 In which decade was pop superstar Mick Hucknall born?
26 Crockford's is a register of what?
27 Italy and Germany formed a military alliance in 1939 called what?
28 Who won the Best Director Oscar in 1992 for Unforgiven?
29 What is Dusty Springfield's real name?
30 What's the English name of the constellation Vulpecula?

Hobbies 1 (See quiz 53, page 285)
1 Kerry Packer. 2 River Cafe. 3 The Manager. 4 Plastic shuttlecocks.
5 Abraham Saperstein. 6 144. 7 Armani. 8 Art Nouveau. 9 23m or 75 feet.
10 20 minutes. 11 Silk screen printing. 12 Monoboarding. 13 Son et
lumiere. 14 Macramé. 15 Uruguay. 16 7 & 11. 17 Raymond Blanc.
18 Swimming. 19 28. 20 Bowling green. 21 Cricket. 22 Angling.
23 Dragons. 24 Town or city centres. 25 Small cart in harness racing.
26 Potholing. 27 Basketball. 28 Arms and hands. 29 Taekwondo.
30 Kneeling.

1 In whose stately home was the Tarzan film Greystoke filmed?
2 What was Sharon Stone's first film, in 1980?
3 Uncle Buck was the debut of which movie star?
4 May Day was the Bond girl in which film?
5 What was the occupation of Madame Sousatzka in the Shirley Maclaine film?
6 Who had a lead role in the movie version of Rising Damp who wasn't in the TV sitcom?
7 Who did Alan Rickman play in Die Hard?
8 Who are the two letter writers in 84 Charing Cross Road?
9 Which son of a pop star appears as Jackson's friend in Moonwalker?
10 In which film did Jack Nicholson say the catchphrase "Here's Johnny"?
11 Who played Mrs La Motta in Raging Bull?
12 Which film all but bankrupted United Artist in 1980?
13 Which ailing actor's voice was dubbed by Rich Little in Curse of the Pink Panther?
14 Who played Meryl Streep's eccentric friend in Plenty?
15 Who won an Oscar for his first major role in 1982?
16 Who was Glenn Close's character in Dangerous Liaisons?
17 Which film included the song It Might Be You?
18 Who was the only Cambodian Oscar winner of the 80s?
19 Who was the only winner of an Oscar and a BAFTA for Platoon?
20 Who was nominated as Best Supporting Actress for The Color Purple?
21 In the film A Royal Love Story, who played Princess Diana?
22 The Color of Money recreated the character from which film?
23 Which father and son appeared in Wall Street?
24 Which role did Kevin Kline play in A Fish Called Wanda?
25 Which. presidential candidate's cousin won an Oscar for Moonstruck?
26 Apart from Music and Visual Effects, which other Oscar did E.T. win?
27 Who directed Psycho III?
28 Whose music features on the soundtrack of When Harry Met Sally?
29 Whose novel was Warren Beatty's Reds based on?
30 Who was the aerobics instructor in Perfect?

TV Times 1 (See quiz 56, page 288)
1 Prince Edward. **2** Fiona Armstrong & Michael Wilson. **3** Dudley Moore.
4 Sinead O'Connor. **5** Urquhart in House of Cards. **6** French & Saunders.
7 Greta Scacchi. **8** Tumbledown. **9** Frank Skinner. **10** Tony Hart. **11** Tutti
Frutti & Fortunes of War. **12** Beavis & Butthead. **13** Ethel Merman. **14** Jack
Lemmon. **15** Helen Hewitt. **16** Richard Branson. **17** Jean Marsh. **18** Clive
Anderson. **19** Faith, Hope & Charity. **20** Mike Ahearne. **21** Alan Clark. **22**
Steve Houghton. **23** Phelan. **24** Westward. **25** Jimmy McGovern. **26** Hotel.
27 Lynne Franks. **28** Alec Baldwin. **29** Timothy Dalton. **30** Frank Muir.

Quiz 56 TV Times 1

Answers - see Quiz 55, page 287

1   Who set up the production company Ardent?
2   Which duo first presented the breakfast show on GMTV?
3   Who appeared in a Tesco ad chasing chickens around France?
4   Who tore up a picture of the Pope on US TV in 1993?
5   Which character said, "You might very well think that, but I couldn't possibly comment"?
6   Who originally appeared in cabaret as the Menopause Sisters?
7   Who had a small role in Bergerac before starring in Heat and Dust?
8   Which play told of Falklands casualty Robert Lawrence?
9   How is comedian Chris Collins better known?
10 Who designed the Blue Peter logo?
11 For which two series did Emma Thompson win best actress BAFTAs two years in succession?
12 Who duetted with Cher on I Got You Babe in 1994?
13 Which Hollywood actress played Lola Lasagne in Batman?
14 Who was Frank Ormand, the Pretzel man in The Simpsons?
15 What was the prison chief called in The Governor?
16 Which British entrepreneur once guested on Friends?
17 Who played Joanna in Dr Who and was the wife of a future Doctor?
18 Who said to Lord Archer, "There's no beginning to your talents, Jeffrey"?
19 Which pop band was Dani Behr a member of before her TV career?
20 What was Gladiator Warrior's real name?
21 Who wrote and presented a History of the Tory Party?
22 Who replaced Craig McLachlan as Ed in Bugs?
23 Which brothers were played by the McGanns in The Hanging Gale?
24 Which TV company was founded by Peter Cadbury?
25 Who wrote the controversial series The Lakes?
26 In which series did Eileen Downey find fame?
27 Ab Fab's Edina was based on which PR lady?
28 Who became narrator for Thomas The Tank Engine in the US in '98?
29 Who played Rhett Butler in the TV sequel to Gone With the Wind?
30 A comedy writing award was introduced in 1998 in whose memory?

Answers

80s Films (See quiz 55, page 287)
1 Duke of Roxburghe's. 2 Stardust Memories. 3 Macaulay Culkin. 4 A View to a Kill. 5 Piano teacher. 6 Denholm Elliott. 7 Hans Gruber. 8 Helene Hanff & Frank Doel. 9 Sean Lennon. 10 The Shining. 11 Cathy Moriarty. 12 Heaven's Gate. 13 David Niven. 14 Tracey Ullman. 15 Ben Kingsley. 16 Marquise de Merteuil. 17 Tootsie. 18 Haing S. Ngor. 19 Oliver Stone. 20 Oprah Winfrey. 21 Catherine Oxenberg. 22 The Hustler. 23 Martin & Charlie Sheen. 24 Otto. 25 Olympia Dukakis. 26 Sound. 27 Anthony Perkins. 28 Harry Connick Jr. 29 John Reed's. 30 Jamie Lee Curtis.

1   Which Saint claimed to have seen the Loch Ness monster in the 6th century?

2   What was Brotherhood of Man's first UK Top Ten hit?

3   In which county did the battle of Edgehill take place?

4   Who directed the films Superman II and Juggernaut?

5   In which decade was TV presenter Eamonn Holmes born?

6   Which theatre foundations were discovered in London in 1988?

7   Who was lead in the films Man of the Moment and The Square Peg?

8   Which ruler led the 7th and 8th Crusades?

9   Which actor won Best Actor Oscar for On Golden Pond aged 76?

10   How many countries surround Botswana?

11   Barbara Trentham was the second wife of which English comic?

12   What is Bordeaux Mixture a blend of?

13   Which Spanish artist painted The Persistence of Memory?

14   Which military group's HQ is at Aubagne near Marseilles?

15   What is the middle name of knighted cricketer Gary Sobers?

16   What was Greta Garbo's last film?

17   The WWSU is the governing body of which sport?

18   What mass is measured in Criths?

19   In which city is the Verrazano Narrows Bridge?

20   Which profession did George Washington start out in?

21   Who was the leading lady in the films McLintock and Rio Grande?

22   Which African country won the 1996 Olympics gold medal for soccer?

23   What was the title of the only UK Top Ten hit for James Brown?

24   Who is the elder – Joanna Lumley or Maureen Lipman?

25   What does the abbreviation 'fz' mean in music?

26   Spaniard Francisco Pizarro founded which city?

27   When was the magazine Cosmopolitan first published?

28   Which city was the first to erect a monument to Lord Nelson in Britain?

29   What was Angel Beast an old type of?

30   What is the county emblem of Lincolnshire?

Answers

Euro Tour (See quiz 58, page 289)
1 Italy. 2 Romania. 3 Tbilisi. 4 Vienna. 5 Gulf of Riga. 6 Brussels.
7 Austria. 8 Koper. 9 Italy. 10 Baltic. 11 Netherlands. 12 9 million.
13 Gulf of Finland. 14 Great Britain. 15 Mount Etna and Stromboli.
16 Grande Dizence in Switzerland. 17 Finland. 18 London. 19 Germany.
20 Liechtenstein. 21 Ormeli in Norway. 22 Belarus. 23 Assisi in Central
Italy. 24 Germany. 25 Italy. 26 Roman Catholic. 27 Corfu. 28 Tourism and
tobacco. 29 Spain. 30 Norway.

Quiz 58 Euro Tour

LEVEL 3

1 Which country is Europe's largest wine producer?
2 Tarom Airlines are based in which country?
3 What is the capital of Georgia?
4 Which capital is further north – Budapest or Vienna?
5 Which Gulf is to the west of Estonia and Latvia?
6 Where is the news agency Centre d'Information Presse based?
7 In which country is Kranebitten International airport?
8 What is the chief port of Slovenia?
9 The Pelagian islands belong to which European country?
10 Bornholm is an island in which Sea?
11 Hoge Veluwe National Park is in which country?
12 To the nearest million, what was the population of Moscow in 1995?
13 St Petersburg is at the head of which gulf?
14 What is the largest island in Europe?
15 Which two Italian volcanoes erupted in 1994?
16 What is the world's highest dam?
17 Which country is called Suomen Tasavalta in its own language?
18 Which capital is further north - Berlin or London?
19 Aero Lloyd Airlines are based in which country?
20 Which European country has the highest life expectancy for men and women?
21 What is the highest waterfall in Europe?
22 Brest is a major town in which country other than France?
23 In which town did an earthquake claim nine lives in 1997?
24 In which country is the city of Bochum?
25 To which country do the islands of Stromboli and Vulcano belong?
26 What is the prominent religion of Lithuania?
27 Which is the northernmost and second largest of the Ionian islands?
28 What are Andorra's two main industries?
29 In which country is Sondica International airport?
30 Hardangervidda National Park is in which country?

Pot Luck 27 (See quiz 57, page 289)
1 St Columba. 2 United We Stand. 3 Warwickshire. 4 Dick Lester. 5 1950s.
6 The Rose Theatre. 7 Norman Wisdom. 8 Louis IX. 9 Henry Fonda.
10 Five. 11 John Cleese. 12 Insecticide. 13 Dali. 14 Foreign Legion.
15 St Aubrun. 16 Two-Faced Woman. 17 Water skiing. 18 Mass of gases.
19 New York. 20 A surveyor. 21 Maureen O'Hara. 22 Nigeria. 23 Living
In America. 24 Joanna Lumley. 25 Accented (Forzato). 26 Lima. 27 1972.
28 Glasgow. 29 A card game. 30 An imp.

Quiz 59   Pot Luck 28

1   What is No in Japan?
2   Who is the elder – David Mellor or Andrew Lloyd Webber?
3   What is a tulwar?
4   Who, with Paul McCartney, composed the Liverpool Oratorio?
5   What were Charles Dickens' two middle names?
6   Which group's only UK Top Ten hit was Word Up from 1986?
7   In which city is Fettes College?
8   Where was the cloth used to make duffle coats first made?
9   On May 21st, 1927, who landed at Le Bourget airport?
10   Where did Joseph of Arimathea's staff take root and bud, in legend?
11   Which song did Frank Sinatra feature in the film Robin And The Seven Hoods?
12   What is a skimmer to an American?
13   What name is given to the Greek letter that is the equivalent of letter O?
14   Which gulf is between the heel and sole of Italy?
15   Which famous leader brought an end to the Pharaohs in Egypt?
16   Which HG Wells' novel is the musical Half a Sixpence based on?
17   To ten years, when was the magazine The Economist founded?
18   What is the final event in a Decathlon?
19   How many unions merged in 1993 to form UNISON?
20   What was Mariah Carey's first UK Top Ten hit?
21   What was Charles De Gaulle's wife known as?
22   Who was the first wicket keeper to claim 50 stumping victims in Tests?
23   Which character was Dustin Hoffman in the film Midnight Cowboy?
24   On which island is Bungee jumping said to have originated?
25   What were the Christian names of the showman Barnum?
26   In mythology what was the special power of Perseus' helmet?
27   Whose one and only hit was Little Things Mean A Lot in 1954?
28   Which monarch introduced the sedan chair into England?
29   What physical property lets a needle float on water?
30   Whom did Dido, the Queen of Carthage, love?

Answers

The Royals (See quiz 60, page 292)
1 Anthropology. 2 Sir Robert Fellowes. 3 Marie Christine von Reibnitz. 4 Samuel Chatto. 5 Viscount Linley. 6 Marina Olgilvy. 7 Geelong Grammar. 8 Sports Science. 9 The Queen Mother. 10 Duke of Roxburghe. 11 Dame Kiri Te Kanawa. 12 Techno. 13 The Duke of Kent. 14 Diana. 15 Princess Margaret. 16 Eight. 17 Diana, Fergie. 18 Young England. 19 His wedding day. 20 Elizabeth Arden. 21 Les Jolies Eaux. 22 Barbara Daly. 23 The Rottweiler. 24 Sir George Pinker. 25 Ludgrove. 26 To ease traffic congestion. 27 Pulled the coach. 28 Martin Bashir. 29 Andrew and Alice. 30 Page boy to Fergie.

Quiz 60 The Royals

Answers - see Quiz 59, page 291

1   Along with Archaeology, which subject did Prince Edward read at Cambridge?
2   Who became the Queen's Private Secretary in 1990?
3   What was Princess Michael of Kent's maiden name?
4   Who was the third great grandson of the Queen Mother's?
5   Which Royal had a financial interest in a chain of hamburger restaurants called Deal?
6   Who was the first unmarried Royal to announce her pregnancy in 1989?
7   Which school was attended by Prince Charles and Kerry Packer?
8   What did Peter Phillips study at Exeter University?
9   Who was portrayed as a school dinner lady on Spitting Image?
10 At whose home did Prince Andrew propose to Sarah Ferguson?
11 Who sang a Handel aria at Charles and Diana's wedding?
12 In a 16th birthday interview what type of music did Prince William say he preferred?
13 Who has the car registration plate K7?
14 Who was the first Royal bride to include her own family's coat of arms on her marital coat of arms?
15 Who retained the number plate 3 GXM for a new Rolls in 1972?
16 How many Princesses of Wales were there before Diana?
17 Who turned up with Pamela Stephenson at Annabel's on Prince Andrew's stag night dressed as police officers?
18 At which kindergarten did Diana Spencer work?
19 When did Prince Philip become Duke of Edinburgh?
20 The Duchess of Windsor employed a make up artist daily from which cosmetics house?
21 What is Princess Margaret's house on Mustique called?
22 Who did Diana's make up on her wedding day?
23 What was Diana's nickname for Camilla?
24 Who delivered Prince William?
25 What was William and Harry's first boarding school?
26 Why did the Queen change the Birthday Parade from Thursday to Saturday?
27 What part did Lady Penelope and St David play at Charles and Diana's wedding?
28 To which reporter did Diana admit her marriage was "a bit crowded"?
29 What were Prince Philip's parents called?
30 What was Prince William's first public duty?

Answers

Pot Luck 28 (See quiz 59, page 291)
1 A type of theatre. 2 Lord Lloyd Webber. 3 A sword. 4 Carl Davis. 5 John Huffham. 6 Cameo. 7 Edinburgh. 8 Duffel in Belgium. 9 Charles Lindbergh. 10 Glastonbury. 11 My Kind Of Town. 12 A straw hat. 13 Omicron. 14 Gulf of Taranto. 15 Alexander the Great. 16 Kipps. 17 1843. 18 1500 metres. 19 Three. 20 Vision of Love. 21 Tante Yvonne. 22 Bert Oldfield (Australia). 23 Ratso Rizzo. 24 Pentecost Island. 25 Phileas Taylor. 26 Made him invisible. 27 Kitty Kallen. 28 James I. 29 Surface tension. 30 Aeneas.

Quiz 61 Pot Luck 29

LEVEL 3

1   The discovery of which plot led to the death of Mary, Queen of Scots?

2   What was Dina Carroll's first UK Top Ten hit?

3   Which Duke commanded the English troops at Culloden?

4   Which letter is one dot and one dash in Morse Code?

5   Which Minister was murdered in 1990 outside his home by an IRA bomb?

6   Which Battle was the first in the Hundred Years War?

7   What is served at a Thyestean feast?

8   Who wrote Goodbye to All That?

9   Who commanded the winning side at the Battle of Marathon?

10   Which eccentric artist is the central character in The Horse's Mouth?

11   Who is the elder – Desmond Lynam or Sir Paul McCartney?

12   In which year did Francis Drake complete the circumnavigation of the world?

13   How do you travel on the Devizes-Westminster race?

14   How old were both Anne Boleyn and Mrs Beeton when they died?

15   Who composed Easter Parade?

16   Which country gained independence in 1908 from Turkey?

17   What is the opening track on the Verve's Urban Hymns?

18   Which hymn was written by Augustus Toplady after sheltering from a storm?

19   In which decade was William Hague born?

20   Who wrote Dr Johnson's biography?

21   Who is the only English monarch to have won a flat race as a jockey?

22   Mary II died of which disease at the age of 32?

23   Whose only UK hit was Patches?

24   What is the correct name for the Ink blot test?

25   Which drill gets women and children into lifeboats first?

26   Which greyhound was the first to win the Greyhound Derby twice?

27   The Sea of Marmara lies between the Bosporus and what?

28   Who designed The Monument in London?

29   Which scale other than the Richter scale measures earthquakes?

30   Who first charted in the UK with Always On My Mind?

Answers

Oldies & Goldies (See quiz 62, page 294)
1 (How Much Is) That Doggie In The Window? **2** Amazing Grace. **3** Oh Pretty Woman. **4** Honky Tonk. **5** I'm Not In Love. **6** Rosemary Clooney. **7** If you're going. **8** So Gay. **9** Spirit In The Sky. **10** Little Jimmy Osmond. **11** I Can't Stop Loving You. **12** Terry Jacks. **13** Lily the Pink. **14** Adam Faith. **15** My Ding-A-Ling. **16** 1973. **17** Needles and Pins. **18** Tab Hunter. **19** Lee Hazelwood. **20** Johnny Remember Me. **21** Jerry Keller. **22** Roy Wood. **23** Moon River. **24** The Good The Bad and the Ugly. **25** Sunny Afternoon. **26** The Next Time/Bachelor Boy. **27** What A Wonderful World. **28** Land. **29** Ernie. **30** You're My World.

Quiz 62 Oldies & Goldies

LEVEL 3

Answers - see Quiz 61, page 293

1   What was the first UK No 1 in which the title posed a question?

2   Which traditional song provided instrumental and vocal versions that charted for 94 weeks?

3   What was Roy Orbison's final chart topper from 1964?

4   Which 'Women' was the longest ever at No 1 for the Rolling Stones?

5   Graham Gouldman and Eric Stewart wrote which 70s classic No 1?

6   Which 1950s vocalist began singing with the Tony Pastor band?

7   What are the first three words of San Francisco?

8   How were the birds singing in the original title of the No 1 Why Do Fools Fall In Love?

9   Which 1986 No 1 was a cover of a 1970 No 1?

10   Which artist took over the title of the youngest No 1 hitmaker in 1972?

11   What is Ray Charles only UK No 1?

12   Which Canadian was next to No 1 after Paul Anka?

13   Which hit gave producer Norrie Paramour his 27th and final No 1?

14   Emile Ford shared his first week at No 1 with which artist?

15   Which Chuck Berry hit was No 1 at the same time in the UK and US?

16   Steve Miller's The Joker hit No 1 in 1990 but when was it recorded?

17   Which hit gave The Searchers their second No 1?

18   Who had a No 1 with the original version of Young Love?

19   Who wrote and produced Nancy Sinatra's These Boots Are Made For Walking?

20   Which John Leyton hit was covered in 1985 by Bronski Beat and Marc Almond?

21   Whose only UK hit was Here Comes Summer?

22   Who wrote See My Baby Jive?

23   What film theme gave Danny Williams his only No 1 in 1961?

24   What was the first instrumental No 1 after the Shadows Foot Tapper?

25   What was the Kinks' third and final No 1 hit in the summer of 1966?

26   What was the only Cliff Richard & the Shadows No 1 double-A-side?

27   Which 1968 No 1 was revived in the film Good Morning Vietnam?

28   What was Wonderful in the Shadows hit which stayed longest at No 1?

29   Which 1971 No 1 was re-released in 1992 as a tribute to its singer?

30   What was Cilla Black's only US Top 40 hit?

Answers

Pot Luck 29 (See quiz 61, page 293)

1 Babington Plot. 2 It's Too Late. 3 Duke of Cumberland. 4 A. 5 Ian Gow.
6 Sluys. 7 Human flesh. 8 Robert Graves. 9 Miltiades. 10 Gully Jimson.
11 Sir Paul McCartney. 12 1580. 13 Canoe. 14 29 years. 15 Irving Berlin.
16 Bulgaria. 17 Bitter Sweet Symphony. 18 Rock of Ages. 19 1960s.
20 James Boswell. 21 Charles II. 22 Smallpox. 23 Clarence Carter.
24 Rorschasch Test. 25 Birkenhead Drill. 26 Mick the Miller. 27 The
Dardanelles. 28 Christopher Wren. 29 Mercalli Scale. 30 Brenda Lee.

Quiz 63 Pot Luck 30

Answers - see Quiz 64, page 296

LEVEL 3

1   Which language do the words kiosk, tulip and caviar come from?
2   Whose Drum can be seen at Buckland Abbey in Devon?
3   Where is the Queen's bank account?
4   What do the initials stand for in the name of ghost story writer M.R. James?
5   Which actor played Major Gowen in Fawlty Towers?
6   In which decade was Lloyd Grossman born?
7   Whose hymn book was first published in 1873?
8   A durmast is a variety of what?
9   Whose only UK Top Ten Hit was Blue Is The Colour from 1972?
10   Which Europeans discovered Lake Tanganyika in 1858?
11   Who said, "I never hated a man enough to give him his diamonds back"?
12   Achulophobia is the fear of what?
13   Which brass instrument is wrapped around the player's body?
14   What colour appears with white and green on the Afghanistan flag?
15   In which US state was there a nuclear accident at Three Mile Island in 1979?
16   Who was the first woman to swim the English Channel in 1926?
17   What is the capital of Angola?
18   Where were a set of rules for football drawn up in 1848?
19   What is indium?
20   Who is the elder – Paul Merton or Richard Madeley?
21   Who lived at No. 1, London?
22   Where are the Aventine, Viminal and Quirinal Hills?
23   What nationality was Sir Robert Helpmann?
24   What is a clerihew?
25   To 10 miles, how far was Piper Alpha off Wick when it exploded?
26   In which European country is the province of Brabant?
27   Where, in the Keats' poem, did Ruth stand "in tears"?
28   What was David Cassidy's first UK Top Ten hit?
29   Where did Kun's Red Terror exist in 1919?
30   Who, in 43 AD, led the resistance against the Romans?

Answers

Olympics (See quiz 64, page 296)
1 Alberto Juantorena. 2 Ice hockey. 3 Yachting. 4 St Moritz. 5 Bars and beam. 6 Michael Johnson. 7 Long jump. 8 Al Oerter. 9 Five. 10 Two. 11 Retained 10,000m and won 5,000m and marathon. 12 Evander Holyfield. 13 Lake Lanier. 14 Simone Jacobs. 15 Michelle Smith. 16 Izzy. 17 Seoul. 18 Allan Wells. 19 Spain. 20 Soling. 21 Poland's Renata Mauer. 22 Tim Henman & Chris Broad. 23 Jayne Torvill. 24 4 x 400m relay. 25 1900. 26 Quarantine laws. 27 Denise Lewis. 28 Montreal. 29 Robin Cousins. 30 Japan.

Quiz 64 Olympics

Answers - see Quiz 63, page 295

LEVEL 3

1 Who won 400m and 800m gold at the '76 Olympics?
2 At which sport did future tennis star Drobny win a medal in 1948?
3 Windsurfing is included in the Olympics as part of which sport's events?
4 Where were the Winter Olympics held in 1928 and 1948?
5 On which apparatus did Nadia Comaneci score perfect tens in 1976?
6 Who was the first man to win Olympic gold at 200m and 400m?
7 In which event did Carl Lewis win his ninth and final gold medal?
8 Who won the first of four discus golds in Melbourne in 1956?
9 How many silver medals did skier Raisa Smetanina win with her four golds and one bronze?
10 How many gold medals did Mark Spitz win in his first Olympics?
11 Which amazing treble did Emil Zatopek achieve at the 1952 Games?
12 Who carried the torch into the stadium at the Atlanta games?
13 On which lake did Steve Redgrave win his record breaking fourth gold medal?
14 Who was the only British woman sprinter to compete in all Olympics between 1984 and 1996?
15 Under what name did Mrs Erik de Bruin win gold at Atlanta?
16 What was the name of the Olympic mascot in Atlanta?
17 Where did Linford Christie run his first Olympic race?
18 Who was the oldest Olympic 100m champion when he won in 1980?
19 Who won women's gold in hockey in Barcelona?
20 Which is the only Olympic yachting event for three person crews?
21 Who won the first medal at the Atlanta games?
22 Who won Britain's first tennis medal since 1924 in Atlanta?
23 Who replaced her partner Michael Hutchinson before winning gold in 1984?
24 Other than 400m hurdles for which event did Sally Gunnell win a medal in Barcelona?
25 In which year did women first complete in the Olympics?
26 Why were equestrian event held in Sweden in 1956 when the Games were held in Australia?
27 Who was Britain's only female medallist at the Atlanta games?
28 Where did Daley Thompson compete in his first Olympics?
29 Which son of a former Millwall goalie won gold in the USA in 1980?
30 What was the first Asian country to have stage the Winter Olympics?

Pot Luck 30 (See quiz 63, page 295)
1 Turkish. 2 Francis Drake's. 3 Coutts. 4 Montague Rhodes. 5 Ballard Berkeley. 6 1950s. 7 Sankey and Moody's. 8 An oak tree. 9 Chelsea F.C. 10 Richard Burton and John Speke. 11 Zsa Zsa Gabor. 12 Darkness. 13 Sousaphone. 14 Black. 15 Pennsylvania. 16 Gertrude Ederle. 17 Luanda. 18 Cambridge University. 19 A metallic element. 20 Richard Madeley. 21 Duke of Wellington. 22 Rome. 23 Australian. 24 A poem. 25 120. 26 Belgium. 27 'Amid the alien corn'. 28 Could It Be Forever/Cherish. 29 Hungary. 30 Caractacus.

Answers

296

Quiz 65 Pot Luck 31

Answers - see Quiz 66, page 298

LEVEL 3

1 Who did the Spice Girls sack as their manager in early 1998?
2 What is a porbeagle?
3 Which bandleader married both Ava Gardner and Lana Turner?
4 What was the family name of artists Jacopo and his sons Gentile and Giovanni?
5 Scottish solicitor William Mitchell drew up the rules for which sport?
6 Which group had a 70s hit with Kiss You All Over?
7 Who was Prince Philip's mother?
8 What two colours go with black and yellow in printing's four-colour process?
9 What did Diana Princess of Wales describe as "a shameful friend"?
10 Who is the elder – Robin Cook or David Blunkett?
11 What was Bad Manners' first UK Top Ten hit?
12 What is a belvedere?
13 In which month is the feast day of St Cuthbert?
14 In which country are the mountains called the Stirling Range?
15 What is tufa?
16 Which soccer club has been managed by both Jimmy Armfield and Brian Clough?
17 Whose one and only hit was Float On in 1977?
18 Who was the first Prime Minister of Israel?
19 Where is New York's Metropolitan Museum of Art?
20 In what year did the London Stock Exchange go computerised?
21 What is a gibus?
22 Who was the first man to hold the post of Astronomer Royal?
23 In which decade was Lord Charles Spencer Churchill born?
24 Who founded the record label Anxious Records?
25 Which Michelangelo statue is in Florence?
26 Vera Caslavska was Olympic and World Champion in which sport?
27 In which year was Wimbledon first televised?
28 Where was the first woman MP to enter the Commons born?
29 Who ceased to be queen when Victoria became queen?
30 What do you do if you siffle?

Answers

Hobbies 2 (See quiz 66, page 298)
1 0 to 36. 2 Finland, playing football. 3 Chess. 4 Scarlet. 5 16lb. 6 Bilbao.
7 Steel links. 8 Tintin. 9 Alton Towers. 10 Giverny. 11 Clarice Cliff.
12 Military combat. 13 10. 14 Baker Street. 15 Caman. 16 Tony Hancock.
17 Curling. 18 Tramp. 19 Aikido. 20 Four (11 and 7 respectively).
21 Stamp collecting. 22 Hang gliding. 23 Harz Mountains (Germany).
24 Mogens Tholstrup. 25 Carry it. 26 Gothenburg, Sweden. 27 Nick Nairn.
28 Bungee jumping. 29 Kung fu. 30 Leiden.

1 What is the range of numbers on a roulette wheel?
2 Where would you watch FC Jazz and what would they be doing?
3 FIDE is the governing body of which game?
4 If you were watching the Queen's horse race, what colour sleeves would the jockey have?
5 In athletics how much does a hammer weigh?
6 Where is the Guggenheim Museum?
7 In abseiling what are karabiners?
8 Who first appeared in a strip cartoon 'in the Land of the Soviets'?
9 Which UK tourist attraction is on the site of an 8th century fortress?
10 Where in Normandy would you visit Monet's garden?
11 If you collected Bizarre pottery whose work would you have?
12 Paintball is a simulation of what?
13 How many zones does an archery target have?
14 In which London street was the first artificial ice rink opened?
15 In shinty what is the curved stick called?
16 Which radio star appeared in films such as The Wrong Box?
17 In which sport does a match last for a certain number of heads?
18 John Gold was the owner of which night club for over 30 years?
19 Which activity has two main types, tomiki and uyeshiba?
20 How many more people are there in an outer handball team than there are in an indoor one?
21 John Tomlinson is credited with starting which hobby?
22 Which form of flying was perfected by Francis Rogallo in the 70s?
23 In which mountains is the Brockenbahn steam railway?
24 Which restaurateur owned Daphne's and founded The Collection?
25 In cyclocross what do you do with your bike when you're not riding it?
26 Where is the Liseberg theme park?
27 Who opened the Braeval restaurant in Scotland in 1986?
28 In which activity do you 'dive for the horizon'?
29 Wing Chun is a popular form of which art?
30 In which Botanic Gardens was the tulip first introduced in 1594?

Answers

Pot Luck 31 (See quiz 65, page 297)
1 Simon Fuller. 2 A shark. 3 Artie Shaw. 4 Bellini. 5 Bowls. 6 Exile.
7 Princess Alice of Battenburg. 8 Cyan, magenta. 9 Bulimia. 10 Robin Cook.
11 Special Brew. 12 A viewing turret. 13 March. 14 Australia. 15 A kind of rock. 16 Leeds. 17 The Floaters. 18 David Ben-Gurion. 19 Central Park.
20 1986. 21 A top hat. 22 John Flamsteed. 23 1940s. 24 Dave Stewart.
25 David. 26 Gymnastics. 27 1937. 28 America. 29 Adelaide.
30 Whistle.

1 Bernard Webb was a pseudonym used by which famous song writer?
2 In which country is the royal family the House of Bernadotte?
3 Acrophobia is the fear of what?
4 In which country is the city of Abidjan?
5 What was the only No 1 UK hit for the Clash?
6 What colour is the circle on the Bangladesh flag?
7 A Brazilian Huntsman is a type of what?
8 Who played director Ed Wood in the 1994 film biography?
9 A Nutmegger is an inhabitant of which American state?
10 In which decade did South Africa resign from the Commonwealth?
11 How many locks are there on the Suez Canal?
12 What was the name of Vivienne Westwood's second shop opened in '82?
13 Who composed Rhapsody on a Theme of Paganini for Piano?
14 What was the number of the British Armoured Division nicknamed the 'Desert Rats'?
15 In which year did James Cook land at Botany Bay, Australia?
16 What is the correct form of address to begin a letter to a Baron?
17 In snooker in which year did the Lada Classic have two champions?
18 Who is the elder – Caroline Quentin or Linda Robson?
19 What was Neneh Cherry's first UK Top Ten hit?
20 What was the Christian name of aeroplane manufacturer Mr Boeing?
21 In which European country are the provinces of Sofiya and Burgas?
22 What size is A4 paper in millimetres?
23 Australia hosted the 1956 Olympics but equestrian events were held in which other country?
24 In which decade was Gary Glitter born?
25 Which artist painted The Watering Place in 1777?
26 What are the initials G.B.E an abbreviation of?
27 Who wrote the novel The Last Testament of Oscar Wilde in 1983?
28 Which magazine has been guest edited by Damien Hirst?
29 Clarence House was built for which monarch when he was still Duke of Clarence?
30 What is the capital of Bahrain?

Answers

TV Times 2 (See quiz 68, page 300)
1 Angus Deayton. 2 Po. 3 Andrew Lincoln. 4 Mark Porter and Emma Norman. 5 Tinky Winky. 6 Ascot. 7 Sara. 8 Lakesiders. 9 Duffy (Cathy Shipton). 10 Papa, Bob. 11 Hot Shoe Show. 12 Jane Asher. 13 My Kind of People. 14 Julia Carling. 15 Tantrums and Tiaras. 16 Francesca Annis. 17 Widows. 18 Helen Rollason. 19 James Naughtie. 20 Ian Hislop. 21 Carla Lane. 22 Twin Peaks. 23 Bedrock (The Flintstones). 24 Heineken. 25 Inventor Black. 26 Gomez Addams. 27 Paul McGann. 28 Fiona Phillips. 29 1313 Mockingbird Heights. 30 The Woodentop twins.

Quiz 68 TV Times 2

LEVEL 3

Answers - see Quiz 67, page 299

1. Who played Mike Channel in KYTV?
2. Who is the smallest Teletubby?
3. Who found fame as Egg in This Life?
4. Who first hosted The Radio Times Show on Sky?
5. Who is the largest Teletubby?
6. Where did the first outside broadcast on Grandstand come from?
7. Who is Postman Pat's wife?
8. In which docu soap did Emma Boundy find fame?
9. Which Casualty character played a midwife in Spice World?
10. Which two words has Nicole uttered to advertise Renault?
11. What was the name of Wayne Sleep's 80s TV show which he later adapted for the stage?
12. Which TV presenter made the cake when Jemima Goldsmith married Imran Khan?
13. What was Michael Barrymore's talent spotting TV show called?
14. Who replaced Anneka Rice on Carlton's Capital Woman?
15. What was the name of the David Furnish directed documentary about Elton John?
16. Who played the Englishwoman in Parnell and the Englishwoman?
17. In which series did Lynda La Plante introduce Dolly Rawlings?
18. Who was the first woman presenter of Grandstand?
19. Who. replaced Richard Baker as the presenter of the Proms?
20. Who presented Channel 4's religious series Canterbury Tales?
21. How is TV playwright Romana Barrack better known?
22. In which show was Harry S Truman the sheriff?
23. In which town would you read The Daily Slate?
24. The music from Raging Bull was used to advertise which lager?
25. Whose magic ray transformed Supergran?
26. Who had a pet octopus called Aristotle?
27. Who played the title role in Alan Bleasdale's The Monocled Mutineer?
28. Anthea Turner was replaced at GMTV by whom?
29. Where did the Musters live?
30. On a Friday, on children's TV who were Jenny & Willy?

Answers

Pot Luck 32 (See quiz 67, page 299)
1 Paul McCartney. 2 Sweden. 3 Heights. 4 Ivory Coast. 5 Should I Stay or Should I Go. 6 Red. 7 Spider. 8 Johnny Depp. 9 Connecticut. 10 1960s. 11 None. 12 Nostalgia of Mud. 13 Rachmaninov. 14 7th. 15 1770. 16 My Lord. 17 1980 (Spencer/ Davis). 18 Linda Robson. 19 Buffalo Stance. 20 William. 21 Bulgaria. 22 210mm x 297mm. 23 Sweden. 24 1940s. 25 Thomas Gainsborough. 26 Knight/Dame Grand Cross of the Order of the British Empire. 27 Peter Ackroyd. 28 The Big Issue. 29 William IV. 30 Manama.

Quiz 69 Pot Luck 33

Answers - see Quiz 70, page 302

LEVEL 3

1   In which decade was actor John Cleese born?
2   After which American General were sideburns named?
3   Freetown is the capital of which country?
4   Who played Test cricket aged 52 years 165 days?
5   Who directed the 1967 film The Dirty Dozen?
6   What is the main language of Angola?
7   What happened to the Olympic flame during the 1976 games?
8   Hartford is the capital of which American State?
9   Which 18th Century artist painted Peasant Girl Gathering Sticks ?
10 To five years, when was the News Of The World founded?
11 What, other than Amazing Grace, was a top ten hit for Judy Collins?
12 A fear of the cold is known as what?
13 In which county is the Rude Man of Cerne?
14 Which country has the dalasi as its currency?
15 What was done in an apodyterium?
16 Emperor Nero was the adopted son of which other emperor?
17 What is the international car index mark for a car from Libya?
18 The spice annatto is made from which part of a plant?
19 Other than Buckingham Palace, which venue sees the daily Changing of the Guard?
20 What is the administrative centre for the Scottish Western Isles?
21 What was the Commodores' first UK Top Ten hit?
22 Who is the elder – George Michael or Anthea Turner?
23 Painter Georges Seurat was born, died and worked in which city?
24 What name is given to elements with atomic numbers 93 to 112?
25 What two colours appear with yellow on the Cameroon flag?
26 Who was the first woman to qualify for the Indy 500 motor race?
27 Which Latin phrase means, 'Let the buyer beware'?
28 In which year did women gain the vote in Switzerland?
29 In which country is the city of Bamako?
30 As a child Jonathan Ross appeared in an ad for which food product?

Answers

90s Films (See quiz 70, page 302)
1 Wag the Dog. 2 Francis Bacon. 3 Arnold Schwarzenegger. 4 River Phoenix.
5 Spanish Civil War. 6 Jean-Claude Van Damme. 7 That Thing You Do!.
8 Pretty Woman. 9 Seal. 10 Ellen Barkin. 11 Frank Drebin. 12 Banker.
13 Julia Roberts. 14 Kevin Kline. 15 Blue Sky. 16 Kennedy & Nixon.
17 James Earl Jones. 18 Abba. 19 Kirsty Alley. 20 Nine Months. 21 Emma
Thompson. 22 Elizabeth Taylor. 23 Kevin McCallister. 24 Jim Carrey , who
played The Riddler. 25 Mars Attacks! 26 Jude. 27 Christopher Walken. 28
Gonzo. 29 Nil By Mouth. 30 2000 AD.

Quiz 70 90s Films

Answers - see Quiz 69, page 301

LEVEL 3

1 Which Barry Levinson film was used to satirise the US presidency during the Lewinsky crisis?
2 Who is the subject of Love is the Devil?
3 Which tough guy directed Christmas in Connecticut?
4 Who died during the filming of Dark Blood in 1993?
5 Which war is depicted in Land and Freedom?
6 Who was Lyon Gaultier in AWOL?
7 In which film did Tom Hanks make his directorial debut?
8 Which film's initial title was $3,000?
9 Who or what is Andre in the film of the same name?
10 Who was Leonardo DiCaprio's mother in This Boy's Life?
11 Who is Leslie Nielsen in the Naked Gun films?
12 What is Jim Carrey's job before he finds the mask in the hit movie?
13 Who was Tinkerbell when Spielberg met JM Barrie?
14 Who was the butler in Princess Caraboo?
15 What was director Tony Richardson's final film?
16 Which US presidents does Gump meet in Forrest Gump?
17 Who was the voice of Mufasa in The Lion King?
18 Muriel is a fan of which band in Muriel's Wedding?
19 Who did Woody Allen cast as his ex wife in Deconstructing Harry?
20 What was Hugh Grant's first Hollywood movie?
21 Who was Oscar winning best screen writer for Sense and Sensibility?
22 Who was John Goodman's mother in law in The Flintstones?
23 What is Macaulay Culkin's full name in the Home Alone movies?
24 Who designed The Riddler's costume in Batman Forever?
25 In which movie did Tom Jones sing It's Not Unusual?
26 In which film did Kate Winslet have her first nude scene?
27 Who played rat catcher Caesar in Mousehunt?
28 Who was the author in The Muppet Christmas Carol?
29 Which film was Gary Oldman's directorial debut?
30 In which comic did Sylvester Stallone's '95 futuristic police character appear?

Pot Luck 33 (See quiz 69, page 301)
1 1930s. 2 Ambrose Burnside. 3 Sierra Leone. 4 Wilfred Rhodes (England).
5 Robert Aldrich. 6 Portuguese. 7 Extinguished by a cloudburst.
8 Connecticut. 9 Thomas Gainsborough. 10 1843. 11 Send In The Clowns.
12 Cheimaphobia. 13 Dorset (figure carved in chalk hillside). 14 Gambia.
15 Clothes were removed before bathing. 16 Claudius. 17 LAR. 18 Seeds.
19 Royal Horse Guards, Whitehall. 20 Stornoway. 21 Easy. 22 Anthea
Turner. 23 Paris. 24 Trans-uranic elements. 25 Green and Red. 26 Janet
Guthrie. 27 Caveat emptor. 28 1971. 29 Mali. 30 Rice Krispies.

Quiz 71 Living World

Answers - see Quiz 72, page 304

LEVEL 3

1 What is another name for the North American nightjar?
2 Where is the world's greatest discharger of radioactive nuclear waste?
3 How is the disease trypanosomiasis also known?
4 What is meant by a haemorrhage which is 'occult'?
5 Which protein is present in a hair?
6 What does it mean if a cell is haploid?
7 In addition to tea and coffee where is caffeine found?
8 Where is the flexor carpi radialis?
9 What is an erythrocyte?
10 How is the sand hopper also known?
11 Guano is used as fertiliser but what is it made from?
12 Cranes are found on all continents except which two?
13 What is an alternative name for leptospirosis?
14 Carragheen is a type of what?
15 Where is a caterpillar's spinneret?
16 Which bird flies highest?
17 What is an insect's Malpighian tubes?
18 How does a mamba differ from a cobra?
19 Which part of the brain controls muscular movements, balance and co-ordination?
20 Which bird can swim as fast as a seal?
21 An urodele is another name for which reptile?
22 Which bird builds the largest nest?
23 The world's largest spider is named after which Biblical character?
24 What is a bird's furcula?
25 Disulfiram is used in the treatment of what?
26 What is a hairstreak?
27 On which island would you find the bee hummingbird?
28 Which bird produces the largest egg in relation to its body size?
29 Why should you avoid a chigger?
30 How many hearts does an earthworm have?

Pot Luck 34 (See quiz 72, page 304)
Answers
1 Louis Washkansky. 2 Denmark. 3 Bela Bartok. 4 Cliff Richard. 5 Albania.
6 George Bush. 7 Elephant. 8 Twiggy. 9 Turkey. 10 Mackerel. 11 1985.
12 Blackheath. 13 Sisserou parrot. 14 1940s. 15 One Day I'll Fly Away.
16 Bovine Spongiform Encephalopathy. 17 43,200. 18 Polish. 19 Sexual
health in the Third World. 20 Martin Amis. 21 Dot, dot, dot. 22 St Clare.
23 Spencer Perceval (British PM). 24 Trumpet. 25 Edo. 26 Excessive
growth. 27 New Zealand. 28 Indiana. 29 Kid Creole and the Coconuts.
30 Touch.

1   Who was the first person to receive a heart transplant?
2   In which European country are the counties of Viborg and Aarhus?
3   Who composed the music for the ballet The Wooden Prince?
4   Who played the lead role in the film Two A Penny?
5   Which country has the lek as its unit of currency?
6   Who was Vice President when Ronald Reagan was President?
7   Which animal head represents the Hindu god Ganesa?
8   Who is the elder – Julie Walters or Twiggy?
9   In which country is the city of Adana?
10   Which type of fish gives its name to a particular patterning of the sky?
11   In which year did Roy Plomley last present Desert Island Discs?
12   The first men's hockey club in England was founded in which London suburb?
13   Which bird stands in the centre of the national flag of Dominica?
14   In which decade was Michael Gambon born?
15   What was Randy Crawford's first UK Top Ten hit?
16   What are the initials BSE an abbreviation of?
17   How many seconds are there in half a day?
18   What was the nationality of the astronomer Nicolaus Copernicus?
19   Geri Halliwell became a UN ambassador specialising in what?
20   Who wrote the novels London Fields and Time's Arrow?
21   How is the letter S formed in Morse Code?
22   Who is the patron Saint of television?
23   Which public figure was shot dead by John Bellingham?
24   Bandleader Quincy Jones chiefly plays which instrument?
25   Changed in 1868 what was the former name of Tokyo?
26   What do you suffer from if you have acromegaly?
27   The yacht Black Magic won the America's Cup for which country?
28   A Hoosier is an inhabitant in which American state?
29   Who had hits with Stool Pigeon and I'm A Wonderful Thing, Baby?
30   Haphephobia is the fear of what?

Answers

Living World (See quiz 71, page 303)
1 Whippoorwill. 2 Sellafield. 3 Sleeping sickness. 4 Internal. 5 Keratin.
6 Single set of chromosomes. 7 Kola nuts. 8 Human's forearm. 9 Red blood
cell. 10 Beachflea. 11 Bird droppings. 12 South America & Antarctica.
13 Weil's disease. 14 Seaweed. 15 Head. 16 Ruppell's vulture.
17 Excretory organs. 18 Not hooded. 19 Cerebellum. 20 Penguin.
21 Salamander. 22 Male malle fowl. 23 Goliath. 24 Wishbone.
25 Alcoholism. 26 Butterfly. 27 Cuba. 28 Kiwi. 29 Harvest mite
(which bites). 30 Ten.

Quiz 73 Who Was Who?

Answers - see Quiz 74, page 306

LEVEL 3

1   Who was known as the 'father of the Soviet H-bomb'?
2   In which shipyards did Lech Walesa work before becoming Polish president?
3   Terry Waite was the envoy of which Archbishop of Canterbury when he was kidnapped?
4   Who founded the Police Memorial Trust after PC Yvonne Fletcher's death?
5   Who was the first US Ambassador in London?
6   Who recorded with the Hot Five and the Hot Seven in the 1920s?
7   Who became the youngest ever member of the GLC in 1969?
8   Who was the 20th Prince of Wales?
9   Who succeeded Len Murray as TUC general secretary in 1984?
10 Who was the first Archbishop of Canterbury to be appointed by the Church Crown Appointments Commission?
11 Which children's author was Russian correspondent for the Daily News during WWI and the Revolution?
12 Which advocate of black rights left the US to live in England in the late 50s?
13 Who was the last British monarch to refuse royal assent of a Bill through Parliament?
14 Who was UK Deputy PM between 1942 and 1945?
15 Which UK PM was responsible for the purchase of US Polaris missiles?
16 Who did Douglas Hurd replace as Foreign Secretary in 1989?
17 Who became President of the ANC in 1997?
18 Which Chancellor of the Exchequer introduced old age pensions?
19 Which Fine Gael candidate did Mary McAleese defeat in the 1997 election for Irish President?
20 Which invention improved on Alexander Cummings invention a century earlier?
21 What was Mikhail Gorbachev's wife called?
22 Who founded Standard Oil in 1870?
23 How was entrepreneur Roland Fuhrhop better known?
24 Which son of Findlaech was killed at Lumphanan?
25 Who was the first Archbishop of Canterbury?
26 Which former Enfield MP has the middle names Denzil Xavier?
27 The name of which UK PM was Ronald Reagan's middle name?
28 Who was shot at a rally in the US in 1972 while campaigning for the Democrats?
29 Which Baron began a continental pigeon post in 1849?
30 Who was German foreign minister during WWII?

Pot Luck 35 (See quiz 74, page 306)
1 Fruit pods. **2** Nebraska. **3** Weather With You. **4** His height. (World's tallest man). **5** Eight. **6** RB. **7** 1930s. **8** Vulcan. **9** Mold. **10** Arithmetic and logic unit. **11** Edgar Rice Burroughs. **12** Three. **13** Andrew Bonar Law. **14** Paul Cezanne. **15** 1642. **16** Warren Beatty. **17** Traffic Wardens. **18** Zambia. **19** When he gives up his seat. **20** If You Let Me Stay. **21** My Lord Duke. **22** 1989. **23** Indonesia. **24** David Hockney. **25** Henry VIII. **26** Michael Heseltine. **27** Peacock. **28** 148mm x 210 mm. **29** French. **30** Trumpet.

Answers

Quiz 74 Pot Luck 35

LEVEL 3

Answers - see Quiz 73, page 305

1 The spice cayenne is made from which part of a plant?
2 Lincoln is the capital of which US state?
3 What was the only UK Top Ten hit from 1992 for Crowded House?
4 What was special about Robert Pershing Wadlow?
5 How many singles had Take That released before their first No 1 Pray?
6 What is the international car index mark for a car from Botswana?
7 In which decade was Sir David Frost born?
8 Who was the Roman God of fire?
9 What is the administrative centre for the Welsh county of Clwyd?
10 Mathematically speaking, what is an ALU?
11 In the 1920s who wrote The Land That Time Forgot?
12 How many stripes are on the national flag of Estonia?
13 Who is the only British prime minister to have been born outside the UK?
14 Which artist painted Le Jardinier in 1906?
15 In which year was the Battle of Edgehill?
16 Who directed the 1990 film Dick Tracy?
17 A Chief Constable is responsible for which uniformed force other than the police?
18 Lusaka is the capital of which country?
19 When does an MP apply for the Chiltern Hundreds?
20 What was Terence Trent D'Arby's first UK Top Ten hit?
21 What is the correct form of address to begin a letter to a Duke?
22 In which year did Frank Bruno first fight with Mike Tyson?
23 In which country is the city of Banjarmasin?
24 Who painted The Rake's Progress and A Bigger Splash in the 1960s?
25 Saint John Fisher was martyred during the reign of which English king?
26 Who is the elder – Lester Piggott or Michael Heseltine?
27 What's the English name of the constellation Pavo?
28 What size is A5 paper in millimetres?
29 What is the main language of the Republic of Benin?
30 Miles Davis is associated with which musical instrument?

Answers

Who Was Who? (See quiz 73, page 305)
1 Andrei Sakharov. 2 Gdansk. 3 Robert Runcie. 4 Michael Winner.
5 John Adams. 6 Louis Armstrong. 7 Jeffrey Archer. 8 The future Edward VIII. 9 Norman Willis. 10 Robert Runcie. 11 Arthur Ransome. 12 Paul Robeson. 13 Queen Anne. 14 Attlee. 15 Macmillan. 16 John Major. 17 Thabo Mbeki. 18 Asquith. 19 Mary Bannotti. 20 Flushing toilet. 21 Raisa. 22 John D Rockefeller. 23 Tiny Rowland. 24 Macbeth. 25 St Augustine. 26 Michael Portillo. 27 Wilson. 28 George Wallace. 29 Paul Julius Reuter. 30 Joachim von Ribbentrop.

Quiz 75 Rockers

Answers - see Quiz 76, page 308

LEVEL 3

1   What was Eddie Cochrane's next UK single after Three Steps To Heaven?
2   Who played Jerry Lee Lewis in the 1989 biopic of his life?
3   How does Roger Peterson figure in rock history?
4   What was Billy Fury's first UK Top Ten hit from 1960?
5   In which city were R.E.M. formed?
6   As a teenager Morrissey ran a fan club for which group?
7   Who wrote the Holly classic It Doesn't Matter Anymore?
8   Which Elvis No 1 is the only one written solely by Lieber and Stoller?
9   Which hard-rock band did the Scottish Young brothers form in Australia?
10 Rock Around The Clock came out on which label?
11 Who did Keith Richard work for before coming a full-time Stone?
12 Which Slade hit was No 1 when US soldiers left Vietnam in 1973?
13 What did Rick Allen of Def Leppard lose in 1984?
14 What did an electrician fitting a burglar alarm find in Seattle in 1984?
15 Who first charted with Rip It Up?
16 James Jewel Osterberg took the stage under which name?
17 At which studio did the 'Million Dollar Quartet' get together in the 50s?
18 In which month did Jim Morrison die in 1971?
19 Where in London was the Sex Pistols first concert?
20 Which Dickie Valentine hit replaced Rock Around The Clock at No 1?
21 Which place used to form part of The Stranglers name?
22 Who was Francis Rossi's school mate and long time bass player in Status Quo?
23 How were the Rolling Stones billed for their first live concert?
24 Which Jerry Lee Lewis hit is the only version of the Ray Charles' classic to reach the British charts?
25 Who ran the Clovis, New Mexico studio where Buddy Holly recorded?
26 Who was Phil Lynott's father in law?
27 Who recorded the album Ma Kelly's Greasy Spoon?
28 Which Led Zeppelin drummer died in 1980?
29 Who ran the Chelsea clothes shop called Let It Rock?
30 Which 1955 Glenn Ford movie featured Rock Around The Clock?

Pot Luck 36 (See quiz 76, page 308)
1 Wales. **2** Jeffrey Archer. **3** Court of Chief Pleas. **4** Blue. **5** Divine Brown.
6 Belmopan. **7** Cygnus. **8** Eloise. **9** 8000. **10** A fish. **11** Knight/Dame
Grand Cross of the Royal Victorian Order. **12** Cat. **13** US Civil War.
14 Kazakhstan. **15** Australia. **16** 1960s. **17** Nepal. **18** Madame Tussaud's
(In 1997). **19** Fog. **20** Patricia Hodge. **21** A small pail. **22** 1969. **23** Chris
Evans. **24** Charlie Daniels Band. **25** Chilterns. **26** Benjamin Britten.
27 Evelyn Waugh. **28** Billy Ocean. **29** Philadelphia. **30** With fun.

Quiz 76 Pot Luck 36

Answers - see Quiz 75, page 307

LEVEL 3

1　Which part of the UK does not receive Channel 4?
2　In the 1980s, who wrote the novel A Twist in the Tale ?
3　What is the Parliament of Sark called?
4　What colour appears with white and red on the Faroe Islands flag?
5　In 1995 Hugh Grant got into trouble for performing a lewd act with whom?
6　What is the capital of Belize?
7　The North American Nebula is a region in which constellation?
8　What was The Damned's one and only UK Top Ten hit?
9　To the nearest thousand, how many different species of ant are there?
10　What is a golomyanka?
11　What are the initials GCVO an abbreviation of?
12　Bombay, Chartreux and Japanese bobtail are all types of what?
13　Which war is Stephen Crane's novel The Red Badge of Courage set in?
14　In which country is the city of Alma-Ata?
15　The writer Thomas Keneally comes from which country?
16　In which decade was actor Colin Firth born?
17　Prithwi Narayan Shah was the first King of which kingdom?
18　Where were William Hague, Jesse Owens and Pele brought together?
19　Homichlophobia is the fear of what?
20　Who is the elder – Patricia Hodge or Judy Finnigan?
21　Who or what was a piggin?
22　In which year was the Women's International Bowling Board formed?
23　Which media presenter left his wife Carol McGiffin in 1993?
24　Which band had a 70s UK hit with The Devil Went Down to Georgia?
25　Among which hills does Chequers lie?
26　Who composed the opera Noye's Fludde?
27　Who wrote Decline and Fall?
28　Under which name did Leslie Charles sail to pop success?
29　Which city has the oldest stock exchange in the USA?
30　What does the musical term 'giocoso' mean?

Rockers (See quiz 75, page 307)
1　Sweetie Pie. 2　Dennis Quaid. 3　Pilot in the crash that killed Holly.
4　Colette. 5　Greece. 6　The New York Dolls. 7　Paul Anka. 8　Jailhouse Rock.
9　AC/DC. 10　Decca. 11　The Post Office. 12　Cum On Feel The Noize.
13　An arm (in a car crash). 14　Kurt Cobain's body. 15　Little Richard.
16　Iggy Pop. 17　Sun Studio, Memphis. 18　July. 19　St Martin's School Of
Art. 20　Christmas Alphabet. 21　Guildford. 22　Alan Lancaster. 23　Rollin'
Stones. 24　What'd I Say. 25　Norman Petty. 26　Leslie Crowther. 27　Status
Quo. 28　John Bonham. 29　Malcolm McLaren. 30　Blackboard Jungle.

Quiz 77 Hobbies 3

Answers - see Quiz 78, page 310

LEVEL 3

1 CIPS regulates which sport?

2 Where were Haagen-Daz ice creams first sold?

3 Where is Rick Stein's famous seafood restaurant?

4 What is octopush?

5 Where is the world's largest nightclub, Gilley's Club?

6 Who jointly opened La Gavroche in 1967?

7 Which venue was designed by George London and Henry Wise?

8 What colour might your balls be in croquet?

9 What is the nearest town to the Lightwater Valley Theme Park?

10 Which game was originally called Lexico?

11 The Toucan Terribles are prolific champions at what?

12 What is the name of England's smallest pub in Bury St Edmunds?

13 Which UK town has the longest shopping mall?

14 Where was the Grand National run during WWI?

15 Who founded the London restaurants Quaglino's and Mezzo?

16 In judo which Dan grades are awarded a red belt?

17 How many points is the gold circle on an archery target worth?

18 In 1848 William Mitchell drew up the rules to which modern game?

19 In shinty what is the opponent's goal called?

20 Which musical instrument was the creation of Charles Wheatstone?

21 Which soccer club has a fanzine called Fly Me to the Moon?

22 Who opened his first restaurant Harveys in 1987?

23 In paddle tennis what is the ball made from?

24 Which game was derived from baggataway?

25 What is important dress code at France's Domaine de Lambetran?

26 What is a gricer?

27 Where is the UK's largest amusement park?

28 What name is given to the circular target in curling?

29 What is Denmark's Rutschebahnen?

30 What do you wear on your feet in street hockey?

Pot Luck 37 (See quiz 78, page 310)
1 Francis Ford Coppola. **2** Earl Of Liverpool. **3** The Valley of the Queens.
4 Alexander. **5** John Constable. **6** New Orleans. **7** Fruits. **8** 1969. **9** The
Ivy League (US colleges). **10** RC. **11** Doctor. **12** Yasmin Le Bon. **13** String.
14 Walter F Mondale. **15** Sir William Walton. **16** Lord Lovat (1747). **17** 1970s.
18 Sugarbush. **19** The Hob. **20** Ecuador. **21** The Milan - San Remo
(Primavera). **22** Fred Titmus. **23** Solomon Islands. **24** Gordonstoun. **25** A
black star. **26** Four. **27** Milk and Alcohol. **28** Buenos Aires. **29** Gordon
setter. **30** Madagascar.

Quiz 78 Pot Luck 37

Answers - see Quiz 77, page 309

LEVEL 3

1   Who directed the 1992 film Bram Stoker's Dracula?
2   Robert Banks Jenkinson was British PM under which title?
3   Which cemetery is to the south of the Valley of the Kings?
4   What is Nick Faldo's middle name?
5   Which artist painted The White Horse in 1819?
6   The Lake Pontchartrain Causeway links Mandeville, Louisiana with where?
7   The spice coriander is made from which part of a plant?
8   When was The Sun newspaper founded?
9   Brown, Cornell and Dartmouth are all members of what?
10 What is the international car index mark for a car from Taiwan?
11 Neil Diamond started to train – but didn't qualify – as what?
12 Who is the elder – Liz Hurley or Yasmin Le Bon?
13 What type of musical instrument is the Japanese koto?
14 Who was Vice President when Jimmy Carter was President of USA?
15 Which British composer died on the island of Ischia in 1983?
16 Who was the last person to be executed by beheading in the UK?
17 In which decade did Agatha Christie die?
18 What was Doris Day's first UK Top Ten hit?
19 In quoits, what name is given to the target at which the rings are thrown?
20 Which country had a guerrilla group whose name translated as 'Alfaro lives, dammit'?
21 In cycling what is the first major classic of the season?
22 Which England cricketer lost four toes in a swimming accident while touring the West Indies?
23 In which island group is Guadalcanal?
24 Prince Charles, Prince Edward and Prince Philip were all head boys at which school?
25 What appears in the centre of the national flag of Ghana?
26 How many symphonies did Brahms compose?
27 What was the title of Dr. Feelgood's only Top Ten hit?
28 Which South American city has a name meaning 'fair winds'?
29 Alexander Gordon 1743-1827 gave his name to what?
30 In which country is the city of Antananarivo?

Answers

Hobbies 3 (See quiz 77, page 309)
1   Angling. 2   New York. 3   Padstow, Cornwall. 4   Underwater hockey.
5   Houston, Texas. 6   The Roux Brothers. 7   Hampton Court maze. 8   Blue,
red, yellow or black. 9   Ripon. 10   Scrabble. 11   Marbles. 12   The Nutshell.
13   Milton Keynes. 14   Gatwick. 15   Terence Conran. 16   9th to 11th.
17   10. 18   Bowls. 19   Hail. 20   Harmonica. 21   Middlesborough.
22   Marco Pierre White. 23   Sponge. 24   Lacrosse. 25   None (it's a naturist
site). 26   Trainspotter. 27   Blackpool. 28   House. 29   Roller coaster.
30   Roller skates.

Answers - see Quiz 80, page 312

LEVEL 3

1 What is the real name of Renault's Nicole?
2 Mrs Peter Hook is best known on TV as whom?
3 Who co presented The Big Breakfast with Zoe Ball?
4 Who played Kadi Toura in the drama series Roots?
5 Who was the antiques dealer in the Paddington stories?
6 Who used to say, "The next Tonight will be tomorrow night"?
7 Which was the English port in the Triangle drama series?
8 Mrs Robert Powell was a member of which famous dance group?
9 Who was the first Teletubby to have its alter ego sacked?
10 Who composed the Barcarolle which advertised Bailey's Irish Cream?
11 In which series did Charles Dance play Guy Perron?
12 Who does the daughter of Band of Gold's creator play in Coronation Street?
13 Who directed a documentary called Genderquake after leaving a top soap?
14 Who followed Phillip Schofield as link man on Children's BBC?
15 Whose final TV role was as Daniel Reece?
16 In May to December what was Zoe's name before she married Alec?
17 Who composed the music for ITV's coverage of Grand Prix racing?
18 Who are the parents of Live & Kicking's first female presenter?
19 What is the profession of Postman Pat's Mrs Goggins?
20 Which series took place in Lochdubh?
21 Who was Bamm Bamm's dad?
22 What was Alan B'Stard's constituency?
23 Which magazine did Amanda work for in Girls On Top?
24 Who were Father Ted's colleagues?
25 Which disgraced ex MP is the uncle of Jack Davenport from This Life?
26 What did Angela Rippon dance to on The Morecambe and Wise Show?
27 George Baker aka Inspector Wexford appeared as which special agent in Up Pompeii?
28 What were the goldfish on Playschool called?
29 Who played Liz Shaw in Bodyguards?
30 What did Peter do in The Peter Principle?

Answers

Pot Luck 38 (See quiz 80, page 312)
1 Shetlands. 2 Bob Monkhouse. 3 Plum. 4 Colombia. 5 Lawrence Durrell. 6 Brazil. 7 My Lord Mayor. 8 Three Coins In The Fountain. 9 Crowds. 10 Dog. 11 Bromley. 12 Piracy. 13 Benjamin Britten. 14 Gin and beer. 15 1880s. 16 Archbishop of Canterbury. 17 Argentina. 18 Witch (Tam O'Shanter). 19 Chess. 20 Aestivation. 21 Carl Douglas. 22 International Phonetic Alphabet. 23 Waterloo & City Line. 24 Germany. 25 Melvyn Bragg. 26 Francis Coppola. 27 Peas. 28 Ireland. 29 Volto subito. 30 Blue and White.

Quiz 80 Pot Luck 38

Answers - see Quiz 79, page 311

1 Where is Baltasound Airport?

2 Who is the elder – Bob Monkhouse or Princess Margaret?

3 Grand Duke, Stanley and Lombard are all varieties of which fruit?

4 In which country is the city of Cali?

5 Who wrote The Alexandria Quartet novels?

6 Against which country did David Platt make his first full England appearance?

7 What is the correct form of address to begin a letter to a Lady Lord Mayor?

8 What was Frank Sinatra's first UK No 1?

9 Demophobia is the fear of what?

10 Which creature is represented in the year the Chinese call gou?

11 What is the most southerly London borough?

12 Anne Bonney and Mary Read famously carried out which trade?

13 Who composed the opera Death In Venice?

14 What have you had if you've just had a dog's nose?

15 During which decade did the Orient Express first run?

16 The Court of Arches is the chief court of whom?

17 Which country has the austral as a unit of currency?

18 Who was the ship Cutty Sark named after?

19 Emanuel Lasker was undisputed world champion for over 26 years at what?

20 What is the summer equivalent of hibernation?

21 Whose one and only UK Top Ten hit was Kung Fu Fighting?

22 What are the initials IPA an abbreviation of, as well as being an ale?

23 Which part of the London Underground is called the Drain?

24 The landau carriage takes its name from a town in which country?

25 Who wrote the novel A Time to Dance?

26 Talia Shire is the sister of which film director?

27 What have you got with a plateful of Pisum satvium?

28 Which country left the Commonwealth in 1949?

29 In music what does the abbreviation VS stand for?

30 Which two colours appear on the national flag of Honduras?

Answers

TV Times 3 (See quiz 79, page 313)
1 Estelle Skornik. 2 Mrs Merton. 3 Mark Little. 4 O.J. Simpson. 5 Mr Gruber. 6 Cliff Michelmore. 7 Felixstowe. 8 Pan's People. 9 Tinky Winky. 10 Offenbach. 11 Jewel in the Crown. 12 Judy Mallett. 13 Susan Tully. 14 Andy Crane. 15 Rock Hudson in Dynasty. 16 Angell. 17 Jay Kay of Jamiroquai. 18 Bryan Forbes & Nanette Newman. 19 Postmistress. 20 Hamish Macbeth. 21 Barney Rubble. 22 Haltemprice. 23 Spare Cheeks. 24 Douglas & Jack. 25 Jonathan Aitken. 26 Let's Face the Music and Dance. 27 Jamesus Bondus. 28 Bit & Bot. 29 Louise Lombard. 30 Bank Manager.

Quiz 81 Rugby

Answers - see Quiz 82, page 314

LEVEL 3

1   Who has been an Irish international and the head of HJ Heinz?
2   In which decade of which century did the first league varsity match take place?
3   In which city were Barbarians RFC founded?
4   Which was the first league side to score 1,000 points in a season?
5   Who was Wales' youngest ever captain?
6   Rob Andrew is qualified in what profession?
7   Where did Brian Moore begin his career?
8   How old was Will Carling when he played for Terra Nova Under 11s?
9   Against which side did Jeremy Guscott make his international debut?
10 Which league side was the first to win all its league games in a season?
11 Which of Wigan's 1994-5 trophies is no longer played for?
12 In 1986 St Helens beat Carlisle 112-0 in which competition?
13 Who was the first union player to kick eight penalties in an international?
14 What was Jason Leonard's first club?
15 Who were the beaten finalists in the first league Knockout Trophy?
16 Who captained Ireland in their centenary season?
17 Who did the All Blacks beat 106-4 in 1987?
18 Where was the first floodlit rugby union match played?
19 What name was given to the breakaway clubs from the Rugby Union in 1895?
20 Which club won the first Middlesex Sevens at Twickenham?
21 What position did J.J. Williams play for Llanelli?
22 Who in 1998 held the world record for the most capped hooker?
23 Who recorded the then highest score draw 46-46 in 1994?
24 Who sponsored the rugby league before Courage?
25 In which country was the first rugby league World Cup held?
26 Who was the first UK rugby league club side to play in Australia?
27 Who played a record 17 appearances on five tours with the British Lions?
28 What was the score when Salford beat Wigan's unbeaten 43 game run?
29 Who made the lowest score (0-0) in the BBC's Floodlit Rugby League competition?
30 Who were the first Scottish rugby union club champions?

Answers

Pot Luck 39 (See quiz 82, page 314)
1 Hungary. **2** Oneirophobia. **3** Kiss Me. **4** 100 miles (161 km). **5** Armoured Fighting Vehicle. **6** The Chicken Song. **7** I. **8** 1960s. **9** Swaziland. **10** Marquis of Granby. **11** Green. **12** God willing. **13** Matthew Broderick. **14** North Carolina. **15** 250mm x 353mm. **16** Salvador Dali. **17** Hyde Park. **18** Llandrindod Wells. **19** Liam Neeson. **20** Under the Coronation Chair. **21** RCH. **22** 1897. **23** Joe Dante. **24** China. **25** Orcus. **26** Winston Churchill's. **27** Seeds. **28** Love's Gotta Hold On Me. **29** A dolphin. **30** Joe DiMaggio.

Quiz 82 Pot Luck 39

Answers - see Quiz 81, page 313

1 Which country has the forint. as its unit of currency?
2 A fear of dreams is known as what?
3 What was Stephen 'Tin Tin' Duffy's only Top Ten hit?
4 How long is the Suez Canal?
5 In the military, what is an AFV?
6 Which UK No 1 was written by Red Dwarf creators Robert Grant and Doug Naylor?
7 Which letter is two dot in Morse Code?
8 In which decade was Rory Bremner born?
9 Mbabane is the capital of which country?
10 What popular pub name comes from the title held by soldier John Manners?
11 What colour are the stars on the national flag of the Republic of Iraq?
12 What does the Latin deo volente mean?
13 Which actor is married to actress Sarah Jessica Parker?
14 Raleigh is the capital of which US state?
15 What size is B4 paper in millimetres?
16 Which artist painted Christ of St John of the Cross in 1951?
17 Where was the Prince's Trust charity Party In The Park held in 1998?
18 What is the administrative centre for the Welsh county of Powys?
19 Who is the elder – Jimmy Nail or Liam Neeson?
20 Where in Westminster Abbey was the Stone of Scone?
21 What is the international car index mark for a car from Chile?
22 To five years when was the magazine Country Life founded?
23 Who directed the 1990 film Gremlins 2: The New Batch?
24 In which country is the city of Dalian?
25 Who was the Roman God of death?
26 Whose top hat sold for £22,000 at Sotheby's in 1988?
27 The spice fenugreek is made from which part of a plant?
28 What was Dollar's first UK Top Ten hit in 1979?
29 In the film Ace Ventura: Pet Detective Ace is hired to find what?
30 Who was known as 'Joltin Joe' and 'the Yankee Clipper'?

Rugby (See quiz 81, page 314)
1 Tony O'Reilly. 2 1981. 3 Bradford. 4 St Helens. 5 Gareth Edwards.
6 Chartered surveyor. 7 Nottingham. 8 Six. 9 Romania. 10 Hull.
11 Regal Cup. 12 Lancashire Cup. 13 Canada's Mark Wyatt. 14 Barking.
15 Wakefield Trinity. 16 Willie John McBride. 17 Japan. 18 Rodney Parade, Newport. 19 Northern Union. 20 Harlequins. 21 Right wing. 22 New Zealand's Sean Fitzpatrick. 23 Sheffield Eagles & Leeds. 24 Slalom lager.
25 France. 26 St Helens. 27 Willie John McBride. 28 26-16. 29 Salford & Warrington. 30 Hawick.

Quiz 83 World Tour

Answers - see Quiz 84, page 316

LEVEL 3

1　What is the currency of Bolivia?
2　Between which two rivers does Manhattan lie?
3　To the nearest million, what was the population of Seoul in 1995?
4　In which country is the city of Curitiba?
5　What is the capital of Brunei?
6　In which country is the deep-water port of Lobito?
7　The islands of Taipa and Coloane are part of which possession?
8　Pluna Airlines are based in which country?
9　Which capital is further north – Khartoum or Addis Ababa?
10　What is the official language of Bhutan?
11　In which country is Kakadu National Park?
12　Which country is due north of Uruguay?
13　Which two countries border Morocco?
14　Which desert lies between the Kalahari and the Atlantic Ocean?
15　Where is the news agency Colprensa based?
16　What is Madison Square Garden situated over?
17　On which island is Nassau, the capital of the Bahamas?
18　In which US state was the first National Park?
19　How is Denali in Alaska also known?
20　The Negev desert tapers to which port?
21　Who designed New Delhi?
22　What is the third longest river in Africa?
23　Which country has the largest oil resources in Africa?
24　To the nearest million, what was the population of the largest US city in 1994?
25　In which country is the city of Medan?
26　What is the capital of Burundi?
27　What is South Africa's judicial capital?
28　What is the most north-eastern US state?
29　SAHSA Airlines are based in which country?
30　Which island is situated between Sumatra and Bali?

Blockbusters (See quiz 84, page 316)
Answers

1　It Happened One Night. **2**　Elwood P Dowd. **3**　Lewis Gilbert. **4**　Miracle on 34th Street. **5**　Philadelphia Story. **6**　A Night at the Opera. **7**　Walter Pidgeon. **8**　Dodi Fayed. **9**　Robert Newton. **10**　Dances With Wolves. **11**　James Cameron. **12**　Busby Berkeley. **13**　Waterworld. **14**　Gary Oldman. **15**　Blenheim. **16**　Amon Goeth. **17**　Bruce Springsteen & Neil Young. **18**　Ben Hur. **19**　Gandhi. **20**　Ellen Burstyn. **21**　King Kong, 1933. **22**　Bolivia. **23**　Endora in Bewitched. **24**　The Shadows. **25**　Costume. **26**　Liv Ullmann. **27**　Cary Grant. **28**　Mammy (Gone With the Wind). **29**　The Full Monty. **30**　How to paint.

Quiz 84 Blockbusters

LEVEL 3

Answers - see Quiz 83, page 315

1 Which 30s classic was originally called Night Bus?
2 Who does James Stewart play in Harvey?
3 Who did Carol Reed replace at the last minute on Oliver!?
4 In which 40s classic did Edward Gwenn play Kris Kringle?
5 Katharine Hepburn bought the rights to a Philip Barry play to make which movie?
6 What was the Marx Brother's first film for MGM?
7 Who played Mr Miniver in the Greer Garson Oscar winner?
8 Which film producer who died in 1997 co produced Chariots of Fire?
9 Who played Bill Sikes when Alec Guinness was Fagin?
10 What was the first Western to win a Best Picture Oscar after a 60 year gap?
11 Who directed the first Terminator films?
12 Who choreographed 42nd Street?
13 Titanic overtook which movie as the most costly ever made?
14 Which actor kidnapped Harrison Ford in Air Force One?
15 Which palace was used for Kenneth Branagh's Hamlet?
16 What is the name of Ralph Fiennes' character in Schindler's List?
17 Whose songs were on the soundtrack of Philadelphia?
18 Which 50s film cost $4 million, twice the maximum of the time?
19 Which film begins with "No man's life can be encompassed in one telling"?
20 Which star of The Exorcist also used the name Edna Rae?
21 Which film has the quote, "It wasn't the airplanes. It was beauty killed the beast"?
22 Where were Butch Cassidy and Sundance finally tracked down?
23 What is the most famous TV role of actress Agnes Moorehead?
24 The composer of the only Oscar nominated song from Grease was from which famous quartet?
25 John Mollo won an Oscar in Star Wars for what?
26 Who was the only woman to have top billing in A Bridge Too Far?
27 Who was originally sought for the role of Shears in The Bridge on the River Kwai?
28 Hattie McDaniel was the first black actress to win an Oscar, but for which role?
29 Which movie did Titanic overtake as a record UK earner?
30 The ex GI is in Paris to learn what in An American in Paris?

Quiz 85 Pot Luck 40

Answers - see Quiz 86, page 318

LEVEL 3

1 Both Emma Bunton's dad and Robert Redford's dad worked as what?
2 London's Royal College of Music is in which regal sounding road?
3 Which actress starred in Thelma and Louise and Lorenzo's Oil?
4 In which European country are the regions of Kitaa and Tunu?
5 In which decade was Lord Archer born?
6 What name is given to the Greek letter that is the equivalent of letter M?
7 What is the Scottish equivalent of the Countryside Commission in England?
8 Who joined the European Union in 1995 with Finland and Sweden?
9 Which sea would you cross if you sailed from Corfu to Cephalonia?
10 Who is the elder – Paula Yates or the Duke of York?
11 What are the initials KCVO an abbreviation of?
12 What was Celine Dion's first solo UK Top Ten hit?
13 Which US state is called the Bullion State?
14 What name did former Mayfair hairdresser Nigel Davies adopt in the 1960s ?
15 What colours appear with black and red on the Jordanian flag?
16 In which year did Dennis the Menace first appear in the Beano?
17 Which British army officer invented shells containing bullets to inflict more casualties?
18 Who was the longest serving British PM?
19 What is a cutty sark according to Robert Burns?
20 What is the capital of Djibouti?
21 Which English seaside resort is associated with Count Dracula?
22 What was Donny Osmond's last UK No 1?
23 Who wrote Chicken Soup With Barley?
24 Doraphobia is the fear of what?
25 What was the pirate Blackbeard's real name?
26 What is the name Blimp derived from in the character Colonel Blimp?
27 Which fund pays the Queen's private expenses as sovereign?
28 What is tattooed on Robert Mitchum's knuckles in the film The Night of the Hunter?
29 Where was Captain James Cook killed in 1779?
30 Who composed the opera Billy Budd?

1   How is the maidenhair tree also known?
2   Which acid makes rhubarb leaves poisonous?
3   What is a tissue which forms on a damaged plant surface called?
4   The Sequoia takes its name from what?
5   What makes the death cap mushroom so toxic?
6   Which European country produces more than half of Europe's rice?
7   Where would you find the home of the bristlecone pine?
8   The Venus flytrap is found naturally in which US states?
9   A meadow clary has flowers of what colour?
10 What sort of plants are cryptogams?
11 The world's tallest tree is native only to where?
12 If a leaf is sessile what is missing?
13 What is another name for the Saintpaulia?
14 How does a bladderwort receive its nourishment?
15 If a plant suffers from chlorosis what happens to it?
16 How is the entada known in Australia?
17 What is the only plant which can change its shape?
18 What does a mycologist study?
19 What type of plant is a saguaro?
20 To which family does the greater celandine belong?
21 The largest known giant redwood is named after whom?
22 How is the plant lactuca sativa better known?
23 If something is coprophilous where does it grow?
24 The tree sometimes known as Wellingtonia is native to which mountains?
25 Atropine is derived from which plant?
26 Which part of the flax plant is used to make linen?
27 If a plant is halophytic where does it grow?
28 Which tree is the tallest native to Europe?
29 On which two islands would you find the sea coconut?
30 Which plant has the largest leaves?

Answers

Pot Luck 40 (See quiz 85, page 317)
1 Milkmen. 2 Prince Consort Road. 3 Susan Sarandon. 4 Greenland.
5 1940s. 6 Mu. 7 Scottish Natural Heritage. 8 Austria. 9 Ionian. 10 Duke
of York. 11 Knight Commander of the Royal Victorian Order. 12 The Power of
Love. 13 Missouri. 14 Justin de Villeneuve. 15 White and green. 16 1951.
17 Shrapnel (Sir Henry). 18 Earl of Liverpool. 19 Short shirt. 20 Djibouti.
21 Whitby. 22 Young Love. 23 Arnold Wesker. 24 Fur. 25 Edward Teach.
26 The word for an airship in WWI. 27 Privy Purse. 28 Love and Hate. 29
Hawaii. 30 Benjamin Britten.

1   A sentence containing all the alphabet's letters is known as a what?
2   What is the international car index mark for a car from Singapore?
3   Who is the elder – Terry Wogan or Bill Wyman?
4   What are Tony Blair's middle names?
5   In which decade did Fiji leave the Commonwealth?
6   Who wrote the novel The Pathfinder?
7   Columbus is the capital of which US state?
8   Who directed the 1991 film The Silence of the Lambs?
9   What was Duran Duran's first UK Top Ten hit?
10 Which post was held by William Gilbert at the courts of Elizabeth I and James I?
11 Which poet was awarded an Order of Merit in 1953, three years before his death?
12 A fear of dust is known as what?
13 Which river was explored by Scotsman Mungo Park?
14 Bill Robertie became the first person to win which World Championship twice?
15 Mogadishu is the capital of which country?
16 Where did the married Princess Elizabeth live before she came to the throne?
17 In music what does the expression 'pesante' mean?
18 Who was the Greek goddess of victory?
19 On the first of which month is Canada Day celebrated?
20 What is the title of the head of the College of Arms?
21 Which mathematician wrote the book The Elements?
22 Which TV character drove a yellow car called Bessie?
23 In which country is the city of Douala?
24 Whose only UK Top Ten hit was Jeans On?
25 For which film did Geena Davis first win an Oscar?
26 In 1860 Willie Park became the first winner of which sporting trophy?
27 What is the correct form of address to begin a letter to a Rabbi?
28 What colour separates the black, red and green bands on the Kenyan flag?
29 What part of your body is initialised as the ANS?
30 Which artist painted Dancer at the Bar around 1900?

Music Superstars (See quiz 88, page 320)
1 Jumping Jack Flash. 2 David Cassidy. 3 Neil Diamond. 4 Girls! Girls! Girls!
5 Sorry Seems To Be the Hardest Word. 6 When I Need You. 7 1960s.
8 Bohemian Rhapsody. 9 Bob Dylan. 10 Eleven. 11 Kate Bush.
12 Dancing Queen. 13 Turandot. 14 Barry, Robin & Maurice Gibb. 15 Let's
Dance. 16 Jean Terrell. 17 The Wonder of You. 18 Madonna. 19 Epic.
20 1962. 21 Mick Jagger. 22 Roxy Music. 23 Rod Stewart. 24 Thunderclap
Newman. 25 Celine Dion and Peabo Bryson. 26 Love Me For A Reason. 27
Zubin Mehta. 28 Hot Chocolate. 29 Blinded By The Light. 30 Rock On.

Answers

1   What did the Rolling Stones sing to close their 1981 USA shows?
2   Who replaced Cliff Richard in the West End Musical Time in 1987?
3   Who wrote I'm A Believer for The Monkees?
4   From which film was Elvis Presley's 1962 No 1 Return to Sender?
5   What was Elton John's first solo hit on his own Rocket label?
6   Which Leo Sayer hit gave the Chrysallis label their first No1?
7   In which decade did Barbra Streisand first make the UK charts?
8   Which hit was the first to be No 1 over two separate Christmases?
9   Which singer/songwriter penned the lines, "The carpet, too, is moving under you"?
10   How many consecutive UK No 1 hits did the Beatles have?
11   Who duetted with Peter Gabriel on Games Without Frontiers?
12   What was Abba's only No 1 in the USA?
13   Which opera does Pavarotti's anthem Nessun Dorma come from?
14   Which of the Gibb brothers wrote their first UK No 1 Massachusetts?
15   Which David Bowie hit was his fourth UK and second US No 1 in '83?
16   Who replaced Diana Ross when she left The Supremes?
17   What was Elvis Presley's penultimate UK No 1 hit?
18   Stephen Bray and Patrick Leonard have both co-written No 1s with which singer?
19   Michael Jackson's Thriller and Bad came out on which label?
20   When did Tony Bennett first record I Left My Heart In San Francisco?
21   Which group singer put out a solo album called Primitive Cool?
22   A John Lennon song gave which group their only UK No 1?
23   Which singing superstar once had a trial for Brentford FC?
24   Pete Townshend first No 1 as a producer was for which group?
25   Who sang the theme song to the film Beauty and the Beast?
26   What was the final No 1 by any of the Osmond family?
27   Who conducted the Three Tenors for their Italia 90 concert?
28   Who is the only group to appear in the charts in every year of the 70s?
29   Which Springsteen song was a hit for Manfred Mann's Earth Band?
30   Which David Essex hit was the sound track for That'll Be The Day?

Pot Luck 41 (See quiz 87, page 319)
1 Pangram. 2 SGP. 3 Bill Wyman. 4 Charles Lynton. 5 1980s. 6 James Fenimore Cooper. 7 Ohio. 8 Jonathan Demme. 9 Girls On Film. 10 Royal Physician. 11 Walter de la Mare. 12 Amathophobia. 13 River Niger. 14 Backgammon. 15 Somalia. 16 Clarence House. 17 Heavy, ponderous. 18 Nike. 19 July. 20 Earl Marshall. 21 Euclid. 22 Dr Who. 23 Cameroon. 24 David Dundas. 25 The Accidental Tourist. 26 Golf's British Open. 27 Dear Sir. 28 White. 29 Autonomic Nervous System. 30 Edgar Degas.

Answers

Quiz 89 Pot Luck 42

LEVEL 3

Answers - see Quiz 90, page 321

1 Which US state is called the Gopher State?
2 From which musical is the song June is Bustin' Out All Over?
3 In which decade was Frankie Dettori born?
4 The French physician Laennec invented which medical aid?
5 Nelophobia is the fear of what?
6 Who wrote Death In The Afternoon?
7 In which country is the city of Fortaleza?
8 Which French rugby union player holds the record for the most tries for his country?
9 Which tree appears on the Lebanese flag?
10 What's the English name of the constellation Dorado?
11 Whose only UK Top Ten hit was The Final Countdown?
12 Who is the most photographed person to attend Riddlesdown High school, Croydon?
13 In which country are the regions of Liguria and Calabria?
14 Which artist painted the famous painting The Ambassadors?
15 The majority of tourists to the USA are from which country?
16 Who composed the opera The Golden Cockerel?
17 What type of roses were in Lady Diana Spencer's wedding bouquet?
18 Which country has the ngultrum as a unit of currency?
19 Who is the elder – Ruby Wax or Victoria Wood?
20 How old was James Herriot when he began writing books?
21 Which King of Spain was known as Charles the Mad?
22 Who joined the European Union in the same year as Portugal?
23 What is the Swedish plattar?
24 Which media celeb founded a magazine called Passing Wind?
25 Who wrote the novel The Sound and the Fury?
26 What was Earth, Wind and Fire's first UK Top Ten hit?
27 The wall, bar and frog are all part of a horse's what?
28 What is the capital of the Dominican Republic?
29 What is Julie Andrews' full real name?
30 In which decade was the first Archery World Championship?

Answers

TV Times 4 (See quiz 90, page 322)
1 Colin Firth. 2 AA. 3 Robert Lindsay. 4 Boyzone. 5 Nero. 6 Eric Idle.
7 British Rail. 8 Robert de Niro. 9 Crossroads, King's Oak. 10 TISWAS.
11 Cedric Charlton. 12 Cricket St Thomas. 13 No one, he was never seen.
14 A moose. 15 Play Your Cards Right. 16 Letitia Dean. 17 The Winchester.
18 Michael Cole. 19 Alan Alda. 20 World's biggest one man band. 21 Fleur.
22 Geoffrey Lancashire. 23 Charlie Gimbert. 24 Seymour Utterthwaite. 25 Susan Hampshire. 26 Crimewatch UK. 27 Rathouse International. 28 It Ain't Half Hot Mum. 29 Purple. 30 Bill Treacher (aka Arthur Fowler).

Quiz 90 TV Times 4

Answers - see Quiz 89, page 321

1   Who played John McCarthy in Hostages?
2   Which emergency service did Anthea Turner work for before her media career?
3   Who played the scheming city council chief in GBH?
4   Who did Andrew Lloyd Webber appear on Top of the Pops with in 1998?
5   What was the caterpillar called in Dangermouse?
6   Who founded Rutland Weekend Television?
7   Which company did Colin work for in Colin's Sandwich?
8   In a Comic Strip Hollywood spoof of the miners' strike Peter Richardson played which actor supposedly playing Arthur Scargill?
9   What did Crossroads change its name to in 1987?
10   Which show had a punk dog called Spit?
11   In The Darling Buds of May what was Charley's real name?
12   To The Manor Born was set in which village?
13   Who played Joe Maplin in Hi De Hi!?
14   What strolled across the opening title in Northern Exposure?
15   How was the US series Card Sharks known when it transferred to the UK?
16   Who played Lucinda in Grange Hill?
17   What was the name of the pub in Minder?
18   Who left the employ of Mohammed Fayed to host a daytime chat show on satellite TV?
19   Who hosted That Was the Week That Was in the US?
20   What record did Roy Castle break on the very first Record Breakers?
21   What was Zoe and Alec's baby called in May to December?
22   Which father of a former Corrie barmaid wrote The Lovers?
23   In Lovejoy who bough Felsham Manor after Lady Jane left?
24   Who replaced Foggy Dewhurst when Michael Aldridge joined the Last of the Summer Wine cast?
25   Which TV actress became President of the Dyslexia Institute?
26   Which series was based on Germany's File XY Unsolved?
27   Which company did Terence 'Twiggy' Rathbone own in Hot Metal?
28   In which series were jungle sequences shot in Norfolk and desert scenes in Sussex?
29   What colour hair did Crystal Tipps have?
30   Which actor was digging an allotment to advertise BT?

Pot Luck 42 (See quiz 89, page 321)
1 Minnesota. 2 Carousel. 3 1970s. 4 Stethoscope. 5 Glass. 6 Ernest Hemingway. 7 Brazil. 8 Serge Blanco with 38. 9 Cedar tree. 10 Swordfish. 11 Europe. 12 Kate Moss. 13 Italy. 14 Holbein. 15 Canada. 16 Rimsky-Korsakov. 17 Mountbatten roses. 18 Bhutan. 19 Ruby Wax. 20 50 years old. 21 Charles II. 22 Spain. 23 Pancake. 24 Ian Hislop. 25 William Faulkner. 26 September. 27 Hoof. 28 Santo Domingo. 29 Julia Elizabeth Wells. 30 1930s.

Quiz 91 Pot Luck 43

Answers - see Quiz 92, page 324

1 In which country is the city of Ibadan?
2 What do the initials for the chemical DDT stand for?
3 Who directed the film trilogy Lethal Weapon?
4 Arthur Scargill and the Duchess of York were removed from where in 1996?
5 What was Pigmeat Markham's only UK Top Ten hit?
6 What is the main language of the Republic of Chad?
7 Douroucouli, de Brazza's guenon and red colobus are types of what?
8 Which artist painted Black Paintings in the 1820s?
9 Who invented the word 'frabjous'?
10 Salem is the capital of which US state?
11 What is Robson Green's middle name?
12 In which decade was Comtesse Raine de Chambrun born?
13 Windhoek is the capital of which country?
14 A fear of fear is known as what?
15 What invaded the town of San Antonio de los Caballeros in June '98?
16 What was Rod Stewart's last UK No 1?
17 Who was the Roman goddess of horses?
18 What does the green pentacle on the Moroccan flag depict?
19 What is the international car index mark for a car from Burundi?
20 What did the M stand for in J.M.W. Turner's name?
21 Where are the headquarters of the French Foreign Legion?
22 What is the drug thiopental used for?
23 Desmond Tutu's middle name is Mpilo, which means what?
24 How is Patricia Andrejewski better known?
25 Who had an 80s hit with She Means Nothing To Me?
26 Fergie was made Chancellor of which university?
27 In 1998 Tommy Dixon was arrested at home after what was mistaken for a gunshot?
28 In which city is the 305 metre long cable braced Erskine bridge?
29 The spice sassafras is made from which part of a plant?
30 Who is the elder – Earl Spencer or Sinead O'Connor?

Answers

Performing Arts (See quiz 92, page 324)
1 French & English. 2 Michael Crawford. 3 English National Ballet.
4 A cappella. 5 Cell Mates. 6 Vanessa Mae. 7 Louis B Mayer. 8 John Ogdon. 9 Rowan Atkinson. 10 Quintet du Hot Club de France. 11 Dash.
12 Mississippi. 13 Placido Domingo. 14 Phil Collins. 15 Popcorn.
16 Maureen Lipman. 17 Laurence Olivier. 18 Bournemouth Sinfonietta.
19 Tony Richardson. 20 Jerome Robbins. 21 Alan Ayckbourn. 22 Napoleon III. 23 Jim Steinman. 24 Steve Coogan. 25 Jim Davidson. 26 Hello Dolly.
27 Arpeggio. 28 Leslie Bricusse. 29 South Pacific. 30 Sir Peter Hall.

Quiz 92 Performing Arts

Answers - see Quiz 91, page 323

LEVEL 3

1 In which languages did Irishman Samuel Beckett write his plays?
2 Who performed his one man show EFX in Las Vegas?
3 Princess Diana was patron of which ballet company?
4 Which type of singing means 'in the style of the chapel'?
5 Which play did Stephen Fry walk out of in 1995?
6 Who went on a Red Hot world tour in 1996?
7 Who founded the American Academy of Motion Picture Arts and Sciences?
8 Who won the 1962 Tchaikovsky competition with. Ashkenazy?
9 Who, in '81, became the youngest star of a West End one-man show?
10 Grappelli and Reinhardt were leaders of which Quintet?
11 What was the name of Wayne Sleep's 1980 dance company?
12 Tennessee Williams was born in which US state?
13 Which opera singer sang with Sarah Brightman in Requiem?
14 Who played the Artful Dodger in the first stage production of Oliver!?
15 Which Ben Elton novel was the first to be adapted into a West End play?
16 Who had a one woman show called Live and Kidding?
17 Who shared management of the Old Vic between 1944 and 1950 with Ralph Richardson?
18 With which orchestra did Simon Rattle make his professional debut?
19 Who established the English Stage Company with George Devine at the Royal Court in 1955?
20 Who choreographed West Side Story and Fiddler on the Roof?
21 Who was in the Guinness Book of Records for having five plays running in the West End at one time?
22 Which leader is the subject of the play L'Aiglon by Edmond Rostand?
23 Who wrote the lyrics for Lloyd Webber's Whistle Down the Wind?
24 Whose was the star of The Man Who Thinks He's It?
25 Who became the youngest comedian to appear at the London Palladium, in 1977?
26 Thornton Wilder's The Matchmaker was made into which musical?
27 Which musical term means 'like a harp'?
28 Who wrote the songs for Doctor Dolittle?
29 Sean Connery's first West End appearance was in which chorus line?
30 Who founded the RSC aged 30?

Answers

Pot Luck 43 (See quiz 91, page 323)
1 Nigeria. 2 Dichloro-diphenyl-trichloroethane. 3 Richard Donner.
4 Madame Tussaud's displays. 5 Here Comes The Judge. 6 French.
7 Monkey. 8 Goya. 9 Lewis Carroll. 10 Oregon. 11 Golightly. 12 1920s.
13 Namibia. 14 Phobophobia. 15 Butterflies. 16 Baby Jane. 17 Epona.
18 The Seal of Solomon. 19 RU. 20 Mallord. 21 Corsica. 22 General
anaesthetic. 23 Life. 24 Pat Benatar. 25 Phil Everly and Cliff Richard.
26 Salford. 27 A balloon bursting. 28 Glasgow. 29 Root bark.
30 Earl Spencer.

Quiz 93 Pot Luck 44

Answers - see Quiz 94. page 326

LEVEL 3

1. In which Hawaiian island is Pearl Harbor?
2. What was Cliff Richard's first 1980s No 1?
3. JF Kennedy was one of how many children?
4. Under what name did Helen Porter Mitchell sing her way to success?
5. What was John Schlesinger's first US film?
6. In which month is the US holiday President's Day?
7. In which European country are the areas of Telemark and Troms?
8. Joe Fagin's 80s hit was a theme tune for which TV series?
9. Which country has the pula as a unit of currency?
10. What is the correct form of address to begin a letter to an Earl?
11. Which US state is called the Bay State?
12. Who is the elder – Michael Flatley or Stephen Fry?
13. Hypegiaphobia is the fear of what?
14. Who did Joe Louis beat to first become world heavyweight champ?
15. What was Eva Braun working as when she met Adolf Hitler?
16. What does the second S stand for in the initials SSSI?
17. Which Battle was the last in the Hundred Years War?
18. Who joined the European Union in the same year as UK and Denmark?
19. Who composed the opera Punch and Judy?
20. What was American hero Paul Revere's day job?
21. Who founded the Pakistan People's Party?
22. In which country is the city of Guayaquil?
23. What was the name of the Queen's first corgi?
24. Who played Sally Bowles in the 1955 film I am a Camera?
25. What did Rajiv Gandhi study at the University of Cambridge?
26. Kurt Weill and Henrik Ibsen were born in which month?
27. Who was the first Austrian to top the UK charts?
28. Which country has the only national flag which is not rectangular?
29. Who played the lead role in the film Finders Keepers?
30. To five either way, how many weeks did Sinatra's My Way spend in the UK charts between 1969 and 1971?

Tennis (See quiz 94, page 326)
Answers
1 Borotra, Brugnon, Cochet & Lacoste. 2 Vijay Amritraj. 3 Martina Navratilova. 4 Arthur Ashe. 5 Gabriela Sabatini. 6 Pete Sampras. 7 French Open. 8 Margaret Smith. 9 Plus an Olympic gold medal. 10 Karen Hantze. 11 1968. 12 Michael Stich. 13 Richard Krajicek. 14 Jensen brothers. 15 Cyril Suk & Helena Sukova. 16 Chris Evert. 17 The Queen. 18 Men's doubles. 19 French. 20 Martina Navratilova. 21 Michael Stich. 22 Lindsay Davenport. 23 Kevin Curren. 24 Tony Pickard. 25 Stefan Edberg. 26 Tim Gullikson. 27 Roger Taylor. 28 Kosice, Slovakia. 29 Sue Barker. 30 Sukova.

Quiz 94 Tennis

Answers - see Quiz 93, page 325

1 Who were tennis's 'Four Musketeers'?
2 Which tennis player appeared in Octopussy?
3 Who had the car number plate X CZECH?
4 Who won the first US Men's Open?
5 Who, in 1986, became the youngest woman semi finalist at Wimbledon for 99 years?
6 Who won the inaugural Grand Slam Cup in Munich in 1990?
7 What was Monica Seles's first Grand Slam title?
8 Who was the first Australian woman to win the Wimbledon Singles?
9 How does a Golden Grand Slam differ from a Grand Slam?
10 With whom did Billie Jean Moffitt win her first Wimbledon Doubles title?
11 What year was the world's first Open tournament?
12 Who was the first German to win the Wimbledon Men's Singles after reunification?
13 At Wimbledon who won an unseeded Men's final in the 90s?
14 Which brothers asked to wear England shirts on Centre Court during the 1996 championships?
15 Which brother and sister won the Wimbledon Mixed Doubles in successive years in the 90s?
16 Who was the first woman to win $1 million in prize money?
17 Who gave Virginia Wade her trophy when she won Wimbledon?
18 Which new competition was included in the Wimbledon championships in 1884 along with the Women's Singles?
19 Which Grand Slam title has Boris Becker never won?
20 Who did Miss Kiyomura beat in the Wimbledon Junior Final in 1973?
21 In 1992 John McEnroe won the Wimbledon Doubles title with whom?
22 Who replaced Martina Hingis as World No 1 in October 1998?
23 Who did Boris Becker beat to become Wimbledon's youngest Men's Singles winner?
24 Who did Greg Rusedski sack as his coach during Wimbledon 98?
25 Who won his first Open title in 1985 two years after winning the Junior Grand Slam?
26 Which mentor of Pete Sampras died in May 1996?
27 Who was the last British man before Tim Henman to reach a Wimbledon quarter final?
28 Where was Martina Hingis born?
29 How is Wimbledon semi finalist Mrs Lampard better known?
30 Which Helena won two titles in one day at Wimbledon 96?

Answers

Pot Luck 44 (See quiz 93, page 325)
1 Oahu. 2 Mistletoe and Wine. 3 Nine. 4 Nellie Melba. 5 Midnight Cowboy. 6 February. 7 Norway. 8 Auf Wiedersehen, Pet. 9 Botswana. 10 My Lord. 11 Massachusetts. 12 Stephen Fry. 13 Responsibility. 14 James Braddock. 15 Photographer's assistant. 16 Special. 17 Castillon. 18 Republic of Ireland. 19 Harrison Birtwistle. 20 Silversmith. 21 Zulfikar Ali Bhutto. 22 Ecuador. 23 Susan. 24 Julie Harris. 25 Engineering. 26 March. 27 Falco (Rock Me Amadeus). 28 Nepal. 29 Cliff Richard. 30 122.

Quiz 95 Pot Luck 45

Answers - see Quiz 96, page 328

LEVEL 3

1 What was the christian name of chocolate founder Mr Cadbury?
2 In which country is the city of Gwangju?
3 Bill Perks the son of a bricklayer became known as who?
4 What does the Latin mea culpa mean?
5 Which creature is represented in the year the Chinese call 'long'?
6 Which country has the rufiyaa as a unit of currency?
7 Who was Willie Vernon to James Cagney?
8 Where does the Symphony of the Stars take place annually in Hollywood?
9 What was Foreigner's first UK Top Ten hit in 1981?
10 Who is the elder – Bob Geldof or Nigel Kennedy?
11 Which Hitchock film title ties in with his father's field of work?
12 Which three colours make up the Sultanate of Oman flag?
13 Whose nickname was 'Stormin' Norman'?
14 Who directed the 1987 film Good Morning Vietnam?
15 Columbia is the capital of which US state?
16 What is a honey locust?
17 Born Marie Grosholtz, under what name is this French lady remembered?
18 Who were Waiting For a Train in their only UK Top Ten hit?
19 Which saints share their names with three of the five inhabited Scilly Isles?
20 Maputo is the capital of which country?
21 What does the medical term D & C stand for?
22 A fear of floods is known as what?
23 Which artist painted Toledo Landscape around 1610?
24 How is the letter O formed in Morse Code?
25 How many square chains make one hectare in surveying?
26 In which county was Sir Humphry Davy, inventor of the miner's safety lamp, born?
27 What did Terry Wogan study at Belvedere College, Dublin?
28 Who was the Greek god of vegetation and re-birth?
29 Which seasonal rose is from the genus Helleborus?
30 What is the international car index mark for a car from Lebanon?

Answers

Famous Names (See quiz 96, page 328)
1 Earl of Lichfield. 2 West Green. 3 Robin. 4 George Michael. 5 Helen Mirren. 6 Vic Reeves. 7 His hair was too long. 8 Duchess of Kent. 9 Mountbatten's. 10 Bernard Ingham. 11 Roger Moore. 12 Catherine Walker. 13 Marco Pierre White. 14 Malcolm McLaren. 15 Jane and Jonathan Ross. 16 Fascinating Aida. 17 Samira Khashoggi. 18 Duke Of Westminster. 19 Ryan Giggs. 20 Michael Grade. 21 Sir Peregrine Worsthorne. 22 Gary & Michelle Lineker. 23 Sean Bean. 24 Soft drinks. 25 Chloe. 26 First cousin. 27 Her favourite restaurant. 28 Ralph Fiennes. 29 Swansea. 30 Alexander McQueen.

Quiz 96 Famous Names

Answers - see Quiz 95, page 327

LEVEL 3

1 Whose stately home is Shugborough Hall?
2 Lord McAlpine is Lord of where?
3 What is the first name of the person who preceded Eddie George as Governor of the Bank of England?
4 Who is known to his family as 'Yog'?
5 Who became Mrs Taylor Hackford in 1997?
6 Who changed his name from Jim Moir so it didn't clash with the BBC's Head of Light Entertainment?
7 Why was Cliff Richard banned from entering Singapore in 1972?
8 How is the former Miss Katharine Worsley better known?
9 In whose family home did Charles and Diana spend the first night of their honeymoon?
10 Who was Margaret Thatcher's Press Secretary when she resigned?
11 Who aged 19 who married fellow drama student Doorn van Steyn?
12 Who founded the Chelsea Design Company in 1976?
13 Which Leeds born chef won three Michelin stars by his early thirties?
14 Who opened the punk boutique Seditionaries in the 70s with Vivienne Westwood?
15 Who has children called Betty Kitten, Harvey Kirby and Honey Kinny?
16 How were Issy Van Randwyck, Dillie Keane and Adele Anderson known collectively?
17 Who was Mohammed Fayed's first wife and Dodi Fayed's mother?
18 Who is London's largest landowner?
19 Who is the son of former rugby league international Danny Wilson?
20 Who was raised by his grandmother Olga Winogradsky?
21 Which former editor is Lady Lucinda Lambton's third husband?
22 Who are the parents of George, Harry, Tobias and Angus?
23 Who has '100% Blades' tattooed on his left arm?
24 William Hague's father's business produced what?
25 In '98 Stella McCartney designed for which fashion house?
26 What relation is Natasha Richardson to Jemma Redgrave?
27 After who or what did Lady Helen Taylor (nee Windsor) name her first son?
28 Which Hamlet ran off with his mother Gertrude in 1995?
29 Where was Michael Heseltine born?
30 Who succeeded John Galliano at Givenchy in 1996?

Answers

Pot Luck 45 (See quiz 95, page 327)
1 John. 2 South Korea. 3 Bill Wyman (Rolling Stones). 4 Through my fault.
5 Dragon. 6 Maldives. 7 His wife. 8 Hollywood Bowl. 9 Waiting For A
Girl Like You. 10 Bob Geldof. 11 The Birds (Dad a poultry trader). 12 Red,
white and green. 13 US General Norman Schwarzkopf. 14 Barry Levinson.
15 South Carolina. 16 A tree. 17 Madame Tussaud. 18 Flash and the Pan.
19 Agnes, Mary & Martin. 20 Mozambique. 21 Dilation and Curettage.
22 Antlophobia. 23 El Greco. 24 Dash, dash, dash. 25 Ten. 26 Cornwall.
27 Philosophy. 28 Adonis. 29 Christmas Rose. 30 RL.

Quiz 97 Pot Luck 46

LEVEL 3

Answers - see Quiz 98, page 330

1 Which occupation was shared by the fathers of Roger Moore and Burt Reynolds?
2 What are the two colours of the national flag of Pakistan?
3 Who is the elder – Liam Gallagher or Ryan Giggs?
4 What is Gerald Ford's middle name?
5 What was the profession of escapologist Harry Houdini's father?
6 Over 700 people died in Greece in July 1987 due to what?
7 Who composed the opera The Rape of Lucretia?
8 What are the initials TARDIS an abbreviation of?
9 Whose one and only UK hit which reached No 1 was Float On ?
10 Which writer is actress Rudi Davies' mother?
11 Which prince was born in the year Ted Hughes became Poet Laureate?
12 If a wine is said to be flabby what does it lack?
13 What is the capital of Greenland?
14 In music, what does the expression 'strepitoso' mean?
15 For a role in which film did Vanessa Redgrave shave her head?
16 Which country has the lev as a unit of currency?
17 For what offence did Sophia Loren spend 17 days in prison in 1982?
18 In which decade was Richard Branson born?
19 In which European country are the regions of Beja and Guarda?
20 Which playwright was born in Whiston on Merseyside in 1947?
21 Which American state is called the Hawkeye State?
22 Which vitamin is also known as biotin?
23 Astraphobia is the fear of what?
24 What common factor links children of Cheryl Baker and children of Mollie Sugden?
25 Who played Ron Jenkins in Coronation Street?
26 DJ Jimmy Young was what sort of instructor in the army?
27 Which hit got to No 2 simultaneously in November 1995 with two separate groups?
28 Who created The Simpsons on TV?
29 Who in Gilbert and Sullivan is 'a dealer in magic and spells'?
30 Which soccer side does Eamonn Holmes support?

Screen Greats (See quiz 98, page 330)
1 None. 2 Betty Grable. 3 Peter Lorre. 4 Goldfinger. 5 Errol Flynn. 6 20th Century Fox. 7 Charles Bronson. 8 Tony Curtis. 9 Barbara Stanwyck's. 10 Bela Lugosi. 11 Gene Kelly. 12 Audrey Hepburn. 13 Marlon Brando. 14 Ingrid Bergman. 15 Rita Hayworth. 16 Rebecca. 17 Sophia Loren. 18 One Night in the Tropics. 19 Dustin Hoffman. 20 George C Scott. 21 Julie Andrews. 22 Lola-Lola. 23 His wife Carole Lombard. 24 Ginger Rogers. 25 Charlotte Bronte. 26 Twenty. 27 Anchors Aweigh. 28 The Big Broadcast. 29 The Barkleys of Broadway. 30 Making A Living.

Answers

Quiz 98 Screen Greats

Answers - see Quiz 97, page 329

LEVEL 3

1 What is the total number of Oscars won by Errol Flynn, Peter Cushing and Richard Burton?
2 Who once had her name changed to Frances Dean by Goldwyn?
3 Who is mentioned by name in Al Stewart's song The Year of the Cat?
4 Which Bond film did Sean Connery make prior to Hitchcock's Marnie?
5 Eric Porter played Soames on TV but who played Soames in That Forsyte Woman?
6 Which was the first US studio Richard Burton worked for?
7 Who is known in Italy as 'Il Brutto'?
8 Who changed Bernie for Tony in his first film Criss Cross?
9 Bette Midler recreated whose 30s role in Stella?
10 Which screen great did Martin Landau play in Ed Wood?
11 Who was lent to Columbia by MGM for Cover Girl?
12 Sean Ferrer was the son of which Hollywood Oscar winner?
13 Whose first Oscar was for playing Terry Malloy in a 50s classic?
14 Who was the mother of actress Isabella Rossellini?
15 Whose pin up was pinned to the atomic bomb dropped on Bikini?
16 What was Hitchcock's first Hollywood film?
17 Who was the first performer to win an Oscar for a performance entirely in a foreign language?
18 What was Abbot and Costello's first feature film?
19 Who played Sean Connery's son in Family Business?
20 Who was the first actor ever to refuse an Oscar?
21 Who was the first British born British actress of British parents to win an Oscar?
22 What was the name of Marlene Dietrich in The Blue Angel?
23 Whose death in 1942 spurred Clark Gable to join the US Air Corps?
24 Whose first film was Campus Sweethearts with Rudy Vallee?
25 Which author did Olivia de Havilland play in Devotion?
26 How old was Debbie Reynolds when she made Singin' in the Rain?
27 What was the first film which teamed Gene Kelly with Frank Sinatra?
28 In which film did Bob Hope find his theme tune?
29 In which 1949 film were Rogers and Astaire reunited after a 10 year break?
30 In which film did Chaplin make his screen debut, in 1914?

Pot Luck 46 (See quiz 97, page 329)
Answers
1 Police officers. **2** White and green. **3** Liam Gallagher. **4** Rudolph. **5** A Rabbi. **6** Heatwave. **7** Benjamin Britten. **8** Time and Relative Dimensions in Space. **9** Floaters. **10** Beryl Bainbridge. **11** Prince Harry. **12** Acidity. **13** Godthab. **14** Noisy, boisterous. **15** Playing For Time. **16** Bulgaria. **17** Tax evasion. **18** 1950s. **19** Portugal. **20** Willy Russell. **21** Iowa. **22** B6. **23** Lightning. **24** Twins. **25** Ben Kingsley. **26** Physical training. **27** Wonderwall. **28** Matt Groening. **29** John Wellington Wells (The Sorcerer). **30** Manchester United.

LEVEL 3

Answers - see Quiz 100, page 332

1 What was the last ruling dynasty of China?
2 The Isle of Man belonged to which two countries before it came under UK administration in 1765?
3 What name meaning 'achievement of universal peace' is given to the reign of Emperor Akihito?
4 How did the former Princess Alix of of Hessen meet her death?
5 Who did not seek re election as Austrian President in 1991 after revelations about his activities in WWII?
6 Who was the first President of Israel?
7 How many days after Waterloo did Napoleon resign?
8 Which governor of Sumatra was responsible for the founding of Singapore?
9 What did the Rarotonga Treaty secure in 1987?
10 What does Rasputin mean, as a name given to Grigory Efimovich?
11 Where were all but six French kings crowned?
12 Which country had a secret police force called the securitate which was replaced in 1990?
13 Which President Roosevelt was Republican?
14 What name was given to the incorporation of Austria into the Third Reich?
15 What did Haile Selassie's title Ras Tafari mean?
16 Who was Nazi minister of eastern occupied territories from '41-44?
17 Who was secretary of state to Kennedy and Johnson?
18 Who was the first president of an independent Mozambique?
19 In which country was the Rosetta Stone found in in 1799?
20 What name was given to the socialist movement which carried out the Nicaraguan Revolution?
21 Which Conference drew up the United Nations Charter?
22 Where was the explosive Semtex manufactured?
23 Which city has the oldest university in the world?
24 Who succeeded Ian Smith as Prime Minister of Rhodesia which then became known as Zimbabwe?
25 Where was the first Marxist state in Africa created?
26 Where was the Maoist guerrilla group Sendero Luminoso active in the 80s?
27 Who became New Zealand PM in December 1997?
28 Who was joint secretary general of the ANC with Mandela in 1964?
29 Who were the first three states to break away from Yugoslavia in '91?
30 Where did the Hundred Flowers Movement encourage government criticism in the 50s?

Pot Luck 47 (See quiz 100, page 332)
1 When I Fall In Love - Rick Astley and Nat 'King' Cole. 2 Brighton & Hove Albion. 3 South Dakota. 4 Joan Crawford. 5 Johnny Briggs (Mike Baldwin). 6 Boa snakes. 7 Rosemary Conley. 8 Anita Lonsborough. 9 She fell down a flight of stairs. 10 Ouranophobia. 11 Ben E King. 12 MC. 13 Henri Matisse. 14 Maroon. 15 Myalgic Encephalitis. 16 Eltham. 17 Steven Spielberg. 18 Mali. 19 Barry Humphries. 20 Catherine Zeta Jones. 21 Delia Smith. 22 Terry Waite. 23 Mauritania. 24 Samuel. 25 From New York to L.A. 26 Lewis Carroll. 27 Taiwan. 28 American. 29 Winifred Holtby. 30 2197.

Answers

Quiz 100 Pot Luck 47

Answers - see Quiz 99, page 331

LEVEL 3

1 Which two versions of the same song were in the Top Ten simultaneously in December 1987?
2 Which football team does Des Lynam support?
3 Pierre is the capital of which American State?
4 Which actress was also known as Lucille Le Sueur?
5 Which member of the Coronation Street cast has sung in the chorus of an Italian opera company?
6 Which reptiles come from the family Boidae?
7 Who produced a fitness video called Ultimate Fat Burner?
8 Who was the first female winner of the BBC Sports Personality of the Year?
9 How did fashion empress Laura Ashley die?
10 A fear of heaven is known as what?
11 Which singer's real name is Benjamin Earl Nelson?
12 What is the international car index mark for a car from Monaco?
13 Which artist painted La Desserte in 1908?
14 What colour appears with white on the State of Qatar flag?
15 What is the full name for the medical condition known as ME?
16 Where in the UK did Bob Hope have a theatre named after him?
17 Who directed the 1992 film Hook?
18 Bamako is the capital of which country?
19 Who is the elder – Barry Humphries or Eddie George?
20 Who duetted with David Essex on True Love Ways in 1994?
21 Whose first book was How to Cheat at Cooking?
22 Who is taller – Terry Waite or Frank Bruno?
23 Which country has the ouguiya as a unit of currency?
24 What was the christian name of shipowner Cunard?
25 Where was Patsy Gallant going from in her 70s UK Top Ten hit?
26 Which children's author appeared on the cover of Sergeant Pepper?
27 In which country is the city of Kaohsiung?
28 What is the nationality of writer and chef Ken Hom?
29 Testament of Friendship is about Vera Brittain's friendship with which author?
30 What is 13 cubed?

Answers

World History (See quiz 99, page 331)
1 Manchu or Qing ('Ching'). 2 Norway & Scotland. 3 Heisei. 4 Shot with her husband Tsar Nicholas II. 5 Kurt Waldheim. 6 Chaim Weizmann. 7 Four. 8 Thomas Stanford Raffles. 9 Nuclear-free South Pacific. 10 Dissolute. 11 Reims. 12 Romania. 13 Theodore. 14 Anschluss. 15 Lion of Judah. 16 Alfred Rosenberg. 17 Dean Rusk. 18 Samora Machel. 19 Egypt. 20 Sandanista. 21 San Francisco Conference. 22 Czechoslovakia. 23 Cairo (El Azhar). 24 Bishop Abel Muzorewa. 25 Congo. 26 Peru. 27 Jenny Shipley. 28 Walter Sisulu. 29 Slovenia, Macedonia & Croatia. 30 China.

1   Who starred with Steve Coogan on The Dead Good Show?

2   Who was the real life husband of the first girl in the famous Nescafe commercials?

3   How was comedy writer Gerald Wiley better known?

4   Who found fame with Emma Thompson playing Danny McGlone?

5   Who starred in and produced a mini series called Sins?

6   Who was a regular in Crown Court as barrister Jeremy Parsons QC?

7   In which series has Philip Franks been a tax inspector and a policeman?

8   Who stormed out of a TV interview when Robin Day called him a "here today gone tomorrow politician"?

9   Whose first pop TV series was called The Power Station?

10   Which Moll Flanders lost husband Ralph to Francesca Annis?

11   Who was the first male presenter of Live & Kicking?

12   What was Lenny Henry's Rastafarian community police officer called?

13   Who came to fame as 'Q' of The Little Ladies?

14   Who was Cherie Lunghi's character in The Manageress?

15   Who played Fletch's son Raymond in Going Straight?

16   Who runs the Amy International production company with wife Susan George?

17   Who are the two youngest. McGann brothers?

18   Who was the first female presenter of Top Gear?

19   Who wrote the Magic Roundabout scripts when they were first broadcast in the UK?

20   Which actresses created The House of Eliot?

21   Who appeared in Dixon of Dock Green aged 10 and found fame as Mrs Theodopolopoudos?

22   What is the real name of the comedian who had a No 1 with a cover version of Tommy Roe's Dizzy and wanted a One-2-One with Terry-Thomas?

23   Which EastEnders star used to be better known by his catchphrase 'Terr-i-fic'?

24   Who played Marjory in The Outside Dog in the Talking Heads series?

25   Who won New Faces and went on to present it?

26   Who is the real life mum of Grace and Henry Durham?

27   Who left Sherwood Forest for oil in Denver?

28   Who adapted his novel of the same name into Men Behaving Badly?

29   Who played the seventh Doctor Who?

30   Who was the only female presenter at the Live Aid concert?

Answers

Pot Luck 48 (See quiz 102, page 334)
1 Betty Joan Perske. 2 Margaret Thatcher. 3 Tennyson. 4 Jeweller. 5 Harvey Goldsmith. 6 Scilly Isles. 7 RM. 8 Queen Margarethe of Denmark. 9 Oops Up Side Your Head. 10 Conakry. 11 Karpov. 12 Oriental rug. 13 Liberator. 14 Bolivia & Peru v Chile. 15 Little Sioux River. 16 Children. 17 Conservatives. 18 Michael Ramsey. 19 Brighton. 20 Jane Seymour. 21 (I Was Made For) Dancin'. 22 Kris Kristofferson & Rita Coolidge. 23 Complete works of Shakespeare. 24 Maine. 25 Phil Collins. 26 Myanmar. 27 Yellow. 28 Gannex. 29 Romania. 30 Glenn Hoddle and Chris Waddle.

Quiz 102 Pot Luck 48

Answers - see Quiz 101, page 333

LEVEL 3

1   What is Lauren Bacall's full real name?
2   About whom did Cliff Richard say, "She really is a woman just like my Mum"?
3   Who wrote the poem The Idylls of the King?
4   What was the profession of fizzy drinks maker Jacob Schweppes?
5   Who is the elder – Harvey Goldsmith or Sir Elton John?
6   Saint Mary's airport serves which Isles?
7   What is the international car index mark for a car from Madagascar?
8   Who opened Europe's longest suspension bridge in 1998?
9   What was the Gap Band's first UK Top Ten hit?
10 What is the capital of Guinea?
11 Who did Kasparov beat to become world chess champion in 1985?
12 What is a kelim?
13 What was the by-name for the B24 bomber?
14 Which countries fought the Pacific War in the 19th century?
15 On which river does the US city of Cherokee lie?
16 What or who does UNICEF benefit?
17 Which political party did Mrs Pankhurst join in 1925?
18 Who was the first Archbishop of Canterbury to meet a Pope since the 16th century?
19 The first Bodyshop opened in which town?
20 Who was Elizabeth I's first stepmother?
21 What was Leif Garrett made for in his only UK Top Ten hit from 1979?
22 Which husband and wife team had a hit with A Song I'd Like to Sing?
23 What was the first text to be 'bowdlerised' by Thomas Bowdler?
24 Which American state is called the Pine Tree State?
25 Who is taller – Mick Jagger or Phil Collins?
26 Which country has the kyat as a unit of currency?
27 What colour appears with red and blue on the Romanian flag?
28 What make of raincoat did Harold Wilson popularise?
29 In which European country are the counties of Arad, Arges and Cluj?
30 Which duo got to No 30 with the hit Diamond Lights in 1987?

Who's Who? (See quiz 101, page 333)
1 Caroline Aherne. 2 Trevor Eve. 3 Ronnie Barker. 4 Robbie Coltrane.
5 Joan Collins. 6 Richard Wilson. 7 The Darling Buds of May, Heartbeat. 8 John Nott. 9 Chris Evans. 10 Alex Kingston. 11 Andi Peters. 12 PC Ganja.
13 Rula Lenska. 14 Gabriella Benson. 15 Nicholas Lyndhurst. 16 Simon MacCorkindale. 17 Mark & Stephen. 18 Angela Rippon. 19 Eric Thompson.
20 Jean Marsh & Eileen Atkins. 21 Pauline Quirke. 22 Jim Moir (Vic Reeves).
23 Mike Reid. 24 Julie Walters. 25 Marti Caine. 26 Victoria Wood.
27 Michael Praed. 28 Simon Nye. 29 Sylvester McCoy. 30 Janice Long.

Quiz 103 The Media

LEVEL 3

Answers - see Quiz 104, page 336

1 What was Bob Geldof's TV production company called?
2 What is Kerry Packer's media company called?
3 Which mag did Jennifer Saunders and Joanna Lumley guest edit?
4 What was the first INR radio station?
5 Kelly's Directories catalogue what?
6 What is the signature tune of the BBC World Service?
7 What was the first magazine in the UK in 1691?
8 In which magazine did the Addams Family first appear?
9 Which American syndicated a newspaper column called 'My Day'?
10 Who founded the Daily Mail?
11 Where is the newspaper ABC from?
12 Which two UK national newspaper were founded in 1990?
13 Apart from the Tribune, which other US newspaper has Chicago in its name?
14 Which press agency has the abbreviation IRNA?
15 Which newspaper proprietor was born Jan Ludvik Hoch?
16 In '89 Richard Murdoch bought a 50% stake in which Hungarian tabloid?
17 Which Sunday Times editor made headline news himself regarding details of his affair with Pamella Bordes?
18 Lloyd Grossman was restaurant critic of which magazine in the 80s?
19 Who took over The Observer in 1981?
20 Apart from the Guardian, which other newspaper did James Naughtie work for before joining the BBC?
21 What type of correspondent for the BBC was Michael Cole before he went. to work for Mohammed Fayed?
22 Who was chairman of Saatchi & Saatchi when they took over the Tory Party account?
23 Which agency did the Saatchi brothers found in 1995?
24 Which famous columnist is married to Lady Camilla Harris?
25 Whose affair with David Mellor brought media man Max Clifford into the public gaze?
26 Which media man's sons all have the middle name Paradine?
27 Which soccer side does Tony Blair's press Secretary support?
28 Which co founder of TV am was married to a future Leader of the House of Lords?
29 What was Ted Turner's family business before he turned to TV?
30 Which media magnate has owned AC Milan and been his country's PM?

Pot Luck 49 (See quiz 104, page 336)
1 Blue and white. 2 Maldives. 3 20th. 4 BDS. 5 Rob Reiner. 6 Record collection. 7 Paradise. 8 Paramount Studios. 9 Angola. 10 Mona Lisa. 11 Debbie Gibson. 12 Mongolia. 13 Lyndon Baines Johnson. 14 Prince Edward Island. 15 Jacopo Robusti. 16 Ulrika Jonsson. 17 Arabian Sea. 18 Sierra Leone & Liberia. 19 Iris. 20 British United Provident Association. 21 House painting. 22 David Thewlis. 23 Texas. 24 Securities and Investments Board. 25 Reptiles. 26 Sea. 27 Games Without Frontiers. 28 Sylvia Syms. 29 John Osborne. 30 Spanish.

1 What two colours appear on the flag of San Marino?
2 Male is the capital of which country?
3 In which century was Dame Barbara Cartland born?
4 What is the international car index mark for a car from Barbados?
5 Who directed the 1992 film A Few Good Men?
6 What did Paul Gambaccini sell at auction in 1997?
7 Which Persian word means 'pleasure garden'?
8 Which film production company began as the Famous Players Film Company?
9 In which country is the port of Lubango?
10 Which painting did Arthur Scargill choose as his luxury on Desert Island Discs?
11 Which vocalist had Top Ten hits with Shake Your Love and Foolish Beat?
12 Which country has the tugrik as a unit of currency?
13 Who was President of the USA before Richard Nixon?
14 In which Canadian province is the novel Anne of Green Gables set?
15 What was painter Tintoretto's real name?
16 Who is the elder – Patsy Kensit or Ulrika Jonsson?
17 Which Sea, after the Coral Sea, is the largest in area in the world?
18 From which countries do the Mende people originate?
19 Who was the Greek Goddess of the rainbow?
20 What does BUPA stand for?
21 What trade did playwright Brendan Behan learn on leaving school?
22 Who played Paul Verlaine in the film Total Eclipse. to Leonardo DiCaprio's Rimbaud?
23 What is the only US state to have been an independent republic?
24 In monetary and banking terms, what do the initials SIB stand for?
25 The Gladys Porter Zoo in Texas is noted for its collection of what?
26 Thalassophobia is a fear of what?
27 What was Peter Gabriel's first UK Top Ten hit?
28 Which actress is the mother of actress Beatie Edney?
29 Who wrote the screen play for the 1963 film Tom Jones?
30 What is the main language of the Dominican Republic?

Answers

The Media (See quiz 103, page 335)
1 Planet 24. 2 Consolidated Press. 3 Marie Claire (UK). 4 Classic FM.
5 Towns and cities. 6 Lilliburlero. 7 Compleat Library. 8 New Yorker.
9 Eleanor Roosevelt. 10 Lord Northcliffe. 11 Madrid. 12 The Independent on Sunday & The European. 13 Chicago Sun-Times. 14 Islamic Republic News Agency. 15 Robert Maxwell. 16 Reform. 17 Andrew Neil. 18 Harpers and Queen. 19 Tiny Rowland. 20 The Scotsman. 21 Royal. 22 Tim Bell. 23 M & C Saatchi. 24 Nigel Dempster. 25 Antonia de Sancha. 26 David Frost. 27 Burnley. 28 Peter Jay. 29 Advertising. 30 Silvio Berlusconi.

Quiz 105 Who's Music?

Answers - see Quiz 106, page 338

LEVEL 3

1　Who was knocked off No 1 position by Wannabe?

2　Whose record has the longest playing time of any to make No 1?

3　Who was Mike McGear's famous elder brother?

4　Whose one hit wonder replaced Honky Tonk Women at No 1 in US and Britain?

5　Which singer left school in 1961 to appear in the film It's Trad, Dad?

6　Which No 1 singer was born Arnold George Dorsey in Madras?

7　Which top musician produced Shakin' Stevens Merry Christmas Everyone?

8　Who sang lead vocal on the chart topper Babe?

9　Who wrote the lines, "All alone, without a telephone"?

10　Who has recorded singles with Paul McCartney, Julio Iglesias and Diana Ross?

11　Who was the first drummer with The Stone Roses?

12　Joyce Vincent and Thelma Hopkins were the girls in which 70s group?

13　Who joined Wendy Richard in the No 1 from 1962 Come Outside?

14　Which female singer did Peter Skellern ask to join his Oasis in 1983?

15　Which chart topper started life at Leigh, Lancashire as Clive Powell?

16　Who set up the DEP record label?

17　Which 60s artist was the first British born artist with three No 1 hits?

18　How is James Michael Aloysious Bradford better known?

19　Who wrote Chain Reaction for Diana Ross?

20　Who joined the Beatles on their first hit to enter the charts at No 1?

21　Who recorded the 1993 No 1 written and produced by Shaw and Rogers?

22　Which actor was talking to the trees on the B side of Wand'rin' Star?

23　Who was No 1 in the UK and US singles and album charts at the same time in 1971?

24　Who covered the Searchers' No 1 Sweets for My Sweet in 1994?

25　Which Creation Records boss signed Oasis?

26　Which duo made up the Righteous Brothers?

27　Who joined the Beautiful South after being roadie for The Housemartins?

28　Whose death moved Don McLean to write American Pie?

29　The Beatles apart, who first took a Lennon & McCartney song to No 1, with the Dakotas?

30　In the 1950s who was the first instrumentalist to achieve two No 1s?

Pot Luck 50 (See quiz 106, page 338)

Answers

1 Liberia. 2 Arnold Wesker. 3 Man City. 4 Five. 5 A tiny diamond studded golden horseshoe. 6 Thomas Middleton. 7 God. 8 Alaska. 9 John Donne. 10 Dreams. 11 Physics. 12 Spain. 13 An antelope. 14 Harrison Birtwistle. 15 1900. 16 The Red House Mystery. 17 Five. 18 Jim Gilstrap. 19 European Coal and Steel Community. 20 Charles Buchinski. 21 MA. 22 San Quentin prison. 23 Rho. 24 Veterans Day. 25 Great Ultimate Boxing. 26 Princess Michael of Kent. 27 Mozambique. 28 Brian Johnston. 29 Michael Tippett. 30 Derby County.

Quiz 106 Pot Luck 50

Answers - see Quiz 105, page 337

LEVEL 3

1   Which country has the ports of Buchanan and Grenville?
2   Who wrote Chips With Everything?
3   Who were the first English team outside London to claim the European Cup Winners' Cup?
4   In Scrabble what would the word DOG score without any bonus points?
5   What was sewn into the hem of Princess Diana's wedding dress for luck?
6   Who co-wrote The Changeling with William Rowley around 1622?
7   Theophobia is the fear of what?
8   Which American state is called the Last Frontier?
9   "For whom the bell tolls" is a quote from whom?
10 What was Gabrielle's first UK Top Ten hit?
11 What did Olivia Newton-John's grandfather win a Nobel Prize for in 1954?
12 In which European country are the regions of Vigo and Murcia?
13 What type of animal is a kudu?
14 Who composed the opera Mask of Orpheus?
15 In which year did Michelin produce the first of its Red Guides?
16 Which detective novel did A A Milne write in 1922?
17 How many stripes are there on the Thai flag?
18 Whose first UK Top Ten hit was Swing Your Daddy?
19 What does ECSC stand for in European Community Organisations?
20 What is Charles Bronson's full real name?
21 What is the international car index mark for a car from Morocco?
22 Where had Jim Rockford been in the years preceding The Rockford Files?
23 What name is given to the Greek letter that is the equivalent of letter R?
24 What is Remembrance Sunday called in the US?
25 What does 'tai chi chuan' mean in Chinese?
26 Who is the elder – Princess Michael of Kent or Felicity Kendal?
27 In which country is the city of Maputo?
28 Which cricket commentator was awarded the Military Cross in WWII for his 'cheerfulness under fire'?
29 Who wrote the opera The Knot Garden?
30 Which soccer side does actor Robert Lindsay support?

Who's Music? (See quiz 105, page 337)
1 Gary Barlow. 2 Meat Loaf. 3 Paul McCartney. 4 Zager and Evans - In the Year 2525. 5 Helen Shapiro. 6 Engelbert Humperdinck. 7 Dave Edmunds. 8 Mark Owen. 9 Marc Bolan (Metal Guru). 10 Stevie Wonder. 11 Alan 'Remi' Wren. 12 Dawn. 13 Mike Sarne. 14 Mary Hopkin. 15 Georgie Fame. 16 UB40. 17 Frank Ifield. 18 Jimmy Nail. 19 The Gibb Brothers. 20 Billy Preston on Get Back. 21 Mr Blobby. 22 Clint Eastwood. 23 Rod Stewart. 24 C.J.Lewis. 25 Alan McGhee. 26 Bill Medley and Bobby Hatfield. 27 Dave Stead. 28 Buddy Holly. 29 Billy J. Kramer. 30 Eddie Calvert.

Quiz 107 Who's Sport?

LEVEL 3

Answers - see Quiz 108, page 340

1   Who beat Jahangir Khan's five year unbeaten record in 1986?
2   Who had the car number plate 1 CUE?
3   How was Walker Smith better known?
4   What was boxer Paul Ryan's nickname?
5   Who won the Oaks and the St Leger for the Queen in 1978 on Dunfermline?
6   What was the nickname of baseball player Ty Cobb?
7   Which woman was undefeated over 400m between 1977 and 1981?
8   Which horse did Willie Shoemaker ride in his last race?
9   Who was the only person to beat Sugar Ray Leonard in a professional fight?
10 Which athlete was nicknamed 'The Flying Finn'?
11 Who beat Babe Ruth's long standing record of 714 home runs in '74?
12 Who was the first jockey to saddle more than 8,000 winners?
13 Who was the first skier to overtake Pirmin Zurbriggen's four overall world championship titles?
14 Which American football player was nicknamed 'Sweetness'?
15 Who in 1985 was the first man for 30 years to hold the 1500m and 5000m world records at the same time?
16 Whose Triple Jump World Record did Jonathan Edwards break?
17 Who was the first South African to win the Benson & Hedges Masters snooker title?
18 Where did Nelson Piquet win his first Grand Prix?
19 Who did Giancarlo Fisichella drive for in 1998?
20 Who won the Moto Cross des Nations for the first time in 1975?
21 Who was dubbed the Louisville Lip?
22 Whose record of 24 Grand Prix wins was broken by Jim Clark?
23 Who was the first non European to win the Tour de France?
24 Who won the 1988 Jesse Owens Award as the year's most outstanding athlete?
25 Fiona May represents which country at which sport?
26 Who won the Fosters World Doubles with Stephen Hendry in 1989?
27 Which French cyclist's nickname means 'The Badger'?
28 Gene Tunney was only beaten once, by whom?
29 Who was the first Australian to win the Women's World Open Snooker Championship?
30 Who was the first racing driver to win 500 points in Formula 1?

Quiz 108 Pot Luck 51

LEVEL 3

Answers - see Quiz 107, page 339

1   What's the most number of raised dots in a single letter of Braille?
2   Which 'E' number is used to represent riboflavin in products?
3   Who was actress Jane Seymour's first father in law?
4   In which country is the city of Maracaibo?
5   In which decade was Mohammed Fayed born?
6   Who, on the cover of Sergeant Pepper, was known by his three names?
7   Picasso's Guernica is a comment on what?
8   What is the correct form of address to begin a letter to a Roman Catholic Archbishop?
9   Which two colours form the background for the Vatican City flag?
10 What is the capital of the American state of Wisconsin?
11 Who was Henry IV's father?
12 Who has larger feet – Gladiator Hunter or Nick Faldo?
13 A fear of the number thirteen is known as what?
14 Which Spice Girl once appeared as an extra in Emmerdale?
15 What's the English name of the constellation Pictor?
16 What was Blondie's last UK No1?
17 Which country has the dirham as a unit of currency?
18 What is the main food of baby whales?
19 What is the international car index mark for a car from Tanzania?
20 In which US state is a university endowed by Cornelius Vanderbilt?
21 Which comedian played Tollmaster in Doctor Who in 1987?
22 What is the main language of Ethiopia?
23 Who played the black film detective Shaft?
24 Which Nobel Prize was won in 1975 by Andrei Sakharov?
25 Who had a No 1 UK hit with Seven Tears in 1982?
26 Who is the elder – Jemima Khan or Kate Moss?
27 Who wrote the Leatherstocking Tales?
28 Tegucigalpa is the capital of which country?
29 What was the Christian name of frozen food man Mr Birdseye?
30 Who directed the 1991 film JFK?

Who's Sport? (See quiz 107, page 339)
1 Ross Norman. 2 Jimmy White. 3 Sugar Ray Robinson. 4 Scrap Iron.
5 Willie Carson. 6 The Georgia Peach. 7 Marita Koch. 8 Patchy Groundfog.
9 Roberto Duran. 10 Paavo Johannes Nurmi. 11 Hank Aaron. 12 Willie
Shoemaker. 13 Marc Girardelli. 14 Walter Paynton. 15 Said Aouita.
16 Willie Banks. 17 Perrie Mans. 18 Long Beach USA. 19 Benetton.
20 Czechoslovakia. 21 Muhammad Ali. 22 Juan Manuel Fangio. 23 Greg
LeMond. 24 Florence Griffith-Joyner. 25 Italy, long jump. 26 Mike Hallett.
27 Bernard Hinault. 28 Harry Greb. 29 Lesley McIlraith. 30 Alain Prost.

Quiz 109 Exploration

Answers - see Quiz 110, page 342

LEVEL 3

1 What is chiefly grown in Alabama's Canebrake country?
2 The Julian and Dinaric Alps extend into which two countries?
3 The Amur river forms much of the boundary between which two countries?
4 What is the Maori name for New Zealand?
5 Which two main metals are found in the Atacama Desert in Chile?
6 What is the currency of Malaysia?
7 Which country has the highest density of sheep in the world?
8 Which African country takes its name from the Shona for 'House of Stone'?
9 Which volcanic peak is west of Cook inlet in Alaska?
10 San Miguel is the main island of which group?
11 What is the capital of the Lazio region of Italy?
12 What is the former name of the capital of Dominica?
13 Which Brazilian state is the centre of Amazonian tin and gold mining?
14 Aqaba is which country's only port?
15 On which island of the Philippines is Manila?
16 What is the world's flattest continent?
17 Which former fort in New York State is the home of the US Military Academy?
18 Which US state capital lies on the river Jordan?
19 In which country is Africa's lowest point?
20 What is the largest primeval forest left in Europe?
21 The Red Sea is the submerged section of which valley?
22 Regina in Saskatchewan was originally called what?
23 How many countries do the Andes pass through?
24 In which country do the Makua live?
25 What is the highest peak of the Apennines?
26 Which city south east of St Malo was the old capital of Brittany?
27 Which Alps lie north east of the Sea of Showers?
28 Robben Island is a prison in which Bay?
29 What is Malawi's largest city?
30 Which south American port's name means River of January?

Pot Luck 52 (See quiz 110, page 342)
Answers
1 New Delhi. 2 Wood not metal resonators. 3 Indonesia. 4 Tippett. 5 Dick Tracy. 6 Amy Grant. 7 Tea. 8 Freud. 9 Six. 10 Henry. 11 Crimean. 12 Doris Kappelhoff. 13 Kansas. 14 Z. 15 Jawaharlal (Pandit) Nehru. 16 Lieutenant of the Royal Victorian Order. 17 Sousaphone. 18 Journalism, literature & music. 19 Turkey. 20 Ghosts. 21 Czech Republic. 22 Elaine Paige. 23 Max. 24 Ice cream. 25 Muscat. 26 The Phantom. 27 Ecuador. 28 Puppetry. 29 Kidney. 30 William I.

Quiz 110 Pot Luck 52

Answers - see Quiz 109, page 341

LEVEL 3

1   Where was Paddy Ashdown born?
2   How does a marimba differ from a xylophone?
3   In which country is the city of Surabaya?
4   Who composed the opera The Ice Break?
5   Which comic strip character was played by Warren Beatty?
6   Whose first UK Top Ten hit was Baby Baby ?
7   What would you drink from a cha-no-yu?
8   Whose theories did Jeffrey Masson attack in Against Therapy?
9   How many stripes are there on the Ugandan national flag?
10 What did the last emperor of China Hsuan Tung ask to be called after he was deposed?
11 In which war was the Battle of Inkerman?
12 What is Doris Day's full real name?
13 Which American state is called the Sunflower State?
14 Which letter is two dashes and two dots in Morse Code?
15 Who preceded Lal Shastri as Prime Minister of India?
16 What are the initials LVO an abbreviation of?
17 According to the Bonzo Dog Doo-Dah Band's The Intro and the Outro what is Princess Anne playing?
18 The Pulitzer Prize is awarded in which three categories?
19 In which European country is the region of Anatolia?
20 Phasmophobia is the fear of what?
21 Which country has the koruna as a unit of currency?
22 Who is the elder – Elaine Paige or Lily Savage?
23 Who is the male hero of the children's book Where the Wild Things Are?
24 What is cassata a type of?
25 What is the capital of Oman?
26 In the first Pink Panther film what was the professional jewel thief called?
27 In which country is the sculpture Monument to the Equator?
28 In Japan what type of entertainment is bunraku?
29 Pyelitis affects which organ of the body?
30 Which king of England was crowned on Christmas Day? ·

Exploration (See quiz 109, page 341)
1 Cotton. 2 Albania & Yugoslavia. 3 China & Russia. 4 Aotearoa. 5 Silver & copper. 6 Ringgit. 7 Wales. 8 Zimbabwe. 9 Mount Redoubt. 10 Azores. 11 Rome. 12 Charlotte Town. 13 Rondonia. 14 Jordan. 15 Luzon. 16 Australia. 17 West Point. 18 Salt Lake City. 19 Djibouti. 20 Hainburg in Austria. 21 Great Rift Valley. 22 Pile of Bones. 23 Seven. 24 Mozambique. 25 Gran Sasso d'Italia. 26 Rennes. 27 Lunar Alps. 28 Table Bay. 29 Blantyre. 30 Rio de Janeiro.

Answers

Quiz 111 Transport

Answers - see Quiz 112, page 344

LEVEL 3

1. What was the name of Helen Sharman's space craft?
2. Over which part of Paris was the first successful balloon flight?
3. What was Boeing's first sea plane made from?
4. Who built the oil tanker Jahre Viking?
5. In which craft did Kenneth Warby set a water speed record in 1978?
6. The space probe Magellan went into orbit where in 1990?
7. What are the terminal cities of Japan's Hikari trains?
8. Why were Britain's first traffic lights built?
9. Which was the last country in Europe to change from driving on the left to the right?
10. Who produced the first mass produced four wheel drive saloon car?
11. The world's highest railway line runs between which countries?
12. Who designed and owned the eight engine Spruce Goose in the '40s?
13. What are the two termini of the Volga-Baltic Waterway?
14. Where is Narita airport?
15. In which craft did Charles Yeager first break the sound barrier in the air?
16. Who built Concorde with BAC?
17. What was the first ocean-going oil tanker called?
18. What was the first space station called?
19. Who built the B17 Flying Fortress in WWII?
20. How many passengers did the first hovercraft carry?
21. What was the name of the first nuclear powered ship?
22. Where was the Volkswagen factory before WWII?
23. In which country was the launch site of the European Ariane rocket?
24. How many people can ride a Frankencycle?
25. What was the cruise ship Norway called before a Norwegian bought it?
26. How many capital cities do you pass through on the Pan American Highway?
27. What was the name of the first balloon to cross the Atlantic?
28. If you took the India Pacific train where would you be?
29. Where did the Hindenberg explode in May 1937?
30. What was the first ship launched by Queen Elizabeth II?

Who's Movies? (See quiz 112, page 344)

Answers

1 Michael J Fox. **2** Charles Laughton & Noel Coward. **3** Bryan Forbes. **4** Max Shreck. **5** Jill Balcon. **6** Jack Lemmon. **7** David Duchovny. **8** George Segal. **9** John Travolta. **10** Writer Jonathan Lynn. **11** Rowan Atkinson. **12** Betty Grable's. **13** Michael Keaton. **14** Robin Williams (Flubber). **15** John Huston. **16** Going My Way. **17** Steve Martin. **18** Sofia Coppola. **19** Woody Allen. **20** Tony Curtis. **21** Meryl Streep. **22** Anthony Shaffer. **23** Simian Films. **24** John Quincy Adams. **25** Rupert Everett. **26** Timothy Leary. **27** Anjelica Huston's. **28** Jason Gould. **29** Cuba Gooding Jr. **30** Chris Columbus.

Quiz 112 Who's Movies?

Answers - see Quiz 111, page 343

LEVEL 3

1 Who duetted with Joan Jett on Light of Day in 1986?
2 Which two actors rejected Bridge on the River Kwai before Alec Guinness got the lead role?
3 How is actor/director Nobby Clarke better known?
4 Who played the first cinema vampire in Nosferatu?
5 Who was Daniel Day-Lewis' actress mother?
6 Who has a production company called Edited?
7 Which TV hero played a movie villain in Beethoven?
8 Who walked off the set of 10 and gave Dudley Moore a movie break?
9 Who did Schwarzenegger's love interest in Twins marry after the movie was made?
10 Who links TV's Yes Minister and the film Nuns on the Run?
11 Who was the voice of Zazu in The Lion King?
12 Whose legs were insured for more – Fred Astaire's or Betty Grable's?
13 Who did Val Kilmer replace as Batman?
14 Who had the title role in the remake of The Absent Minded Professor?
15 Which director was an amateur lightweight boxing champion in the early 20s?
16 In which film did Bing Crosby first play Father O'Malley?
17 Who adapted the play Cyrano de Bergerac into the movie Roxanne?
18 Who appeared in her father's Godfather Part III?
19 Who directed the first two films in which Dianne Wiest won Oscars?
20 After landing a weekend with this actor the winner said she really wanted the second prize of a fridge.
21 Who did Kristin Scott Thomas beat to win the role in The Horse Whisperer?
22 Who adapted Agatha Christie's Evil Under the Sun for the big screen?
23 Which production company was set up by Hugh Grant and Elizabeth Hurley?
24 Who is the president played by Anthony Hopkins in Amistad?
25 Who played Prinny in The Madness of King George?
26 Which 60s activist was the godfather of Winona Ryder?
27 Which actress's husband designed the Olympic Gateway in LA. '84?
28 Who played Streisand's son in Prince of Tides?
29 Who won supporting actor Oscar for Jerry Maguire?
30 Who directed Mrs Doubtfire?

Answers

Transport (See quiz 111, page 343)
1 Soyuz TM-12. 2 Bois de Boulogne. 3 Spruce. 4 Japan. 5 The Spirit of Australia. 6 Venus. 7 Tokyo & Osaka. 8 To make access easier to the Palace of Westminster. 9 Sweden. 10 Audi. 11 Peru & Bolivia. 12 Howard Hughes. 13 Astrakhan to St Petersburg. 14 Tokyo. 15 Bell X-1 rocket plane. 16 Aerospatiale. 17 Gluckauf. 18 Salyut 1. 19 Boeing. 20 Three. 21 Lenin. 22 Wolfsburg. 23 French Guiana. 24 Four. 25 France. 26 17. 27 Double Eagle II . 28 Australia. 29 Lakehurst, New Jersey. 30 Britannia.

HOW TO SET UP YOUR OWN
PUB QUIZ

It isn't easy, get that right from the start. This isn't going to be easy. Think instead of words like; 'difficult', 'taxing', 'infuriating' consider yourself with damp palms and a dry throat and then, when you have concentrated on that, put it out of your mind and think of the recognition you will receive down the local, imagine all the regulars lifting you high upon their shoulders dancing and weaving their way around the pub. It won't help but it's good to dream every once in a while.

What you will need:

 A good selection of biros (never be tempted to give your own pen up, not even to family members)

A copy of *The Best Pub Quiz Book Ever*

A set of answer sheets photocopied from the back of the book

A good speaking voice and possibly a microphone and an amp

A pub

At least one pint inside you

At least one more on your table

A table

What to do:

Choose your local to start with, there is no need to get halfway through your first quiz and decide you weren't cut out for all this and then find yourself in the roughest pub in Christendom 30 miles and a long run from home.

Chat it through with the landlord and agree on whether you will be charging or not, if you don't then there is little chance of a prize for the winners other than a free pint each and this is obviously at the landlord's discretion – if you pack his pub to bursting then five free pints won't worry him, but if it's only you and a two others then he may be less than unwilling, as publicans tend to be.

If you decide on a payment entry keep it reasonable, you don't want to take the fun out of the quiz; some people will be well aware that they have very little hope of winning and will be reluctant to celebrate the fact by mortgaging their house.

Once location and prize are all sorted then advertising the event is paramount, get people's attention, sell sell, sell or, alternatively, stick up a gaudy looking poster on the door of the bogs. Be sure to specify all the details, time, prize and so on – remember you are selling to people whose tiny attention span is being whittled down to nothing by alcohol.

After this it is time for the big night, if you are holding the event in the 'snug' which seats ten or so you can rely on your voice, if not you should get hold of a good microphone and an amplifier so that you can boom out your questions and enunciate the length and breadth of the pub (once again, clear this with the landlord and don't let liquid anywhere near the electrical equipment). Make sure to practice, and get comfortable with the sound of your own voice and relax as much as possible, try not to rely on alcohol too much or "round one" will be followed by "rown' too" which will eventually give way to "runfree". Relax with your voice so that you can handle any queries from the teams, and any venomous abuse from the 'lively' bar area.

When you enter the pub make sure you take everything listed above. Also, make sure you have a set of tie-break questions and that you instruct everybody who is taking part of the rules – and be firm. It will only upset people if you start handing out impromptu solutions and let's face it the wisdom of Solomon is not needed when you are talking pub quiz rules; 'no cheating' is a perfectly healthy stance to start with.

Finally, keep the teams to a maximum of five members, hand out your answer papers and pens and, when everybody is good and settled, start the quiz. It might not be easy and it might not propel you to international stardom or pay for a life of luxury but you will enjoy yourself. No, really.

ANSWERS

Part One

1 _____

2 _____

3 _____

4 _____

5 _____

6 _____

7 _____

8 _____

9 _____

10 _____

11 _____

12 _____

13 _____

14 _____

15 _____

16 _____

17 _____

18 _____

19 _____

20 _____

21 _____

22 _____

23 _____

24 _____

25 _____

26 _____

27 _____

28 _____

29 _____

30 _____

ANSWERS

Part Two

1 _____	**16** _____
2 _____	**17** _____
3 _____	**18** _____
4 _____	**19** _____
5 _____	**20** _____
6 _____	**21** _____
7 _____	**22** _____
8 _____	**23** _____
9 _____	**24** _____
10 _____	**25** _____
11 _____	**26** _____
12 _____	**27** _____
13 _____	**28** _____
14 _____	**29** _____
15 _____	**30** _____

ANSWERS

Part Three

1 _____   16 _____

2 _____   17 _____

3 _____   18 _____

4 _____   19 _____

5 _____   20 _____

6 _____   21 _____

7 _____   22 _____

8 _____   23 _____

9 _____   24 _____

10 _____   25 _____

11 _____   26 _____

12 _____   27 _____

13 _____   28 _____

14 _____   29 _____

15 _____   30 _____

ALSO AVAILABLE

The Best Pub Quiz Book Ever!

Containing over 10,000 questions
and answers, this book is divided
into over 300 quizzes on all of your
favourite subjects. A must for every
Pub Quiz fanatic.

ISBN 1 85868 182 0
£6.99
Available from all good bookshops

The Best Pop Pub Quiz Book Ever!

Containing 6,000 questions and
answers, this book is divided into
over 100 individual quizzes on all of
your favourite pop music subjects.
Essential reading for Pub Quiz
fanatics.

ISBN 1 85868 258 4
£6.99
Available from all good bookshops